DOCKLAND

An illustrated historical survey of life and work in east London

Frontispiece
Thames Sailing Barge Xylonite.
(Museum of London)

Published by North East London
Polytechnic in conjunction with the
Greater London Council

Edited by SK Al Naib
with the assistance of RJM Carr

Published by North East London
Polytechnic in conjunction with the
Greater London Council

ISBN 0-901987-80-8

© **1986 North East London Polytechnic**

Distributed by Thames and Hudson Ltd

Printed March 1986
Reprinted December 1986
Reprinted March 1988
Reprinted March 1989

Printed for GLC Supplies Department
(CRS)
by Eyre and Spottiswoode Ltd (79412) 12/85

Contents

Contents

"Red" sails in the sunset ?

Foreword by George Nicholson

In 1968 I sailed out of the Royals for the last time on the Blue Funnel ship *Sarpedon*, (previously the Glenline vessel *Denbighshire*). Whilst I had just completed an engineering apprenticeship my brother a long serving deck officer with the Bank Line owned by Andrew Weir and Co had also recently sailed into the Surrey Docks. Further up river there was still an active cargo trade using Hays wharf and other Riverside wharves.

Some commentators and politicians have painted a picture which would have one believing that the Port of London had been in decline since the war. The truth is rather different. Up to the late 1960s, it was still possible to share the view of Sir Patrick Abercrombie set out in the 1943 County of London Plan. He said:

"The Thames, by virtue of its great width, its sweeping and varied curves, its tidal ebb and flow and its shipping activities is one of the finest rivers in the world. It presents unequalled opportunities for public enjoyment, civic splendour and public amenity; it makes London the first port of Great Britain; as a great waterway it provides a cheap means of freight transport and it is the backbone of London's industrial areas."

Since the early 70s, by a combination of design and neglect that vision has been squandered. An industry which employed many thousands of workers and which touched the lives of millions of people not directly employed in the docks has all but disappeared. London's river, from being the world's busiest working waterway, has become a playground. The seemingly endless traffic, bringing cargoes from the ends of the earth, past Gravesend, Woolwich and Greenwich to the Royal, Millwall, Surrey Docks and the Pool of London has drastically declined.

The old dockland is still clear in the minds of Londoners. Generations of children grew up in streets where the houses were dwarfed by ships, whose sides rose like cliffs over their back gardens. Even City commuters, looking out of train windows from the elevated viaducts, were made daily aware of the bustling life of Rotherhithe and Wapping by thickets of cranes and the massive silhouette of the *London Mammoth*.

If the image of the past is powerful, so is curiosity about what can still be seen. This book is an attempt to satisfy that curiosity. If history is to be useful, however, it should be a tool not just for recollection, but reflection. What remains is important to us as Londoners, not only as a vital part of our history but also because it provides the only foundation on which the future of Dockland can be built.

Visible reminders of the past, whether in the form of old photographs or buildings in a street, contain those shared memories which give every group, from a family to a nation, a sense of identity. For thinking Londoners the recent history of dockland ('dockland' is an older and more inclusive term than the statutorily defined

1 George Nicholson, engineer, M V Sarpedon (ex Denbighshire) about 1968.

'Docklands') contains some quite painful shared memories.

For the majority of families whose livelihood depended on river trade activity, the abandonment of the upstream docks was as unexpected and destructive as a natural catastrophe. It was their Great Fire. They could only watch and accept the consequences of a process which they had no part in initiating and little chance of controlling.

What should have been a long anticipated, carefully planned and sensitively controlled restructuring, looks in retrospect more like a collapse. Opportunities were squandered. No census was made of the sound, adaptable buildings being vacated in their thousands. As the demolition and burning went on and as the waterways were filled, a living part of a great city was turned into a wilderness. A pathetic handful of listed buildings — those that had not been destroyed by neglect — stood as lonely monuments.

Even where, as at the St Katharine Docks, an isolated enclave has been given some kind of new life and achieved noticeable commercial success it has taken on the character of an artificially created historical 'theme park'. Comparison with what happened a little later at Covent Garden is instructive. The Garden is at least as successful in commercial terms and it must be said that the transition from the old life to the new was achieved there without unnecessary destruction or disruption. The market area has remained, in consequence, an integral part of the familiar London scene, rather than an inward-looking, one-stop attraction for tourists.

Farther down river, remarkable buildings like the *Skin Floor,* with its forest of branching iron columns, have been left stranded and disused. On the Southwark side, Shad Thames, one of London's most dramatic streetscapes, decayed for years.

The remedy imposed on London — the creation of a democratically unaccountable authority — was the beginning of a process which we are now seeing driven to a bitter conclusion, with the capital city itself plunged back into its mid-nineteenth century condition, fragmented, controlled not by a unified elected government but by a muddle of quangoes and joint boards.

By one of those ironies only history can provide, 10 years after sailing from the KGV I was elected to represent a riverside ward on Southwark Council and later in 1981, to represent Bermondsey on the GLC. As the Chairman of the GLC's planning committee I became custodian of the baton handed on from Abercrombie's time only to find myself locked in battle with another ex-seaman, the present incumbent of the Chair of the London Docklands Development Corporation.

Anyone who regards as a success story the systematic attacks by the LDDC on local and strategic planning, and on local accountability, the confiscation of practically all the housing land in the Dockland part of Newham,

Southwark and Tower Hamlets, the loss of thousands of jobs traditional to the area, the madcap schemes for an airport, luxury housing, and huge office developments, cannot be said to have the interests of the residents of Docklands at heart. The truth is that dockland is up for sale to the highest bidder. A great opportunity for Londoners has been lost.

Historians of the future will study and judge the events of this extraordinary time. My opinions are firm and clear — with all that I have said and written on the subject who could doubt it! I have not hesitated to let those opinions colour this foreword. But I also feel a keen responsibility for seeing that the facts about dockland, past and present, are carefully recorded. For this task London has been fortunate to have the services of the Docklands History Survey.

The Survey has had its own interesting history. The Council provided a room and secretarial services for its first meeting in 1979, when a number of concerned individuals came together to discuss what studies and records ought to be made in dockland areas. From the beginning, these enthusiasts were able to gather support from all sides. The National Maritime Museum, the Museum of London and many other official and voluntary organisations were represented at their continuing meetings and it soon became clear that, by working together, they could undertake a study which none of them had the resources to tackle alone. With grants from the Docklands Joint Committee, the Greater London Council and others the group was able to appoint a full time Survey Officer, Dr Carr, and begin a systematic investigation.

The Council bore the whole cost of publishing their preliminary report, which was a penny plain affair, designed more to attract specialised interest and invite additional information than to achieve wide sales. I was, nevertheless, struck by its value and potential. Its gazetteer of surviving buildings and objects and its researchers' guide to documentary sources (both of which are updated and reprinted here) prompted me to say that if the Survey could do so well, then they might do better. The bare facts should, I felt, be supported by some topic papers and critical commentary and — not least — by pictures.

The Council committees concerned gave the idea immediate support and this new edition is the result. The additional research was supported by a further Council grant and the Council has again paid for the publication itself, but the benefits will not end there. The North East London Polytechnic, as sponsors and academic supervisors of the project, will undertake the promotion and sale of the book and plough back the income into dockland research and publication.

I should underline the fact that the Council's input has been in providing funds and the services of its Historic Buildings Division. The group has had complete editorial freedom. No attempt has been made to exercise censorship (or 'guidance' as censors prefer to call it). The only guidance from GLC officers has been toward additional sources of information and illustration.

The team of writers reflects the wide range of support and expertise brought together over the last six years. In these pages you will find the work of a docker, a lighterman, social and marine historians, industrial archaeologists, engineers and historic building specialists. They have brought with them a variety of personal views as well as an impressive range of knowledge. I doubt whether they would agree with one another (let alone with me) on their interpretation of the recent past but they have worked together as a team with dedication and enthusiasm. What they have producedd is a vivid and lasting memorial of which all who love London can be proud.

As to the future; it is for all of us to play our part. There is a growing movement determined to bring the river back to life. There is no magic to this, as the experience of ports and rivers in Europe demonstrates.

The port of Paris is *still* seen as an instrument at the service of the economy of the Ile de France region. Would that port operators and shippers in this country were so public minded.

If this book stirs your *imagination* then it will have doubly served its purpose. It brings back vivid memories to me, but it also fires a determination not to be a spectator of events for a second time.

The Thames for Londoners is our new manifesto[1] — join us!

Notes

1 *The Thames for Londoners* — A Manifesto for the Use of the River, January 1985

The Use of the River Thames in London — Conference Papers, July 1985

Foreword to the first edition

Ashley Barker

In the nineteen fifties and sixties planning was so heavily preoccupied with renewal and comprehensive re-development that the existence of the city as a living entity in which every part dependend for its existence on every other part was barely acknowledged.

Planning was not concerned with the simple care and maintenance of what already existed, even if it was seen to be working well. Planning was about change — largely with directing and partly with initiating it but, in either case, with continuous change seen as not merely natural but absolutely necessary. The very word 'plan' meant a document which laid down the ways in which the city might be restructured and renewed and given more opportunities for rapid movement and further change. Chapters 1 and 2 of the plan commonly contained an outline road network and broad land use patterns as if for a new town, with the 'fixes' reduced to the unavoidable minimum. Acknowledgement of the existence of an old and useful fabric was usually relegated to a late chapter (it is Chapter 8 in the Greater London Development Plan Studies) where lip service was paid to a previously ignored option, that of preserving what was called 'the best' of the past. An 'age and condition' survey of buildings was included somewhere (usually in the housing chapter) to underline the fact that longevity was regarded as both undesirable and inevitably linked with deterioration.

Years of disappointing experience have now taught us that maintaining and improving what exists is often the best way to health and happiness, that total renewal is no guarantee against rapid decay and that ill-advised and over-rapid change can generate social distress. It is now perhaps, more clearly understood that effective planning must, of necessity, start from a detailed consideration of what has been inherited, but we are still suffering from the knock-on effects of decades of planning decisions which determinedly ignored the past.

Planning does not lose its vision if it builds on a bedrock of knowledge and takes decisions to change, to leave untouched, to maintain, restore, improve or modify in that knowledge. The London Docklands History Survey provides an authoritative and thorough description of the older physical fabric of Docklands and offers guidance for those who need to research in more detail. It is concerned not only with the important listed buildings and artefacts but with all those objects from the past whose existence may be of significance to planners, developers, historians, industrial archaeologists, and, not least, to Londoners who care to know how London came to be as it is.

This is not a book to be read and put on the bookshelf. It is a reliable tool to be kept ready to hand. I may regret that such a tool was not available to us ten years ago and that so much of value was lost in Docklands before the History Survey was conceived, but it has important work to do now.

1984

Editor's preface

SK Al Naib/RJM Carr

The area covered by the Docklands History
Survey and this book is broadly that of the Port
of London up-river. With the exception of the
south bank in Southwark the area extends from
London Bridge to Beckton and Woolwich,
including Deptford Creek and Bow Creek. The
criterion has been to include parts of the East
End where ships could be seen loading or
unloading at least until the late 1960s and the
areas surrounding such activity where a
maritime influence was still significant. The
activity of the Port did, of course, extend
further, up-river to Brentford and beyond and
down-river to the Estuary. Apart from the
chapter on Royal Docklands the period covered
is principally from the late eighteenth century,
when plans for the building of wet docks for
cargo handling were first drawn up.

The subject matter is not only buildings,
machinery, ships and civil engineering
structures but also the people, living and dead,
who spent their working lives in Dockland. To
achieve publication within the lifetime of the
Greater London Council the greater part of the
project had to be completed within not much
more than 8 months, from the commissioning of
the various authors to the delivery of the index
to the printers. Our expert contributors have all
been forced to leave some interesting avenues of
research unexplored but their enthusiasm for
the project seems to have been sharpened by the
challenge of working to tight deadlines.

Note on the second edition

Dr S K Al Naib

The first printing of 3,000 copies of this book was sold out within six months of publication in March 1986, and it is now reprinted unrevised to meet continuing demand. The book has had many experts amongst its readers and attention is drawn to the invitation at the foot of this note.

Dockland is now recognized as a major account of life and work in London's dockland during the past 200 years. It is a factual guide for those who want to know about the heritage of London's dockland with authoritative text on every aspect of life in the area.

The book, which is a joint venture by the North East London Polytechnic (NELP) and the Greater London Council (GLC), is the culmination of many years' research by the Docklands History Survey, a research group in the Department of Civil Engineering, NELP.

By working in harmony, the GLC, NELP and a whole array of specialised societies were able to produce this fascinating book. The co-operative nature of the enterprise is splendidly evident in the book itself. It brings together the experiences of dockers, lightermen, civil engineers, industrial archaeologists, social and marine historians to provide a vivid portrait of life and work in dockland from the nineteenth century to the present day.

The Port of London was of central importance in the history of Great Britain and the Empire. Today, practically all the docks in London are closed. Since 1976, plans have been made for redevelopment on both banks of the Thames from the Tower to Barking Creek which means that these 8½ square miles of London docklands will undergo fundamental changes for the remaining years of this century.

Sadly during the last decade much evidence of the port's history has disappeared and what remains is at risk. Buildings and warehouses have been demolished, machinery removed for scrap and company records, photographs, drawings and other documents have been destroyed and dispersed. The memories of men and women who spent their lives working in the docks still remain unrecorded. It is hoped that the publication of this book will prompt much more recording and rescue work.

Because of the fundamental changes caused by the redevelopment of the docklands and ensuing destruction of much of the history of the area, the Dockland History Survey was established in 1979 at NELP and supported by the Dockland Joint Committee, the GLC, The National Maritime Museum and the Museum of London. A full-time Research Assistant and Survey Officer, Dr R J M Carr, was appointed in the Department of Civil Engineering at NELP.

The main aims of the survey were:

1   To encourage interest in the industrial, commercial and social history of dockland.
2   To investigate and record all aspects of dockland history and to encourage, co-ordinate and assist research.
3   To inform the public of the results of its work in various ways.
4   To provide advice to local authorities, developers and others on all matters relating to the history of dockland.

The initial results of the research were published at the expense of the GLC in 1984 and entitled 'Dockland History Survey' with a foreword (reproduced on page 3) by Ashley Barker. This gave the lead to what still remained of industrial, technological and sociological history of the area. The published survey provided the first working tool of its kind for the planning of the dockland.

The success of this publication led to further discussions with the GLC for financial support in order to continue research into dockland's history. With the enthusiasm and support of Mr George Nicholson (chair of GLC Planning Committee) and Mr John Earl of Historic Building Division, the research team was able to start work at once on the present volume.

Dockland provides an authoritative and unique reference on the archaeological, engineering and social heritage of dockland for local authorities, planners, private and commercial developers and not least, to Londoners who need to know about the history of their great City. London's dockland is the largest redevelopment area in Western Europe and this book, we hope, will provide an historical foundation on which the future of the area can be built.

We are now trying to ensure that dockland research and related community studies will go on. NELP is pledged to carry out this important work and seek external funding for it.

An Invitation to the Reader

If you are a reader with knowledge and unpublished information on docklands or with interesting stories on life and work in the docklands, or can assist in any Dockland research, please contact:

Dr S K Al Naib
Head of Department
Department of Civil Engineering
North East London Polytechnic
Longbridge Road
Dagenham
RM8 2AS
Tel No 01-590 7722, ext. 2173

Dockland: origins and earlier history

Professor Theo Barker

London's docks, developed over a century and a half, handled more traffic than anywhere else in the kingdom. Despite heavy wartime bombing and the need to carry on in patched-up premises, they revived again and were as busy as ever until the 1960s. But larger vessels, containerization, and growing oil traffic caused more and more business to be handled downstream. Tilbury and the oil terminals became increasingly important. Between the mid 60s and the mid 70s 150,000 jobs were lost as London's dockland was deserted. A prime site of eight square miles — or, rather, a multitude of prime sites — close to the heart of London became available for the enterprising who had the vision and imagination to adapt the area for the needs of the twenty-first century as the dock builders had prepared it to meet the requirements of the nineteenth and twentieth.

Professor Simmons has remarked in another context that 'in England all towns turn away from their rivers as if ashamed of them. Commercial considerations were paramount. Factories and warehouses were allowed to occupy the banks of the river for the ease of communication that it brought them; the river was scarcely ever treated as an amenity'.[1] London now has the opportunity to take pride in its riverside sites and those immediately to the rear of them, including the former dock basins, to carry out the largest and most exciting urban development scheme in Europe. The London Docklands Development Corporation is bringing new life to an area of over 5,000 acres, 450 acres of it open water.

London's river has played a far greater role in national, as well as London, history than is usually realised. It handled the bulk of the country's overseas trade long before any commercial cargo-handling docks were contemplated. This is not difficult to imagine when much of this foreign trade was with the Low Countries, a short voyage from the mouth of the Thames. Later, the East India, Russia, Royal African and other great trading companies, located in the City, sent ships to more distant parts of the globe. By 1700 about 70% or more of England's foreign trade was

handled by London itself. In addition to this, however, was the much less glamorous, but nevertheless very important, traffic passing coastwise between London and other parts of the country not only on or near the coast itself but also along or near rivers such as the Trent or the Great Ouse which penetrated far inland and, with river improvement, could be navigated farther upstream than the natural limits of navigation. London, in fact, became a great engine of economic growth which played a vital role in stimulating activity elsewhere in the country, later giving rise to what we have come to know as the Industrial Revolution.

London's population grew from a mere 40,000 or so early in the sixteenth century to nearly 600,000 in 1700, by which time it had surpassed Paris (already about 200,000 in the early sixteenth century, not a seaport and much slower growing) and had become one of the largest cities on earth. To feed 600,000 people was a major feat, calling for supplies which, as Defoe pointed out, came from remoter, as well as nearer, parts of the kingdom. Some of these supplies came by road; but much, especially grain, the essential foodstuff, and coal, the essential fuel, came by coastal ship. By 1700, for instance, London was probably taking a third of the million tons of coal produced by the collieries of the north-east every year.[2] The capital was also the great distribution centre for imported goods, such as sugar, tea, or linens, which were despatched back around the coast and inland. London then dominated the kingdom. In 1700 no other English town, not even Bristol or Norwich, had populations over 30,000, a twentieth of London's.

Sailing vessels, foreign or coastal, navigated the river right up to London itself, the eastern limits of which then extended only to Wapping and Shadwell on the north bank or to Rotherhithe on the south. The Pool continued to serve the City well, providing over 1,400 ft of frontage between London Bridge and the Tower. The legal quays were supplemented by various sufferance wharves stretching for just under 3,000 ft below London Bridge on the South Bank and for just under 800 ft below the

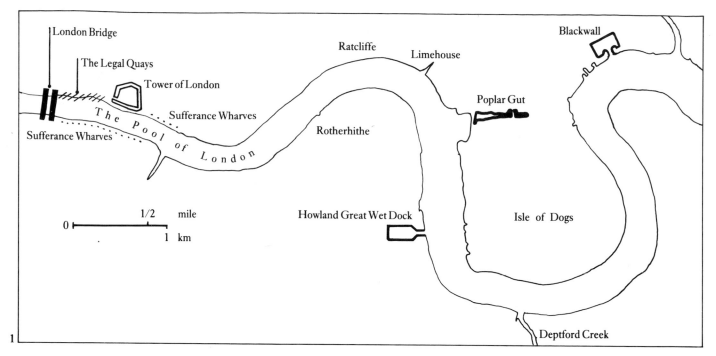

1 *The Port of London in the late 18th century. (C A White)*

Tower on the north.[3] As traffic went on growing during the eighteenth century, however, complaints of congestion and delay began to grow, too. By the 1760s the merchants were petitioning for an extension of the legal quays; but without success.

The volume of shipping doubled during the next 30 years. Congestion and delay grew worse and, eventually, intolerable. By 1797 over 10,000 coasters and nearly 3,500 foreign-going vessels were coming up to London annually. Moored in the river wherever they could find space, they left the narrowest channel for navigation, especially as the coasters, arriving and departing more frequently, traditionally moored nearest to London Bridge. The larger vessels, which took longer to load and unload, dropped anchor in Limehouse, Greenwich or Blackwall Reaches. The 3,400 lighters, needed to carry goods to and from the ships added to the traffic problems.[4]

Congestion was further increased by much of the trade being seasonal. The West India vessels contributed particularly to the river's traffic jam by all arriving between July and October and leaving again by the end of · November. The West India merchants became particularly concerned with the unsatisfactory, indeed growingly unbearable, position and it was a meeting they held in September 1793, in an attempt to resolve it, which was to lead in due course to the building of London's first commercial docks. There had long been wet docks on the Thames, notably the one-and-a-half acre dock at Blackwall, built about 1660, and the better-known Howland Dock, (ten acres), at Rotherhithe; but these had been for the fitting out, repairing and sheltering of shipping, not for commercial purposes.[5]

Pilferage had become a matter of growing concern as the congestion and delay in the open river provided increased opportunity for theft. By the 1790s it had become highly organised, as Patrick Colquhoun, the Metropolitan Police Magistrate, noted in 1797, listing,

"the "river pirates", who were connected with the marine store shops; they reconnoitred by day and made their attacks in armed boats on dark nights, cutting adrift the lighters and barges, and taking out the merchandize. The "night plunderers" — the watermen of the lowest class, who attacked unprotected lighters and made over the stolen goods to receivers. The "light horsemen", comprising mates of ships and revenue officers, who would wink at the robbery of the ship, in which coopers, porters and watermen take part. The "heavy horsemen" — porters and labourers who wore an inner dress, called a guernsey, provided with pockets wherein to stow away small quantities of colonial produce, whilst portering about the ships and quays. Besides these organised depredators, the wine coopers pilfered while opening and refining casks; the mudlarks picked up stolen bits, which others by concert threw into the mud; the rat catchers employed on board the ships carried away produce; the lightermen concealed goods whilst going from the ships to the quays; and the warehousemen, when the sugar reached the warehouses, pilfered and sold the stolen sugar to small dealers at public houses."[6]

One estimate valued the depredations from the West India ships as costing anything between £250,000 and £500,000 a year. Another claimed a loss of upwards of a fiftieth of all the sugar imported and a fortieth of all the rum.[7]

There were, however, many vested interests, both legal in the City and illegal on the river, which opposed the building of docks to the east of the City boundaries, especially as it was originally proposed that they should be used by West India ships alone. The Isle of Dogs, the intended site, was then a lonely, boggy waste used for the pasturing of cattle. It was said to

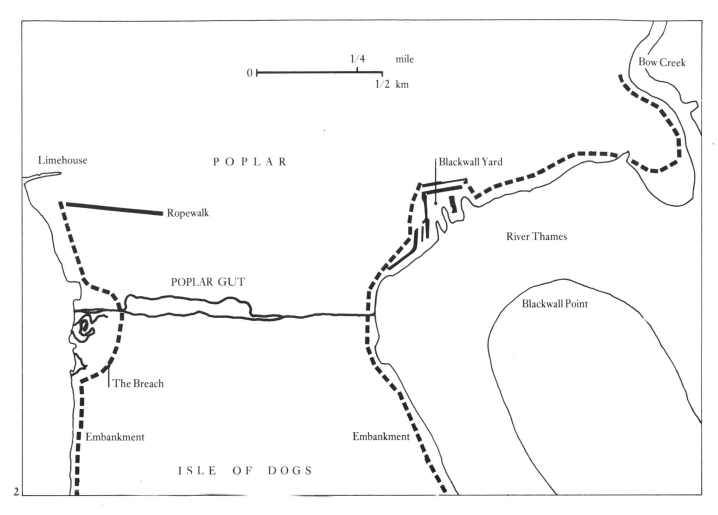

2

have only two inhabitants: one drove the cattle off the marshes and the other operated the ferry to Greenwich.[8] A counter-proposal was put forward, by the North American and European merchants, to knock down property in Wapping and build a dock there, with canal access across the Isle of Dogs to cut off the awkward U-bend in the river. After much debate, both proposals went ahead, each financed by a different company. The West India Dock Act was obtained in 1799 and the London Dock Act in 1800. Each venture had its own legal quays and bonded warehouses. Each was surrounded by impressive walls and defended by a private police force. The West India Docks were also protected by a great ditch 12 ft wide and 6 ft deep to prevent any encroachment too near to the walls.

The West India Docks, the 30 acre import dock and the 24 acre export dock, were opened in 1802 and 1806 respectively and the 20 acre London Dock in 1805, in which year the canal

2   Site of the West India Docks and City Canal in the mid-18th century, from the map by John Rocque 1741-5. (C A White).

3   The West India Docks and City Canal as first built, 1806. (C A White)

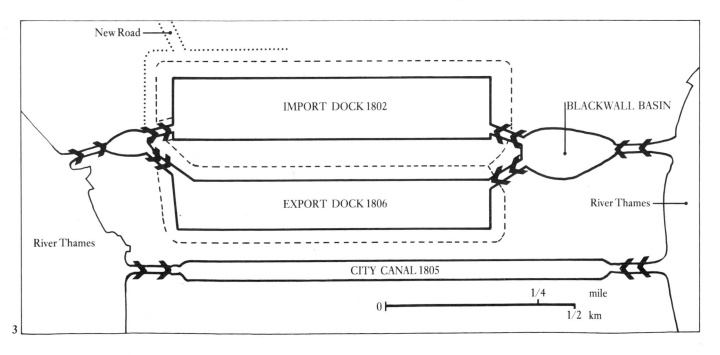

across the Isle of Dogs to the south of the West India Docks also came into use. All West India produce, apart from tobacco, had to be unloaded at the West India Docks, and all tobacco, rice, wine and brandy at the London Dock. Both ventures proved profitable, especially the West India Dock Company, which paid its shareholders the maximum dividend allowed by its Act, 10%, every year from 1803 to 1829 — and free of income tax to 1810. The dock users, too, derived much benefit by having their cargoes handled at lower cost. Yet, although the previous large-scale plunder came to an end, petty theft was never entirely wiped out.[9]

The success of the West India and London Docks encouraged further building. The East India Docks were opened in 1806 unusual in that they contained no warehouses: the Company's imports continued to be carried by road under escort to its City warehouse stronghold in Cutler Street. The Regent's Canal Dock was opened in 1812, originally to accommodate barges only but later greatly extended. To the south of the river, the Grand Surrey Canal Company opened its own dock in 1807, followed between then and 1812 by the independently promoted Commercial, East Country, Norway and Baltic Docks nearby, specialising particularly in timber imports.

The dock companies' monopolies soon came under fire from believers in Free Trade. This led to the ending of the West India Dock Company's monopoly in 1823 and the promotion of the St Katharine's Dock Company, formed in that same year, to build a much smaller dock system on an extraordinarily expensive site between the London Dock and the Tower. It comprised only eight acres of water divided into two basins and was notable both for having Thomas Telford as its designer and, as Dr Gordon Jackson has remarked, for being 'out of date before it was opened'. The warehouses were more grand than useful . . . and the inevitable rate-cutting that ensued showed not that freedom brought cheapness with profits, but that over-capacity reduced profits to a dangerously low level without bringing worthwhile relief to merchants or shipowners, who still had to support more warehousing space than the Port as a whole demanded of its dock system.[10]

While an increasing number of ships continued to use the port, most of them continued to be involved in the coasting or short-haul trades which did not require dock facilities, and from 1815 little steamboats made their appearance on the river, first to provide passenger services upstream and down river to Gravesend, Margate and Ramsgate, and then to challenge sailing vessels in the coastal trade.[11] The building of the docks soon brought great changes to Poplar and called for improved land communication with the City.

When John Stow was writing his *Survey of London* in the later sixteenth century, the highway east of Ratcliffe 'with fayre Elme trees on both sides' led to 'Lime Hurst, Lime Host,

corruptly called Lime House' about a mile away. He reported that "of late yeares ship-wrights and (for the most part) other marine men have builded many large and strong houses for themselves, and smaller for saylers from thence [Ratcliffe] almost to Poplar, and so to Blake wal".[12] Limehouse and Poplar grew as hamlets concerned particularly with shipbuilding and ship repairing. Gascoyne's survey of 1703, for instance, shows rows of buildings inland from the river at Limehouse.[13] The wet dock at Blackwall has already been mentioned. In 1789 another one, the Brunswick, was built, together with a mast house there, seven storeys high.

Looking like a gigantic windmill, it served as an important landmark for homecoming sailors. The Blackwall yard, then known after its owner, Perry, was later taken over by the famous shipbuilding firm of Green and Wigram.[14] There was also much building of small ships of 100 tons and less on the banks of the river itself. In 1790, twice as many of these small craft were being constructed in or near London as in any other port, though most of this traditional form of wooden shipbuilding seems to have been lost by the Thames not long after that.[15]

The East India and the West India Dock Companies joined forces to lay out Commercial Road through open fields to the City, a broader highway along a more direct route than the Ratcliffe Highway. By 1825, when an official census of short-distance stage coaches was carried out, the route to Blackwall came third on the list (after those to Paddington and Camberwell). The service was operated by the West India Dock Company for the carriage of passengers and trade samples.[16] A decade later, a railway was promoted from the City to Brunswick Pier, Blackwall, to serve the dockland communities along the line and to link with steamboats to Gravesend, cutting the journey from there to the City by 45 minutes. The London and Blackwall Railway, opened from a temporary station in the Minories in July 1840 and extended to the new Fenchurch Street terminus in August 1841, is discussed by Alan Pearsall in this volume. Its companion on the other side of the river, the London and Greenwich Railway, had been opened from Deptford to Spa Road, Bermondsey in 1836 and from Greenwich to London Bridge two years later.[17]

The building of the docks and the improvement in land communications to them encouraged industrial growth and housing for the rapidly rising labour force. From the 1830s steam shipbuilding and engineering were developed on the west side of the Isle of Dogs, associated with the names of Napier and Fairbairn. These pioneering ventures, discussed later by Eve Hostettler, failed to reap the real gains of steel and steam shipbuilding, however, which were to come in the latter part of the nineteenth century and the early twentieth. The new industry reached maturity not on the Thames but on the Clyde, the Mersey and the estuaries of the North-East,

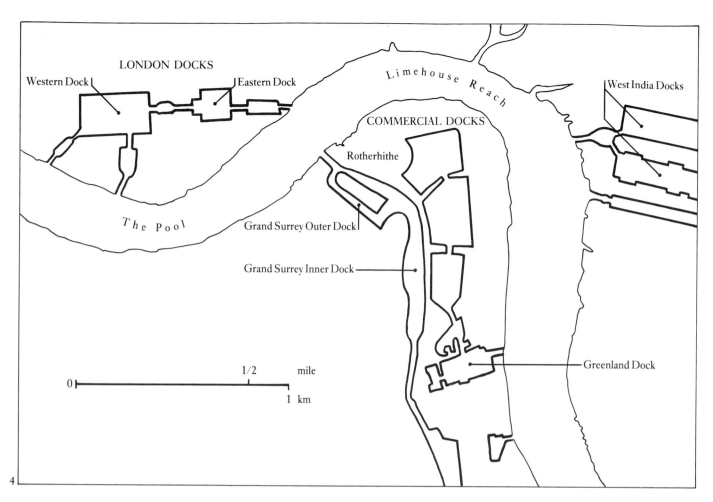

London Docks
Western Dock
Eastern Dock
Limehouse Reach
West India Docks
Commercial Docks
Rotherhithe
Grand Surrey Outer Dock
The Pool
Grand Surrey Inner Dock
Greenland Dock

0   1/2   mile
0   1 km

4

though the Thames Ironworks, having built about 900 vessels, was still of importance after 1900. It also diversified into electrical manufacturing.[18]

Competition between the dock companies became more severe from the 1820s. Although they handled most cargoes from abroad, the UK traffic, unloaded in the river overside, continued to be larger in volume. In 1835, for instance, the docks received only 950,000 tons of goods out of 3,700,000 tons coming into the port as a whole. Moreover, between then and

1850 there was a considerable growth in overside delivery into barges to be taken elsewhere from the docks themselves.[19] Dock capacity was also increased with the opening of the (Royal) Victoria Dock (100 acres) in 1855, Millwall Dock (1868) and the Royal Albert Dock (1880) at a time when overside delivery from the open river still accounted for most of the traffic. This coastwise trade, however, was being competed for by the new railways which had been built into London from the 1830s, especially those from the north. Yet coastal

4   The London and Surrey Docks, 1834. (C A White)

5   The development of the Port of London. (C A White)

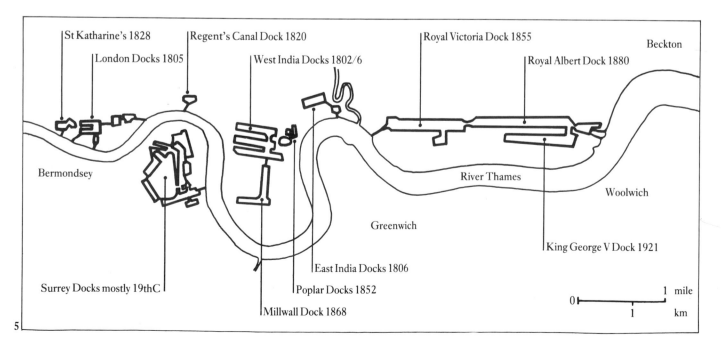

St Katharine's 1828
Regent's Canal Dock 1820
Royal Victoria Dock 1855
Beckton
London Docks 1805
West India Docks 1802/6
Royal Albert Dock 1880
Bermondsey
River Thames
Woolwich
Greenwich
Surrey Docks mostly 19thC
East India Docks 1806
Poplar Docks 1852
King George V Dock 1921
Millwall Dock 1868

0   1 mile
0   1 km

5

shipping managed to hold on to a surprisingly large amount of the traffic. In 1863, for instance, the merchandise tonnage between Edinburgh and Glasgow and London exceeded the rail tonnage by eight times. Until the 1860s half or more of London's coal was still arriving by sea.[20] Perhaps the railways were affecting the dock companies' warehousing business as much as the open river's overside business: when railway branches were opened into the docks, goods could be removed with less delay and storage.[21]

The dock companies responded to this greater competition by amalgamation. The East and West India Dock Companies amalgamated in 1838 and those on the south side, to form the Surrey Commercial Dock Company, in 1864. The upstream London and St Katharine Dock Companies joined forces with the Victoria Dock Company in that same year and later built the Royal Albert Dock with direct access to Gallion's Reach. As vessels became larger, (see Alan Pearsall's contribution on Deep-sea Ships), the East and West India Company stole a march by moving 16 miles down river from the Royal Docks (and 26 miles from London Bridge). They acquired a 450-acre site at Tilbury and built a new dock there. To this the competition responded by building a larger entrance lock at the Royal Albert Dock. But these two main competitors were driven to agreement in 1889.[22] The way was open for the eventual setting up, in 1909, of the Port of London Authority, which also included the other surviving dock concerns.

Fierce competition between dock employers, and between them and those engaged in the important overside business, had its inevitable effect upon the conditions of dock labour. This, in turn, had its influence upon the social conditions, including the housing standards, of a large part of the population of East London, discussed in another chapter by Eve Hostettler. The organisations of the London dockers and the success of the much-publicized London Dock Strike of 1889 was to become a landmark in the history of the British labour movement. It was the signal for the wider mobilisation of workers in other occupations who had not been apprenticed to a trade and were not as yet in trade unions. This was an important step along the road which was shortly to lead to the creation of the Labour Party. Did it lead, too, in the longer run, to mechanization, containerization and the dramatic changes in London's dockland with which this volume is concerned? Or would these events have come about anyway as a result of technical progress: the larger vessels which made up-river docks uneconomic and freed their valuable sites for science-based industries? To this extent, technical progress has released sites for the new technology and for the better-off beneficiaries of the computer age to take advantage of comfortable dwellings by or near a river which, despite enormous change, still holds for many a great fascination and appeal.

Notes

1   Simmons, Jack p 58, *A Selective Guide to England.*

2   Flinn, Michael W p 274, *The History of the British Coal Industry*, Vol II.

3   Bird, James p 205, *The Growth of the Port of London.*
Jackson, Gordon p 54, *The History and Archaeology of Ports.* This part of the chapter relies heavily upon this valuable source and upon Stern.

4   Colquhoun, Patrick pp 10–14, *A Treasure on the Commerce and Police of the River Thames* (1880).

5   Jackson, Gordon pp 43–4, *The History and Archaeology of Ports.*

6   Jackson, Gordon pp 56, *The History and Archaeology of Ports.*

7   Stern pp 51–2.

8   Newton and Others v Cubitt and Others, Court of Common Pleas, Engl Law Reports, Vol 142, pp 1053–1066, q Stern, p 66n.

9   Stern pp 76–2.

10   Jackson, Gordon p 62, *The History and Archaeology of Ports.*

11   Bagwell, Philip S p 64 seq, *The Transport Revolution from 1770.*
Barker, Theo C and Robbins, Michael pp 40–3, *A History of London Transport*, Vol 1.
Gourvish, T R pp 1–8, 14–18, 'The Railways and Steamboat Competition in Early Victorian Britain', *Transport History* Vol 4 No 1, March 1971.
Channon, Geoffrey pp 1–24, 'The Aberdeen Beef Trade with London: A Study in Steamship and Railway Competition 1850–69', *Transport History* Vol II, No 1 March 1969.

12   Stow Vol II, pp 71–2.

13   Rose Map c.

14   Green, Henry and Wigram, Robert pp 33, 45 seq, *Chronicles of Blackwall Yard*, (1881).

15   Account of Ships and Vessels Built in Great Britain from 1790 to 1791 and 1804 to 1805. Parliamentary Papers 1806 [243] XIII. I owe this reference to Dr Stephanie Jones.

16   Barker, Theo C and Robbins, Michael, p 5, Vol I, *A History of London Transport.*

17   Barker, Theo C and Robbins, Michael, p 45, pp 48–9, Vol I, *A History of London Transport.*

18   Barker, Theo C and Robbins, Michael, p 38, p 331, Vol II, *A History of London Transport.* Essex, V C H p 470, Vol II (1907)

19   Lovell, John p 16, *Stevedores and Dockers.*

20   Channon, Geoffrey p 18. Bagwell, Philip S p 73. *The Transport Revolution from 1770.*

21   Lovell, John p 16, *Stevedores and Dockers.*

22   Jackson, Gordon pp 80–3, pp 122–5, *The History and Archaeology of Ports.*

Warehouses in dockland

Malcolm Tucker

One of the principal secondary activities of a seaport until very recently was the storage of goods in transit sheds and warehouses. Short-term storage was required for goods awaiting export or forward shipment, and for newly-arrived imports during customs clearance and breaking of bulk before sale. Longer term storage was also required, since harvests and weather gave the arrival of many commodities a seasonal if not haphazard character, which had to be buffered against consumption spread evenly throughout the year.

In the eighteenth and early nineteenth centuries, when virtually every commodity was subject to import or export duty, the legal requirements of the Customs and Excise influenced the demand for warehousing in London perhaps as much as the general state of trade.[1] Until then, in order to defray the duties to which they became liable as soon as they were landed, imports had to be sold quickly and this discouraged storage in the Port. The East India Company alone, under its charters of 1661 and 1708, was permitted to defer payment of duty, half for six months and half for a year, on goods warehoused under the strict supervision of the Customs. During the eighteenth century, however, this principle was slowly extended to tobacco, pepper, rum, sugar, coffee and wines. They were placed under the joint locks of the Customs and the merchant, who deposited a bond of security.[2]

The Warehousing Act of 1803 allowed all types of high value goods to be placed in approved warehouses for up to fifteen months without payment of duties, and the period was extended to three years, or longer at the Commissioner's discretion, by the Warehousing Act of 1823. Goods were strictly monitored on entering and leaving the warehouses, and during any inspection, re-packing or blending, and maximum allowances for wastage during these processes were prescribed by the Acts. A bond of security of twice the duties payable had to be deposited.

In parallel with the development of bonded warehouses, obstacles to the location of warehouses were gradually relaxed. In the eighteenth century, the Customs came to allow goods to be discharged "on sufferance", and for a fee, at wharves other than the restrictive Legal Quays around the Custom House which had been specified in Acts of 1558 and 1663. The system was regularized in 1789 by the listing of permanent Sufference Wharves, open to all importers, subject to their proprietors giving a bond for fair dealing and paying for Customs officers' attendance. But bonded storage remained restricted. The 1803 Act endorsed the temporary monopolies of the new enclosed docks and the East India Company for handling designated classes of goods. However, the Act of 1823 simply laid down a list of those high-value goods which had to be deposited at warehouses erected in places of special security, such as enclosed docks, while other restrictions were relaxed further. Thereafter, bonded warehouses and the places they might be located were approved by Treasury Warrant, a relatively straightforward procedure.

1   *Internal construction of a 9 storey sugar warehouse, c1835, 40 Dock Street, London E1 — demolished. (Malcolm Tucker)*

The ending of the East India Company's monopoly in tea, in 1835, allowed others to enter this expanding business. From the 1840s, large number of articles were freed from Customs duties, with the intended effect of expansion of trade, although rising population and prosperity ensured there was little diminution of the demand for bonded accommodation for dutiable goods.

Outside the enclosed docks, sites suitable for warehouses were limited, for they had to be on or close to the waterside, preferably below Bridge, yet reasonably near to the City for the convenience of merchants. This led to ever increasing densities of building as trade expanded. To satisfy the needs of the Port at their peak in the early twentieth century, tall warehouses lined the banks of the Thames almost continuously from Blackfriars to Limehouse and from Bankside to Rotherhithe, in addition to the vast accommodation in the docks, the city warehouses and the railway depôts.

Functional requirements

The functional requirements of traditional warehouses were relatively simple — large floor spaces contained within buildings that must be structurally robust, weatherproof and secure against theft and fore so far as the circumstances of the time would permit. External loading doors known as loopholes were provided at each level, and mechanical equipment was needed for hoisting and lowering. Otherwise goods handling within the warehouse was by muscle power and hand barrow, or latterly light electric truck. Subsidiary activities were the checking, sorting, cleaning, blending, re-packing and weighing of goods, which might require limited additional equipment such as portable weigh beams and clerks' desks. More specialised equipment was developed in the late nineteenth century for granaries and cold stores. For goods in transit within the security of the docks, as also for timber, simple sheds sufficed.

The external appearance of the London warehouse was determined by requirements of structural stability and fire protection, formalised in the London Building Acts.[3] These did not change fundamentally from the time of the Great Fire of London until the adoption of reinforced-concrete framed construction early in the twentieth century. The Act of 1667 for the Rebuilding of London after the Great Fire stipulated that all new buildings in the City and its immediate suburbs should have external and party walls of brick or stone, in order to restrict the spread of fire from one building to another, and it laid down minimum thicknesses of construction for buildings of different heights. Under an Act of 1707, party walls, ie between adjoining buildings, had to rise above the levels of the roofs, and overhanging eaves were eliminated, so that all roofs thereafter were concealed behind parapets. The London Building Act of 1774 continued these principles, but removed restrictions on the number of storeys. It reformed the system of

building control by the appointment of district surveyors, responsible for inspecting and approving new buildings. This Act, unique to London, applied to all the parishes of the built-up area, as far downstream as Rotherhithe and Limehouse. The enclosed dock companies subsequently achieved exemption, but maintained high standards of construction.

The standard building material of the area throughout the eighteenth and nineteenth centuries was the London stock brick, made from clay mixed with coal ash, the unburnt cinders assisting in the firing and producing a characteristic clinkered texture. For floors and roofs, timber was the only feasible material initially, but the straight-grained softwoods imported from the Baltic were ideal. Roofs were clad formerly with common tiles or pantiles, but later with slates, which allowed a much shallower pitch. Fine architecture was not a basic requirement of warehouses, but nevertheless the better-capitalised enterprises erected many imposing and well-planned buildings.

The Eighteenth Century

Very few buildings survive to illustrate eighteenth century warehouse construction in London. The earliest would seem to be the lower four storeys of the Old Bengal Warehouse, 1769-70, at Cutler Street in the City. Built for the East India Company, this is unrepresentatively grand, but it exhibits straight-headed sash windows of Georgian proportion set in stock-brick walls, and widely-spaced vertical lines of loading doors, served by cart yards. The internal structure comprises substantial timber columns, (otherwise called storey posts or stanchions), capped with crossheads supporting timber beams and joists. There are brick dividing walls and stone staircases. The ranges of the 1790s at Cutler Street followed a similar pattern. Circular columns with applied Doric mouldings and carved crossheads were an exceptional feature of the showroom floors there.

The Rum Warehouses built by the Navy at Deptford Dockyard in the 1780s also conform to the Georgian architectural tradition. An indication of the style of a smaller warehouse of the period may perhaps be gained at Grice's Granary, Rotherhithe, three storeys of the late 1790s. Its timber stanchions have massive timber "knees" supporting the beams. There are two original queen-post roofs of 1795 at the one-time East India Company's saltpetre warehouses at Free Trade Wharf, Shadwell. At the St Katharine Docks, part of the former G Warehouse of around 1800 has become the inappropriately-named "Dickens Inn". It has steep, queen-post roofs, intended for common tiles, and a rather unscientifically proportioned timber frame with raking struts. The original building had heavy brick walls with small windows, and the modern weatherboarded and galleried exterior is totally contrary to the 1774 Building Act.

The Early Nineteenth Century

After 1800, the warehouses of the early enclosed docks were adorned with Portland stone plinths, sills, string courses and cornices befitting such major public works. A significant innovation, seen in the earliest West India Dock warehouses from 1802, was the cast-iron window frame, often embellished with spikes for greater security and set in a wide opening for the better daylighting of the large internal spaces. The window shape, broader than high under a shallow segmental arched head, became the standard pattern for over a century.

Internal construction remained largely of timber, for the incombustible brick jack arches on cast-iron beams and columns that had been introduced in the 1790s into textile-spinning mills were expensive and not justified by the relatively low fire risks of a secure warehouse. Naked lights were not allowed in the enclosed docks. To control the spread of fire in the unfortunate event, the warehouses were subdivided by fire walls. The 1774 Building Act specified a maximum gross ground floor area between such walls of 3,500 square feet (320 square metres), although this was exceeded in the enclosed docks.[4] Openings in these walls required fire doors of quarter inch (6 millimetre) sheet iron. The walls also gave lateral stability to the buildings and assisted the separation of different consignments for Customs purposes. At the West India and the St Katharine Docks, the divisions were so arranged that goods were hoisted into the warehouses through loopholes on the dockside and subsequently lowered to carts through loopholes on the landside, so ensuring that goods entering and leaving bond were segregated, as well as assisting traffic flow.

Enclosed stone stairs were provided to allow independent access to each bonded area, rather than for fire containment or as means of escape.

These stairs might be of ample proportions, where merchants could come to inspect high-class goods and perhaps carry them away, as at Cutler Street or the London Dock North Stacks. The West India Docks and the London Dock South Stacks, in contrast, used

space-saving semi-spiral stairs. In granaries and similar non-bonded buildings, or where consignments could fill several floors, open-treaded timber stairs were used throughout the nineteenth century.

These large warehouses had long-span wooden roofs, generally clad with slates, although the particularly shallow upper roofs at West India were copper-clad. Impressive trusses similar to those used in the London Dock North Stacks survive in the Pennington Street sheds, completed around 1813.[5]

Storey heights and bay dimensions varied in the nineteenth century according to the goods to be stored. Heavy commodities such as sugar and grain could not be easily stacked above a certain height without overloading the floors, and warehouses for these had low storeys in general. In an extreme case, a nine-storey warehouse of the 1830s at 40 Dock Street, Stepney, had floor to floor heights of only 7 feet 6 inches (2.29 metres). General commodities which might be stacked higher or required good daylighting for inspection were allowed more generous space. At the West India Docks the six storeys at No 2 Warehouse, for sugar, may be compared with the five storeys within the same height at No 1 Warehouse, and a similar situation prevailed around the Eastern Dock at St Katharine's. Column spacings were related to the optimum spans of wooden floors, with joists spanning from 8 feet (2.4 metres) in some heavily loaded granaries to 13 feet or so (4 metres), and beams varying in span from 10 feet to 18 feet, (3 metres to 5.4 metres), according to loading and strength.

An important feature of the London Docks in particular was the vaults for wine and spirits beneath quay level. At the London Docks they covered at least 22 acres (9 ha). The vaults were generally of groined type, upon a grid of columns, with barrel vaults upon the perimeter buttress walls. Although grids of 12 and 18 feet (3.6 and 5.4 metres) were standard, to suit the warehouses above, an exceptional 26 foot (7.9 metre) square grid was used beneath the Old Tobacco Warehouse (1805). Columns of the early vaults were of dressed stone, but cast iron was used at St Katharine's (1827-8).

4   London Docks North Stacks, 1805 — demolished. (Maleolm Tucker)

5   Vaults under London Docks South Quay, c1806 — demolished. (Malcolm Tucker)

4

5

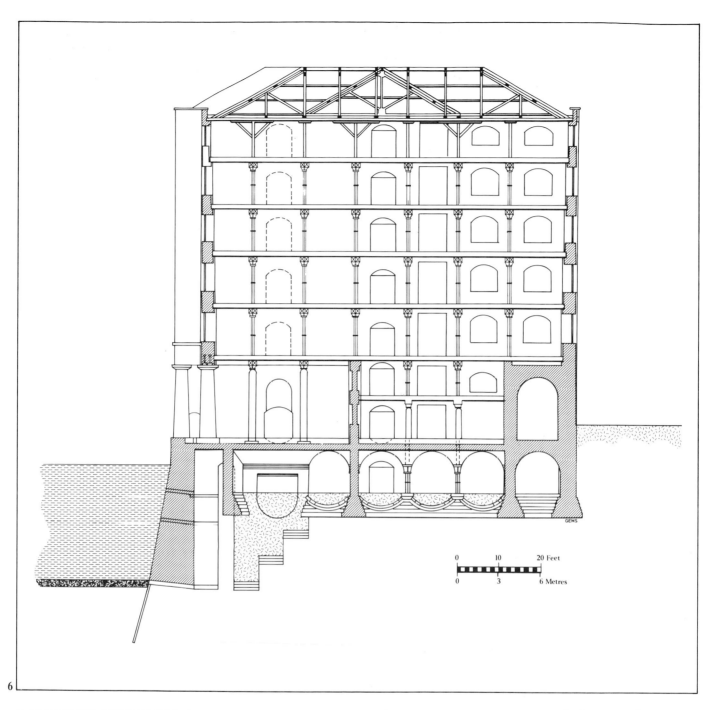

6 Cross section of B Warehouse, 1828, St Katharine Docks. (Gloria E M Shayler)

7 Spacious interior of B Warehouse, 1828, St Katharine Docks. (Malcolm Tucker)

The early foundations at the London and West India docks were on softwood piles driven through waterlogged silt and peat into the underlying gravel. At St Katharine's, firm strata occurred at a higher level and the warehouses were founded via inverted arches onto strip footings of brick. These stepped down the face of the dock excavation where they approached the quay. In later years, foundation piers of mass concrete became common. Bearing pressures were often high by modern standards, the structures being sufficiently flexible to accommodate the resulting settlements.

The arrangement of the St Katharine Dock warehouses on columns on the edges of the quays arose from the acute constrictions of the site. The idea was not new, having been proposed more than once in the 1790s for the improvement of the Legal Quays in the City. It was adopted in the 1840s for one or two warehouses in the London Docks (and on a grand scale in the Port of Liverpool), but elsewhere it found little favour, with only very modest examples along the London riverfront. Though the ability to hoist goods direct from ship to warehouse was an advantage, the sorting and manoeuvring of goods for other destinations was severely restricted by columns and fire walls.

At St Katharine's the cranes for lifting goods onto the quays were placed in shallow embayments of the dockside walls of the warehouses, which had the subsidiary architectural effect of breaking up the otherwise very long facades, as did the cart yards on the landside. Also the architect, Philip Hardwick, applied to his facades the giant blind arcade motif, already used in domestic architecture, which proved popular in various forms for warehouses over the next hundred years.

8 Cast iron staircase of 1828, St Katharine Church House. (Malcolm Tucker)

8

The structural use of iron

The use of cast iron was expanding rapidly in the early 1800s under the influence of engineers such as John Rennie the elder, who was active at the London and West India docks. Its high compressive strength made it an ideal material for the internal columns of warehouses. Timber posts, even of oak, had a tendency to split or to punch into their crossheads under heavy loads. At the London Docks in 1805, cast-iron reinforcements were used at the joints in posts of oak. Cast-iron columns, of heavy cruciform section supporting timber crossheads, were used when the London Dock South Stacks were raised from two to four storeys in 1810-11, possibly their earliest use in the docks, while in 1814 timber columns in No 2 Warehouse at the West India Docks, overloaded with sugar, were replaced with ones of iron. These had detachable iron crossheads. A similar operation must have taken place, probably after 1820, in parts of the Cutler Street warehouses.

The cruciform cross-section used in these early cast-iron columns remained the commonest form in the timber-floored warehouses of London throughout the nineteenth century, being easier to cast and therefore cheaper than the theoretically more efficient hollow circular section. By the time of the St Katharine Dock warehouses, 1827-8, there had evolved a standard type of integral column head, of an elongated plate supported on deep ribs, which altered little thereafter, although pierced or bifurcated varieties were seen occasionally.

A remarkable building in the London Docks illustrates the experimental yet competent nature of the early application of cast iron to building construction. The New Tobacco Warehouse was built in 1811-14 and a substantial portion remains as the "Skin Floor". It is a single-storeyed structure of considerable extent (originally 210,000 sq ft or 20,000 sq metres), with exceptionally elegant timber queen-post roofs of 54 feet (16.5 metres) span. Widely spaced cast-iron columns bifurcate in a tree-like manner, with raking struts to support alternate roof trusses midway between the columns. The arrangement was modelled on the wholly timber Old Tobacco Warehouse of 1805.

A transit shed roofed wholly in iron was ordered by the London Dock Company in 1810. In 1813, the West India Dock Company built several innovative sheds at the Rum Quay. Cast-iron arched beams were introduced, eliminating the need for raking struts as used in the "Skin Floor". One shed by the Butterley Company had roof trusses, beams and columns entirely of cast iron and was 1,330 feet (405 metres) long, with provision for thermal expansion.[6] Two by Thomas Pearsall of Bristol had prototype trusses of rolled wrought-iron flats, which proved unstable. Near by, in 1817, the timber-roofed Mahogany Shed incorporated overhead travelling cranes for handling logs. All these sheds have gone, but small wooden-roofed sheds of 1824, on slim

9 Early cast-iron stanchions, 1810 London Docks South Stacks — demolished. (Malcolm Tucker)

9

circular iron columns, may be seen in the Quadrangle maintenance yard at the West India Docks (now "Cannon Workshops").[7] Around 1829, Henry Palmer invented corrugated iron, which he used compositely with iron frames for roofing sheds at the London Docks.

Cast iron was a routine structural material by the late 1820s and it was used at St Katharine's for the spectacular Doric colonnade of hollow castings 2 inches (50 millimetres) thick and the inverted-T-section beams spanning between them. For economy, the internal beams and joists remained of timber, and only the Navy could afford incombustible construction, of sandstone slabs on cast-iron joists and beams, for its storehouses of the 1820s, as formerly stood at Deptford Victualling Yard.

For strength in tension, the superior properties of the more expensive malleable or wrought iron were increasingly utilised, for instance, the substitution of queen rods for queen posts in timber roofs from the 1830s and the trussing of timber beams with iron rods at the London Docks from the 1840s. Timber beams "flitched" with wrought-iron plates sandwiched vertically within them were commonly employed until supplanted by rolled steel beams at the end of the century.

10 New Tobacco Warehouse, 1813, London Docks. (Malcolm Tucker)

10

11 Queen-rod roof trusses of 58 ft span, New Hibernia Wharf, 1860 — demolished. (Malcolm Tucker)

11

The 1840s saw the development for shipbuilding and railway construction of rolled wrought-iron plates and angles rivetted together into beams, and in 1854 the engineer William Fairbairn, the leading practitioner, published his treatise "On the Application of Cast and Wrought Iron to Building Purposes". This probably influenced the St Katharine Dock Company to build I Warehouse (now "Ivory House") of wholly incombustible construction in 1858-60. It has brick jack arches on wrought-iron plate girders and cast-iron circular columns.

12 Hay's Wharf, 1856 — Dock facades in 1974. (Malcolm Tucker)

12

Fire protection, a dilemma

Fire protection at lesser cost was the ostensible objective in the warehouses at Hay's Wharf, Tooley Street (1856-7) and New Hibernia Wharf), Montague Close (1858-60), both erected by William Cubitt for the wharfinger John Humphery. Incombustible floors of brick jack arches on cast-iron beams alternated with floors of timber, although some of these at Hay's Wharf originally incorporated "concrete and slate" fire protection. The brick floors allowed circumvention of the limit on cubic capacity in the 1855 Building Act, even though the cast-iron columns supporting them relied on the timber intermediate floors for stability. One half of Hay's Wharf was destroyed in the Great Fire of Tooley Street in 1861.

A problem recognised around this time was that cast iron is prone to fracture in fire from stresses of expansion and contraction if unevenly restrained or if rapidly cooled by hoses, and that "fireproof" is a misnomer. Thereafter, one school of thought advocated heavy timber as preferable to iron columns, the timber charring away only slowly in a fire. Although Hay's Wharf was re-built in facsimile with the insurance money, brick jack-arch construction was rarely applied elsewhere in London buildings.[8]

Out of the Tooley Street fire, there arose in 1865 the public fire brigade of the Metropolitan Board of Works, in place of the brigade sponsored by a consortium of insurance companies since 1832. The part-time parish fire brigades had long previously been found inadequate.

Control by the insurance companies also became stricter, with the establishment in 1864 of the Wharves and Warehouses Committee. This inspected premises for hazardous situations and practices, and made recommendations to its member companies on rates of premium and other restrictions appropriate to the risk in each case.[9]

The later Nineteenth Century

The more liberal customs regulations and growth of trade in the Victorian period produced a disproportionate increase in warehousing on the riverfront, since the "Free Water Clause" in each dock company's Act encouraged discharge overside into lighters for delivery outside the docks. The new London Bridge of 1832 gave improved navigation for barges and made the South Bank more accessible by road from the City. Warehouses on the Upper Pool and above Bridge were re-built typically to five or seven storeys' height, with further blocks on the landside connected by spectacular tiers of footbridges across the narrow intervening streets. A few examples remain, in Wapping and, particularly, Shad Thames. There, the 1872 riverside range of Butler's Wharf has six and eight storeys and warehouses of the 1880s to the 1900s extend 150 yards (130 metres) inland, making this the densest packed area of Dockland. Hay's Wharf of 1856-7, with handsome six storey warehouses around their own dock, was in a class apart. Many wharves built jetties into the river for moderate sized ships to berth alongside.

The classical architectural idioms of giant pilasters and stucco cornices were favoured for these riverside sites, but some warehouses ventured into Gothic styles, as Oliver's Wharf, Wapping, of 1870, or used elaborate and colourful brickwork, as the former St Mary Overy Wharf, Clink Street, of 1882. Staffordshire blue engineering bricks and pressed bricks from other sources were introduced for hardwearing areas, at first for the jambs of loopholes. On the other hand, many of the granaries of Bermondsey persisted with plain stock brickwork and unglazed wooden window frames into the 1870s.

Early granaries differed little in principle from other warehouses. Buildings of specialised design began to appear in the 1880s when the Surrey Commercial Dock Company provided

13

their No 7 Granary with hydraulic bucket elevators and conveyors to handle increasing quantities of imported wheat in bulk. The Millwall Dock Company's Central Granary, commenced in 1899, was a particularly massive brick structure, thirteen storeys tall, with pneumatic elevators. Large granaries associated with flour mills were built also at Deptford Creek and the Victoria Dock.

New Zealand dairy produce was first shipped under refrigeration to Hay's Wharf in 1867, and frozen New Zealand lamb in 1882. Cotton's Wharf and others around Tooley Street were converted to cool stores for butter, cheese and bacon, and the South Bank soon became the principal centre for provision merchants. The London and India Docks Joint Committee

converted a warehouse for cold strorage at West India and they built one of the first cold stores at Smithfield meat market in 1895 — the PLA later built a second one there and others at the Royal Albert Dock.

The railways were slow to alter the pattern of handling of goods in the docks, although Poplar Docks and the Victoria Dock were rail-connected from the early 1850s. Two-storey transit sheds were provided at Poplar in the 1860s and 1870s and the Royal Albert Dock of 1880 was laid out for the rapid loading of rail wagons, with single storey transit sheds but no warehouses. Warehouses were constructed at railway goods stations connected to the Blackwall Railway, just east of the City. Notably, the Tilbury Warehouse at Commercial Road Goods Depôt was completed in 1887 for traffic from Tilbury Docks. It had floors of Evans and Swain's solid timber construction on wrought-iron plate girders.

Towards the end of the nineteenth century improved technology made fireproof floors an economic proposition. "Filler joist" floors were coming into use in warehouses from the 1880s, accelerated by the availability of rolled steel joists. The metal joists were encased with lightweight concrete made with brick or coke breeze aggregate, on a principle used since the 1840s in model dwellings and public buildings.

The Twentieth Century

Modern reinforced concrete construction, in which embedded steel bars act compositely with good-quality concrete, was introduced to Britain in 1897 by Francois Hennebique, and its great strength and fire resistance particularly suited it to warehouses. The monolithic concrete frame rendered obsolete the tradition of heavy loadbearing brick walls, although London's by-laws were slow to acknowledge this. Moreover, pre-cast concrete piles or concrete rafts facilitated construction on difficult ground. The new Port of London Authority adopted reinforced concrete for two-storey transit sheds upon jetties at the London and West India Docks (1912 and 1914), and for cold stores and transit sheds at the Royal Albert and King George V Docks (1917-21), where impressive triangulated (Warren) girders of 50 foot (15 metres) span were incorporated.

Reinforced concrete floors were also used in conjunction with traditional brickwork, or with steel beams encased in concrete for protection from fire. Where concrete frames were exposed on the exterior, inter-war warehouses were sometimes exceedingly ugly, as at the Surrey Commercial South Dock, but the Oxo warehouse of 1928 at Blackfriars Bridge conceals its construction behind an ornamental river frontage. The Hay's Wharf Company evolved an effective style of concrete and brickwork in horizontal bands, with staggered loading doors, for its post-1945 cold stores.

Undoubtedly the most striking and unusual modern warehouse was M Shed, alias No 19 Shed, built in 1967 at the South West India

13 Shad Thames, bridges connecting riverside and landside at Butler's Wharf. (Malcolm Tucker)

14

14 *Reinforced-concrete transit
sheds on jetties, 1912, London
Docks — demolished.
(Malcolm Tucker)*

now those of wholesalers and retailers, notably
wine merchants, and they are not specifically
related to the Port.

Dock. It had pre-stressed concrete waffle-slab
floors, steel lattice barrel-vault roofs and a
vehicular ramp to the first floor. Although
intended only for transit purposes, M Shed had
three floors to achieve a high throughput at the
berth.

Pre-cast, pre-stressed concrete frames were
used for a shed at the London Docks during the
1952 Korean War steel shortage. For simple,
single storey sheds, steel frames and lightweight
corrugated cladding normally have strong
economic advantages, however. This style of
construction suited the new, more spacious
transit shed accommodation required by the
PLA in the 1950s when fork lift trucks and
palletised loads were introduced to speed the
discharge and turn-round of vessels.
Steel-framed sheds were built with a 20 foot (6
metre) clear headroom and uninterrupted spans
up to 150 feet (45 metres) at the Millwall Dock
and 200 feet (60 metres) at the Victoria Dock.
Then, in 1966 and 1970, three sheds were built
for the Olsen Line at Millwall with 600 by 200
foot (180 by 60 metre) clear spaces for the
mechanised handling of pallets of fruit.

In the face of new mechanical handling
methods and rising costs of labour, the rundown
of traditional warehousing in the upper docks
and the Pool of London was predictable, but
more of a surprise was the suddenness of this
decline in the period 1967-70, unintentionally
hastened by the decasualisation of dock labour.
After the first container berth was opened at
Tilbury in 1968, the revolution of
containerisation overtook even the recent
investments at Millwall. Containers and
roll-on/roll-off more vehicles can be packed
and unpacked at the ultimate origin or
destination, or at groupage depôts far inland,
and open parking space, not warehousing, is
required at ports for the majority of general
cargoes. In 1969 the Tilbury Bulk Grain
Terminal opened, to handle all the wheat
passing through the Port, while other trades not
in containers have also been concentrated at
Tilbury. Warehouse activities have become a
growth-industry around Heathrow Airport.
Otherwise, London's warehousing needs are

Notes

1   Graham Smith, *Something to Declare. 1,000
Years of Customs & Excise.*

2   Control of tobacco and wine passed in 1786
from the Commissioners of Customs to the
Commissioners of Excise. Thereafter, these
commodities could remain in the warehouse
indefinitely without payment of duties.

3   C C Knowles and P H Pitt, *A History of
Building Regulation in London, 1189-1972.*

4   The limit became 200,000 cubic feet (5,700
cubic metres) in the 8144 Act, 216,000 cubic
feet (6,100 cubic metres) in 1855 and 250,000
cubic feet (7,100 cubic metres) in 1894.

5   The 65 foot (20 metre) span,
triple-king-post trusses of 1774 over the Porter
Tun Room of Whitbread's Brewery, Chiswell
Street, were never equalled in the docks.

6   Described by Charles Dupin, *Memoires sur
le marine et les ponts et chaussées de France et
d'Angleterre*, p 11, and illustrated, Charles
Dupin, *Voyages dans la Grande Bretagne, Part 3,
Force Commerciale*, Plate 11.

7   Innovation in composite cast-iron and
wrought-iron roof trusses was seen around
1818 in the anchor smithery at Woolwich
Dockyard, (also illustrated by Dupin). They are
now partly re-erected at the Ironbridge Gorge
Museum.

8   For contemporary experience, see James
Braidwood, *Fire Prevention and Fire Extinction.*

9   The records of the Wharves and
Warehouses Committee are deposited at the
Guildhall Library.

For a comprehensive review of the history of
fireproofing, see:

Department of Scientific & Industrial
Research, (S B Hamilton), *A Short History of the
Structural Fire Protection of Buildings.*

Acknowledgements

The writer wishes to thank all those owners who
have given access to their warehouses in the
past, David Thomas and other members of the
Greater London Industrial Archaeology
Society who have collaborated in recording and
research, Edward Sargent for sharing the fruits
of his research in the PLA archives, and the
Historic Buildings Division of the Greater
London Council for access to their records.

Lost buildings in dockland

Paul Calvocoressi

It is one measure of the success of conservation policies in Greater London that in large areas of the Metropolis it is still possible without undue exercise of the imagination to see what it looked like fifty or even a hundred years ago. This is not true in Dockland. The two generations since the beginning of the Second World War have seen developments which have changed the area almost out of recognition. Only in a few small enclaves, such as St Saviour's Dock in Bermondsey or the old village centre of Rotherhithe, can one still discern more than traces of an earlier identity.

The "Dockland" character of popular imagination, as illustrated by Gustave Dore and described in the stories of writers such as W W Jacobs and Sir Arthur Conan Doyle, was largely a creation of the nineteenth century; beginning with the construction of the new enclosed docks in the early 1800s and continuing through the rest of the century with the gradual lining of both sides of the river with tall, closely-packed, brick-built warehouses.

London had of course been expanding eastwards from its City limits from at least the end of the middle ages. By the end of the eighteenth century both sides of the river were heavily built up as far as Poplar and Rotherhithe. Thus, when the nineteenth century docks and warehouses came to be built, their construction could only be carried through at the expense of massive destruction of existing properties[1]. The destruction of the church of St Katharine by the Tower, (fig 1), in 1825 gave rise to a public outcry which reached the correspondence pages of The Times[2] but for the most part the displaced families came from the poorest labouring classes and any objections they might have had could be easily ignored.

It is, however, not so much with these changes that we wish to deal here as with those even more comprehensive developments that have taken place in the last 45 years. This is not the place to attempt any detailed analysis of these developments. Space is limited and the causes are complex. All that can be done is to attempt a gross over-simplification and suggest three principal agencies of change: enemy action, economic forces and the public authorities, and illustrate them with pictures of

1 *The medieval church of St Katharine by the Tower, part of the hospital and precinct of St Katharine, which were demolished to make way for St Katharine Docks in 1825. The hospital was founded by Matilda, wife of King Stephen, in 1148. The buildings survived the worst consequences of the Reformation, the Fire of London and the Gordon Riots and its proposed demolition, together with over 1,000 houses created a public outcry. (Gentleman's Magazine, February 1826)*

what seem to be their more important architectural or historic victims.

Enemy action

The unrestricted U-boat campaigns of the First World War had showed how vulnerable Britain was to ruthless attacks on its commerce. It was widely believed between the wars that aerial bombardment could be an even more devastating form of assault. Pre-war official forecasts of what bombing could achieve were so alarming that they had to be kept secret. It was predicted that 3,500 tons of bombs could be expected in the first 24 hours followed by a further 700 tons per day. It was anticipated that each ton would cause 50 or more casualties and that material damage to the value of £550 million would be inflicted in the first three weeks, resulting in the complete breakdown of communications and other public services, mass panic and epidemics[3].

These prophesies proved of course to be grossly exaggerated. Nevertheless, Britain, far more than Germany, depended on overseas trade and one quarter of all British imports came through the Port of London[4]. It was therefore inevitable that the Luftwaffe's planners would soon appreciate the importance of Dockland as a target. A general directive from Göring for the conduct of the air war

against Britain, issued on 20 June 1940, stated as one of its objectives, after the destruction of the RAF, the dislocation of "Britain's supplies by attacking ports and harbour installations"[5].

With the capture of France, the Germans had at their disposal airfields from which their bombers and their escorts could reach London[6]. The first attack came on the afternoon of 7 September 1940 and for 76 successive nights London was raided (with one night off for bad weather). Thereafter, attacks continued sporadically for almost the rest of the war. The Docks were easily identifiable from the air and were attacked more than any other civilian target. Nearly 1,000 high explosive bombs and thousands of incendiaries were dropped[7].

The Port of London Authority lost one third of its warehousing and half of its storage accommodation. Though its activities were disrupted, the port was by no means put out of action. The Port of London Authority described the assault as "serious but not crippling"[8]. At the same time large areas of residential Dockland were devastated. During the whole of the blitz, 30,000 people were killed. Slightly more than half of these casualties were in London and a high proportion of these were in Dockland[9].

Within the Docks it is perhaps surprising how

2 Warehouses on the North Quay of the Import Dock in the West India Docks, destroyed by bombing in 1940. They formed part of a range of nine five-storey warehouses designed by George Gwilt in 1800. H M Colvin in his Biographical Dictionary of British Architects, 1600-1840 (John Murray, 1978) describes these warehouses as Gwilt's finest work and says of them that they were "the finest examples of London's dock architecture". Warehouses 1 and 2 at the west end of the Quay survive and are now Grade I listed buildings. (PLA)

2

many of the major buildings survived. There were, though, inevitably, serious architectural losses. The most important of these were the West India and the St Katharine Docks. In the West India Docks, (fig 2), the North Quay of the Import Dock was hit. Here stood a magnificent range of multi-storey warehouses, dating from 1800-02 onwards and designed by George Gwilt. The West India Docks were the first of the enclosed docks to be built and these warehouses were part of the original construction. They were amongst the oldest warehouses surviving in the Metropolis and among the most important. All but Warehouses 1 and 2 and the Dock Offices at the western end of the quay were destroyed.

The St Katharine's Docks were opened in 1828, (fig 3), and were the last docks of the first phase of the upstream dock development. Their engineer was Thomas Telford and they were notable for Telford's pioneering use of warehouses built right on the edge of the quay so that cargo could be unloaded directly from the ship into the warehouse without any need for intermediate handling. The Docks comprised two principal basins, the East and the West, both surrounded with warehouses. The warehouses round the East basin, (fig 4), were destroyed by bombing. Also destroyed were the Dock Offices at the north west corner of the West basin, (fig 5), a fine stuccoed Greek Revival design by Telford's architectural collaborator, Philip Hardwick, (for the fate of the rest of the West basin, see below).

3   The proposed St Katharine Dock buildings illustrated in the Gentleman's Magazine in January 1826. This view shows the layout of dock basins and warehouses though the detail of the buildings as built was different. At the lower left-hand corner of the East (right) basin can be seen the earlier 'G' warehouse, of which a mutilated fragment is all that now survives.

4   Warehouses in the East basin of St Katharine Dock, destroyed by bombing in 1940. Note the differences from the "proposed" print (fig 3): the massive Doric ground floor colonnade and the more sophisticated articulation of the elevations. To what degree either Telford or Hardwick were responsible for the final designs is not certain. (PLA)

5 St Katharine Dock House,
built to the designs of Philip
Hardwick in 1827-8 and destroyed
by bombing in 1940. (GLC)

5

34

CK HOUSE 1828.

LESLIE & GODWIN LIMITED

ONDED

ORIENT

6 *The church of St George-in-the-East, the Highway, Stepney was one of three Stepney churches designed by Nicholas Hawksmoor and begun in 1714. (The other two were St Anne, Limehouse and Christ Church, Spitalfields). It was bombed in 1941 and the interior was gutted. The tower and the outside walls survived and a new church has been built inside the shell. (Bedford Lemere NMR)*

7 *St John's church, Wapping, which dates from 1756 and was designed by Joel Johnson, photographed in December 1940 shortly after bomb damage. The tower with its distinctive cupola (which can just be seen in the background of fig 23) survives, having been restored in 1964 by the London County Council. (GLC)*

We have already mentioned that destruction spread well beyond the immediate confines of the Docks. One of the most notable architectural victims was the church of St George-in-the-East, built in 1729 to the designs of Nicholas Hawksmoor, whose interior was completely gutted, (fig 6), though the walls and west tower survive. Another ecclesiastical victim was the church of St John, Wapping, (fig 7), though here again the west tower survives.

Economic forces
The construction of the Docks was a solution to the demands of rapidly-increasing trade. The devastating scale of these operations has already been referred to. To build the first part of the London Docks between 1800 and 1805 some 1,300 houses had to be demolished. For the St Katharine Docks 1,033 houses were lost as well as St Katharine-by-the-Tower[10], (fig 1).

6

7

8

8 *St Mary Overy's Dock, Clink Street, Southwark. This photograph shows the houses and wharf that were demolished to make way for Pickford's Wharf in about 1860 and for St Mary Overy's Wharf, which was built in 1882. St Mary Overy's Wharf was itself demolished 102 years later amidst much controversy, (see figs 18, 19 and 20 below). (GLC)*

9 *St Olave's Church, Tooley Street, Southwark. This church, designed in 1739 by Henry Flitcroft, became redundant after the First World War. Despite strong objections from the London County Council and others it was demolished in 1929 and the site was sold to the Hay's Wharf company, who built their new head office on the site. (GLC)*

9

This was only a beginning. Trade continued to expand at an enormous rate and with it came demands for more and more warehousing space. From the 1830s there was strong competition between Dock and Wharf companies. As the century progressed, wharves were increasingly preferred and their construction proliferated along both banks of the river. By 1880 there was already an over-provision but their construction continued well into this century, steadily replacing much of the older riverside property, (figs 8 and 9).[11]

In the 1960s and 1970s this process was drastically reversed. The Port of London Authority moved most of its activities downstream to Tilbury. Changing patterns of goods storage and distribution emptied most of the riverside warehouses.

These changes coincided with the post-war property boom. The "you've never had it so good" years, when vast sums of money were lured into the property market in the hope of large and easy cash profits in what has been described as "one of the biggest misdirections of resources in modern times"[12].

Asset-stripping was the surest way to easy money and few assets could be more easily stripped than land.

A combination of property developers, local councillors and planners made the most of the boom while it lasted. Developable sites within easy reach of the City were obviously attractive to developers. The increased rates these developments could bring to councils whose needs were great but whose income was low also had their attraction. Planners were still dazzled by dreams of comprehensive regeneration. Wharves and warehouses were mostly seen as "dark satanic mills" which were better swept away. Few people, before the early 1970s, saw in

10

10, 11   The West basin of St Katharine Docks represents the worst blot on the Greater London Council's conservation record. The three Telford warehouses to survive the Blitz, 'A', 'B' (fig 10) and 'C' (fig 11) were demolished one by one over a period of ten years with wholly inadequate consideration being given to their architectural and historic importance and to the possibility of their retention and conservation. 'A' Warehouse was the first to go, in 1970, to be replaced by a new hotel. 'B' Warehouse was demolished in 1977-8 to make way for a new office block. 'C' Warehouse was demolished in 1980. (GLC)

11

12

15

13

16

14

17

them either interest or economic potential.

The result was a massive demolition of dock buildings and warehouses. In the St Katharine Docks all the remaining buildings except for "I" warehouse (built in the late 1850s) were demolished, (figs 10, 11 and 12). In the London Docks only the Skin Floor and the Pennington Street sheds survive. Statutory listing was no protection for Telford's warehouses in the St Katharine Docks, nor for D A Alexander's mighty North Quay Stacks in the London Docks, (figs 13 and 14). Outside the Docks, riverside warehouses were either demolished to provide cleared sites or, left empty, caught fire and had to be destroyed, (figs 15 to 21).

A few of these sites, those nearer the City, have actually been redeveloped, (fig 20). Further afield, now that the property boom has

come adrift, warehouses that managed to survive the Gadarene rush are now being converted while many of the cleared sites remain empty and derelict.

The public authorities

The elected authorities played a major part in encouraging and approving and, sometimes, in trying to resist the developments described above. They also had a more direct role to play. From the mid-nineteenth century the local authorities acquired powers to carry out improvements themselves, such as the provision of drainage (fig 22) and major highways. They also had considerable powers of slum clearance. The first slum clearance powers were used as a tool of sanitary engineering, as a way of removing offensive squalor. Subsequently the

18

19

12 'G' Warehouse, St Katharine Dock. This warehouse, dating possibly from the first decade of the nineteenth century, survived most of its original neighbours to be incorporated into the Dock. It was of massive timber-framed construction within its brick outer walls and the framing had been adapted to accommodate large liquor vats. It was largely demolished in 1973 but a fragment of it was retained and survives in a grotesquely mutilated form as the Dickens Inn not far from its original site. (GLC)

13, 14 The five massive Stacks on the North Quay of the West basin of the London Docks formed a group of dock buildings second only to the West India Dock warehouses illustrated in fig 2. They were designed by Daniel Asher Alexander and completed in 1805 just after the opening of the Dock. With the closure of the Dock in 1969 they were left empty and untended. They suffered from serious vandalism so that by the mid 1970s hopes that even one of them might be able to be retained proved vain. A new printing works now occupies their site. (GLC)

15 Carron Wharf, St Katharine Way was of very similar design to New Hibernia Wharf (fig 21) and the Hay's Dock warehouses (fig 27). It probably dated from the 1860's and was demolished in 1974, having been empty and derelict for some time. (GLC)

16, 17 Bennet's Lower Wharf, Bermondsey Wall East (fig 16) and Apollinaris Wharf, Rotherhithe Street (fig 17) are typical examples of the later nineteenth century warehouses that lined the river on the South side between St Saviour's Dock and Rotherhithe. They were mostly demolished with almost indecent haste in the mid 1970s to provide sites for new development, hardly any of which can yet be seen. (GLC)

18, 19 St Mary Overy's Wharf, Clink Street, Southwark. This fine six-storey warehouse with its distinguished polychrome elevations facing St Mary Overy's Dock and the river dated from 1882 and was designed by George Alchin Dunnage. With the decline of the warehousing trade, its site, close to London Bridge, became potentially very valuable for office development. Despite powerful arguments from the Greater London Council and others at a public inquiry in the summer of 1981 that the building was of special interest and was capable of beneficial use, the Secretary of State for the Environment overruled his own inspector and allowed its demolition. (Fig 18, The Architect, 18 November 1882, courtesy of RIBA. Fig 19, GLC)

20 *Conservation for Developers. Or, How to Preserve Links with the Past without the Inconvenience of actually Re-using Old Buildings. All that remains of St Mary Overy's Wharf: a fragment of one corner of the staircase tower facing Winchester Square, squashed between the advancing framework of the new offices, 1984. (P Calvocoressi)*

21 *What happened to all too many warehouses if they were left empty for too long. New Hibernia Wharf, Montague Close, Southwark photographed on the morning of 1 December 1978, just after the fire which damaged it so severely that it had to be demolished. This warehouse, which can also be seen on the left of fig 18, was built in 1858 as West Kent Wharf. A scheme to convert the building was approved in 1978 but was never started. By the time of the fire, another application, this time for its redevelopment, had been submitted. (GLC)*

22 *New Square, Shad Thames, Bermondsey photographed in 1906 shortly before its demolition to form the site for the London County Council's storm water pumping station. (GLC)*

20

emphasis shifted towards the provision of decent housing conditions but slum clearance remained (and remains) an important part of public health and housing departments' armouries.

It can not be said that the use of slum clearance powers has ever been an unqualified success. The early powers, from which requirements that those displaced should be rehoused on the spot had to be removed, tended (like piecemeal road widening) simply to move the problem elsewhere. Later campaigns, once the most overcrowded and insanitary rookeries had been removed, (fig 23), all too often destroyed houses which were perfectly capable of improvement, only to replace them with new monolithic rookeries which respected neither the *genius loci* nor the needs nor wishes of the local inhabitants.

Lessons have been learned since the days of the most enthusiastic clearances in the 1950s and 1960s and the social and economic arguments for repair rather than replacement are now better understood. But the learning process was costly, losing the Dockland communities a great many old buildings, many modest and unpretentious but some of the quality of the eighteenth century Wellclose and Swedenborg Squares. (figs 24, 25 and 26).

21

22

It has not been the purpose in these pages to lament the buldings that have gone. If any readers should wish to look at these pictures and then view the same sites today, they will be able to draw their own conclusions. Nevertheless, there are perhaps one or two questions which they might wish to ask. Does the new Milton-Keynes-on-Thames rapidly being thrown up under the aegis of the London Dockland Development Corporation recognise and continue the powerful character and traditions of the area? Do developments such as the pretentiously-named London Bridge City on the Hay's Wharf site, (fig 27), or the redevelopment of the West basin of St Katharine Docks preserve or enhance the appearance of these important historic sites, or are the developers paying no more than lip-service to a contemporary shibboleth, displaying the outward and visible signs of an inward and spiritual emptiness?

23

23 *The Prusom Street Clearance Area, photographed in September 1926, was typical of many areas of old housing which were demolished as slums. (GLC)*

24, 25 *Wellclose Square was laid out by Nicholas Barbon in 1682-3. Subsequently, the houses, built for wealthy merchants, came down in the world, but they survived the Blitz only to be demolished as slums in the 1960s. The illustrations show Nos 35-39 (fig 24) and No 51 (fig 25). (GLC)*

24

Notes

1 For the unprecedented scale of these operations, see Skempton, "Engineering in the Port of London".

2 Pudney, *London's Docks*, p 64 ff.

3 Calvocoressi, Peter and Wint, Guy. *Total War: Causes and Courses of the Second World War*, Allen Lane, 1972, p 136.

4 Pudney, *London's Docks*, p 166.

5 Jacobsen, H-A and Rohwer, J (eds.), *Decisive Battles of World War II: the German view, (trans E Fitzgerald)*, Andre Deutsch 1965, p 79.

6 Taylor, A J P, *English History 1914-1945*, Oxford University Press, 1965.

7 Pudney, *London's Docks*, p 170.

8 Pudney, *London's Docks*, p 166.

9 Taylor, *English History*, p 150.

10 Jones, Gareth Stedman, *Outcast London, a study in the relationship between classes in Victorian society*, Oxford University Press, 1971, p 164.

11 Jones, *Outcast London*, p 114, ff.

12 Calvocoressi, Peter, *The British Experience 1945-75*, Bodley Head, 1978, p 145.

25

43

26

26 Swedenborg Square dated from the earlier eighteenth century. Originally known as Prince's Square, the name was changed in 1938 to commemorate Emanuel Swedenborg, who was buried in the Swedish Protestant Church, built in 1728, which stood in the Square until 1919. The houses illustrated, Nos 8-17, date from the earlier nineteenth century. Like Wellclose Square (figs 24 and 25), the houses in Swedenborg Square were demolished in the 1960s. (GLC)

27

*"There was an Old Man who supposed,
That the street door was partially closed;
But some very large rats, ate his coats and his hats,
While that futile old gentleman dozed."*
(Edward Lear, A Book of Nonsense, 1846)

Like the security of the Old Man's front door, the listing of the warehouses round Hay's Dock was less than complete. The consequence was similarly unfortunate. These fine warehouses date from 1856 (though the west range had to be rebuilt after the Great Tooley Street Fire of 1861 and the riverward ends were rebuilt in modern style after bomb damage). They were designed by the architectural firm of Snooke and Stock, who were probably also responsible for New Hibernia and Carron Wharves (figs 21 and 15). They form part of the massive Hay's Wharf redevelopment currently under construction. By no means all the buildings on the site are being demolished, but many are, including Fenning's Wharf (partly of 1836 but much altered) and all but a fragment of Cotton's Wharf, which was also rebuilt after the 1861 fire and designed by Snooke and Stock. The Hay's Dock warehouses are to survive but in a seriously mutilated form, with almost all their interiors gutted, their roofs replaced and the Dock de-watered to provide a covered car park. (GLC)

27

The work of the dock engineer

Ivan S Greeves FICE

Introduction

The work of a Civil Engineer is best described in the words of the charter of the Institution of Civil Engineers as "being the art of directing the great sources of power in Nature for the use and convenience of Man." As far as dock engineering in London was concerned it meant the controlling of the River Thames so that ships could navigate safely, and the provision of sheltered water in docks where they could be loaded and unloaded.

With the amalgamation of the various dock companies in 1908 to form the Port of London Authority, Lord Devonport its first Chairman, appointed Sir Frederick Palmer as Chief Engineer. He gathered around him a strong team of Civil Engineers to design and supervise the construction of new works. Between the first and second World Wars the size of ships increased considerably, and the efforts of the Engineering Department were concentrated on the construction of new deep-water docks. The first new dock was the King George V Dock, opened in 1921 with a new large entrance lock. Afterwards, in the 1930s the task of deepening the Albert Dock was tackled, followed by the complete modernisation of Victoria Dock. This provided essentially new linked docks with a system of transit sheds, warehouses, and railway tracks. This chapter describes the work of a Civil Engineer in the Port of London from the 1940s by means of a series of illustrations.

World War II

The war brought devastation to the docks. Those men who had not been called to Military Service were engaged in clearing the bomb rubble. The Eastern Basin of St Katharine's Docks was used as a temporary tip for rubble from the docks and from the City. When in 1943 the Overlord Plan for the invasion of France was decided upon, it was necessary to find sites for the construction of the floating breakwaters. Ideally, dry docks would have been best, but those in the Royal and Millwall docks were full of cruisers, corvettes, and destroyers

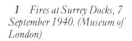

1 *Fires at Surrey Docks, 7 September 1940. (Museum of London)*

2 *Phoenix units for Mulberry Harbour under construction, Russia Yard, winter 1944. (Mowlem)*

3 *Phoenix units for Mulberry Harbour, afloat in Russia Dock prior to D Day, April 1944. (Mowlem)*

had dredged 47 million cubic yards from the docks and river. Theories had been proposed that the practice of dumping dredgings in Black Deep, some 30 miles to the seaward of Southend, might have some connection with the amount of silt deposited in the upper reaches. After model tests, it was decided to go ahead with tests in the river itself. Radio-active isotopes encapsulated in finely ground glass particles were used. It was found that as the tide makes, heavily silt-laden salt water flowed below the lighter fresh water depositing mud in the central part of the estuary. In fact, some went upstream as far as Westminster Bridge before moving downstream again. Mud dredged at Gravesend found its way back to Barking Reach this requiring redredging to take place. The Engineering solution was simple and most effective. In future all dredgings would be pumped ashore at Rainham in Essex where the PLA owned 260 acres of low ground. After a few years the results were far reaching and conclusive. The regime of the Thames settled down naturally and little further maintenance dredging was necessary,

Damage to dock installations by shipping

It was always felt that ships' pilots had little regard for dock installations. The flexible timber lead-in jetties were always being damaged. At the Greenland entrance to the Surrey Docks, after the war, several incidents involving damage took place at the upper arm of the jetty. On investigation it was found that the ships concerned were powered by modern marine diesel engines which had to be stopped, and restarted in the reverse direction. The engine room staff, used to going forward at a steady speed coming up river, were unprepared when ordered suddenly to go full speed astern. The lock gates had not been opened for the ship to enter the dock and it was necessary to wait for a few minutes at the entrance. However, treating the signal as an emergency, the engine was given full power before it had completely stopped. The result was that the ship surged forward into the lead-in jetty, bounced off it and then rammed it again before the engine could be stopped. Since such incidents occurred quite often it was necessary to keep men permanently employed carrying out timber repairs.

In the early 1960s spectacular damage was caused to the entrance to the West India Docks. A new ship on her maiden voyage rammed the solid masonry and outer dock gate, causing a nasty dent in the bows of the new ship. It was carefully reversed into the river and anchored whilst the pilot and captain went below to take a little restorative for their nerves. On making a second attempt they demolished a considerable section of the lead-in jetty. The third attempt after two costly efforts, was successful.

Turning modern ships with flared bows can also cause difficulties when they overhang the quayside. On more than one occasion whilst berthing or turning in the confined waters of an impounded dock, the flare of the bows has caught one of the quayside cranes. The impact

undergoing repair. To provide space in London it was decided to dam the East India Import Dock, and the South Dock in the Surrey Commercial Docks. They were dried out, and later when construction was completed they were reflooded. Some units were built in basins alongside the Thames. Here they were built half-height, floated out, and completed in the deep water of the West India Docks. They were towed around the Straits of Dover and parked at Selsey awaiting the D-Day landings.

Post war years

As soon as the war in Europe was over the PLA Board decided, firstly that the arrears of maintenance should be undertaken to the full capacity of resources available and without financial limit, and secondly that partially damaged buildings should be repaired. Thirdly restoration involving extensive rebuilding should be undertaken. This policy was aimed at getting the highest production from quays, sheds, and warehouses left in the port. This would provide sufficient time for the Engineers to consider the post-war shipping requirements, and to plan new construction for their needs.

Dredging

A major problem was that of dredging the river after the war. Between 1928 and 1956 the PLA

has been such that the rail clamp securing the
crane to the quay has been broken. This has
then caused the crane to topple over
demolishing the shed behind.

On yet another occasion in 1965 a ship
carrying a considerable deck cargo of timber
had it slip. The ship took a list. In an over
enthusiastic attempt to adjust the trim, some
open portholes became submerged, and the list
increased by an alarming amount. A quick
desperate action was required, solved by
sending for the fire brigade who quickly
pumped out the water and restored equilibrium.

Damage to lock sills
In June 1963 a ship finding herself going too fast
when approaching the entrance to Shadwell
Lock for the London Docks did the natural
thing to stop, it dropped anchor! This was to act
as an emergency brake. However, the bottom of
an entrance lock is not like the sea bed. The
fluke of the anchor caught the sill timbers,
making the lock inoperable. As this was the only
entrance to the London Docks, and many ships
were berthed there at the time, it was necessary
to carry out immediate repairs. It was possible to
give limited access for shipping at the top of the
tide when the inner gates could be opened for a
short period to let them out into the river.

Five week-end occupations were arranged to
carry out the engineering works. Fortunately,

emergency gate stops had been incorporated in
the construction of the lock, and after 100 years
were still in perfect condition. An emergency
gate of heavy steel beams and timbers was
quickly fabricateed to fit the stops. The lock was
dewatered and the full extent of the damage
exposed. During four week-end occupations a
new sill was built, and the lock was completely
restored to shipping.

Sometimes a tug's tow rope would break
when turning a ship in the lock entrance.

*4 Building a new sill, Shadwell
entrance lock, 1963. (Mowlem)*

*5 Shipping in Royal Albert Dock
1965.*

Although disconcerting at the time it does not always cause heavy damage.

On visiting the bridge of one of the largest ships in the Royal Docks it has been possible to visualise the difficulties of navigation. From a point some sixty feet above quay level it appeared almost impossible that the ship had ever entered the dock at all without causing damage.

The diving bell
A large diving bell weighing 14 tons was always available for carrying out emergency works on the floor of the entrance locks. When it was handled by a floating crane, or quayside derrick, it provided a simple way for the Engineer to examine the dock bottom himself. This was a more satisfactory way of assessing the damage than relying on the report of a diver working almost blind in the inky waters of the dock.

Such an occasion occurred in 1951 when water found its way under the outer gate platform of the St Katharine entrance lock. The force of the water pushed out some of the stone blocks and deposited them twenty feet away in the entrance to the lock. Emergency repairs were carried out by concreting under water using the diving bell. Later, however, it was found that the whole lock structure had been shaken up in the war by a bomb which fell nearby. This necessitated the rebuilding of the lock with new gates.

Work in tidal reaches
Before the days of the Thames Barrier, works being carried out in the tidal reaches were subject to freak levels of high water. Cofferdams in a vulnerable position were always liable to overtopping. The nature of the tides in London is such that high water spring tides occur between 3 and 4 am and pm. Many of these occasions have been at the week-end. When there is a deep area of low pressure over the North Sea with a strong North Easterly wind blowing, extra high tides can be expected. The Dock Engineer finds himself anxiously watching for the level of water at high tide. A decision has to be made whether to flood the cofferdam, to prevent damage or to hope that the tide will change before overtopping occurs. In any case the position would have to be watched carefully. All thoughts of an afternoon off would have to be put aside until the danger was over.

Repairs to quay
The repair of quay surfaces on busy berths was difficult because they were seldom unoccupied long enough for work to be carried out. Most packets of cargo used to be handled between ship and transit shed by dockers pushing steel-wheeled hand barrows. In time these caused damage to the quay surface, and ruts opened up. If a heavily-laden barrow wheel caught in a rut, it would jar the arms and sometimes the back of the docker pushing it.

When the opportunity arose, it was essential to obtain possession of the quay as quickly as possible. Such an occasion would occur when there was a stoppage due to industrial action. As the dockers left work all available men with compressor tools would be diverted from their normal work to occupy the quay and would start breaking out the worn surfaces. Hopefully, from the Engineers' point of view, the stoppage would last long enough for the repair work to be completed before the dockers returned.

Connaught Road cutting
The dock Engineer has to learn that interference to shipping has to be kept to a minimum whilst essential alterations and repairs are carried out. When the Royal Mail Line ordered three new fast refrigeration ships

6 The St Katharine entrance lock, repairing the sill using the PLA diving bell and M V Ebury, 1951. (Stanley J Coleman)

7 Diver being prepared, about 1930. (Museum of London)

8 Diver about to descend, about 1930. (Museum of London)

6

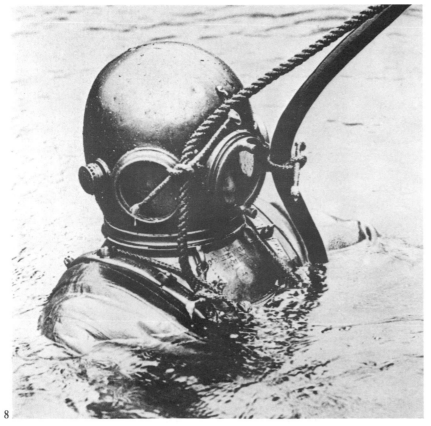

8

50

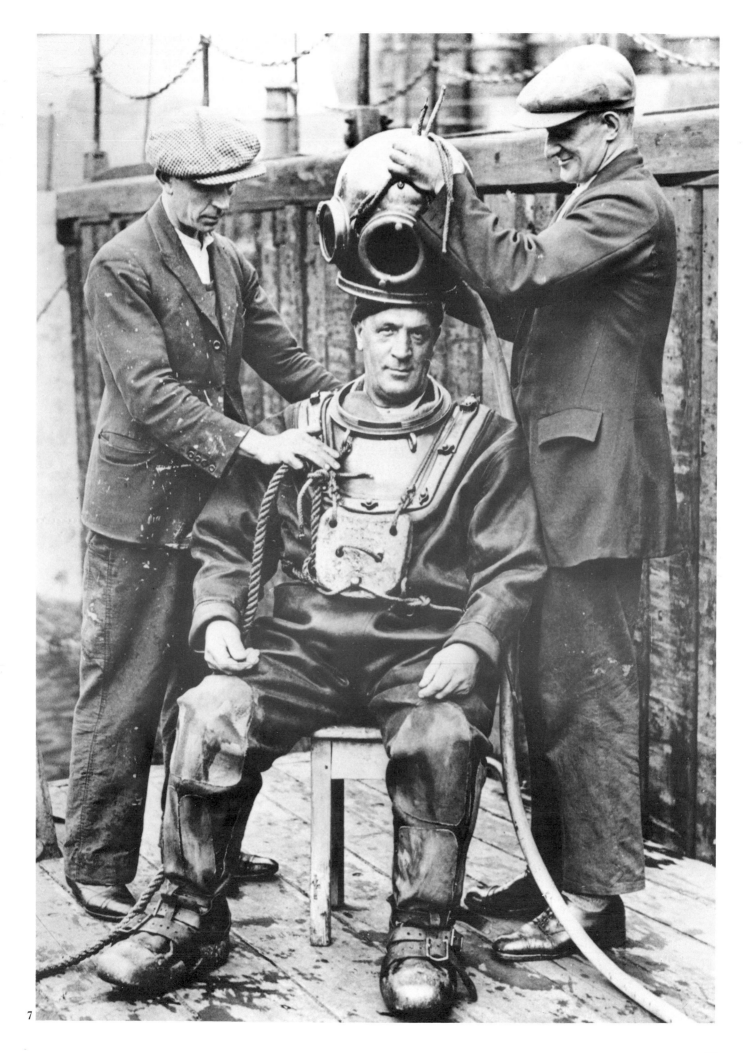

9

for the South American meat trade in 1957, they were too wide to pass through the Conaught Road cutting safely. The cutting would have to be widened before the ships started on their maiden voyages.

It was quite easy to build a new quay wall behind the existing one without causing delay to shipping. However, the demolition of the old concrete wall presented a difficult problem. The use of explosives was considered to be too dangerous, because however carefully the bottom of the cutting had been swept, just one piece of concrete left behind could rupture the hull of a ship.

It was decided to demolish the old wall in the dry inside a cofferdam. Where the railway tunnel passed under the dock wall it was necessary to construct the cofferdam in the form of a limpet. A heavy fender system provided protection of the works and allowed uninterrupted passage for shipping. Men were not allowed to work in the bottom of the cofferdam whilst a ship was passing through. During the six months that the dam was in position 360 ships of varying sizes and 1200 tugs, many of them towing barges, passed through the cutting without delay.

When the bottom of the old wall had been reached, the crown of the railway tunnel was uncovered. To the concern of everyone it was seen that a gap some nine inches high had been left between the steel lining to the tunnel and the surrounding brickwork. This meant that Silvertown could have been flooded should a ship have smashed into the cofferdam at the time and broken the watertight seal. Emergency measures were taken quickly so that the Engineers could sleep peacefully in their beds at night.

The rebuilding of the St Katharine entrance lock and the Western entrance to Victoria Dock

Reconstruction of Thomas Telford's St Katharine's entrance lock in 1957 and George Parker Bidder's Western entrance to Victoria Dock in 1963 afforded a unique opportunity to compare the work of these two highly respected nineteenth-century Civil Engineers.

The St Katharine entrance lock was built in 1827 and lasted 130 years. It had been constructed in the very best traditions of the canal age using good quality workmanship and masonry. However, Thomas Telford in his memoirs speaks of the rapidity with which the works were carried out. In fact he said that he protested at the haste of construction, pregnant as it was with risks which taxed all his experience and skill — no doubt this was when the outer dam failed allowing the river to flood the works.

During the years after the second world war, no doubt partly due to bombing nearby, water was found to be seeping under the gate platforms whenever the gates were closed. This became so bad that in 1957 it was decided to close the lock and rebuild the platforms, taking the opportunity of installing modern

10

bottom-hinged flap gates.

The inner dam comprised a single skin of steel piles driven into the dock bottom and supported by three deep plate girders resting on the ends of the lock wall. Since it would be necessary to cut back the wall masonry to receive the new outer gates, it was necessary to build a self-supporting double skinned gravity dam filled with brick hardcore. The main body of the lock was barrel shaped, and was in direct contact with the London Clay.

When dewatering was completed it was possible to see the quality of workmanship and excellent state of the masonry and brickwork which had been submerged for 130 years. The gate platforms however had completely failed. Instead of building solid platforms in direct contact with the London Clay, Telford had chosen to build a framework of heavy timbers supported on timber piles driven into the London Clay. The space between the timbers had been filled with a gravelly mixture, which it is believed was used as a mat for the carpenters and masons to stand upon without "puddling up" the surface of the clay — blocks of Bramley Fall Stone were laid on the timbers to form the gate platform. With the wartime bombing, water must have found its way under the timbers and

9 *Widening the Connaught Road Passage, view looking West, 1958. British Railway goods trains were still using the swing bridge at this time. (Derby Aero Surveys)*

10 *The St Katharine entrance lock, inner gate, East side, September 1958. Quality workmanship uncovered after 130 years. Note the chain roller and box, the old sluice outlet between the lock and pump chamber, and the curve of the dock wall. (J Flowerday)*

11 *Outer gate platform, St Katharine entrance lock, looking towards the inner dam, October 1958. The timber standing sill has lifted and the missing stone was blown 20 feet by water pressure.* (J Flowerday)

11

12 *The St Katharine entrance lock, lifting the outer gate over the dam by* London Mammoth.

12

through the gravel with sufficient force to displace the stones above. Some of the platform stones were found twenty feet away in the bellmouth of the entrance.

It was found necessary to demolish the whole of the dock wall and sill in the outer position. A new cut-off was provided by means of steel sheet piling which was driven across the sill and returned behind the dock walls. The same procedure was carried out at the inner gate positions.

The new gates were fabricated at a site in the West India Docks, lifted by the PLA floating crane *London Mammoth* and transported on its deck to St Katharine's Docks. Here they were

lifted over the dam into the dock which had been flooded to receive them. The gates, each weighing 60 tons, were equipped with inside buoyancy tanks to control floatation. The gates were uprighted by flooding the lower compartments. When they had reached the vertical position they were turned and offered-up to the meeting faces provided in the new dock wall and lowered on to their trunnions by controlling the level of water in the lock.

The Western entrance lock — Royal Victoria Dock
The Victoria Dock was a private development by three Victorian contractors, Thomas

Brassey, Sir Morton Peto and Edward Betts—
they employed G P Bidder as their design
engineer. The entrance lock, built between
1853 and 1858 was considered to be the most
advanced design of its time. Like the St
Katharine Lock the ground in which the lock
was founded was London Clay. However, in the
30 years between building the two locks,
considerable advancements had been made in
developing new materials and methods of
construction.

The walls in the body of the lock were cast
iron piles driven at 7' 1" (2.16 metres) centres
with cast iron plates tucked into the flanges of
the piles for support. The piles were tied back to
a row of timber anchor piles driven 18 feet (5.5
metres) behind. The space between the rows of
piles was filled with a weak lime-concrete.
During construction the water in the ground
was lowered by steam pumps. In the body of the
lock gravel overlying the London Clay was
removed and replaced by puddle clay. It was not
considered necessary to install a concrete
bottom. However, as soon as pumping was
stopped a section of the north wall moved
forward into the lock without warning. The tie
rods were bent and broken and the anchor piles
broke. A few hours later the south wall failed in
the same way. In carrying out repairs all the
puddle clay was removed and replaced with lime
concrete topped with a 6" (0.15 metres) layer of
Portland Cement concrete. Later, no trace of
the concrete floor could be found. This had no
doubt been taken out over a period of 100 years
by over-enthusiastic dredging when clearing
the lock of mud. By 1928 the original lock gates
had reached the end of their useful life and the
roller paths were giving trouble. When the
Silvertown Way was built in the 1930s it was
decided to restrict the lock to barge traffic. This
caused damage to the cast iron panels, which
broke and allowed water to leach out the lime
from the concrete backing. In some places the
concrete disintegrated and ran out into the river
through gaps in the broken plates. During 1957
loss of water through the lock increased until
there was an unacceptable use of the
impounding pumps to maintain the water level
in the docks. The lock was declared unsafe and
shipping in the Royal Docks had to be protected
by building a dam across the inner end of the
lock.

In 1963 it was decided to lengthen and
deepen the lock, installing new lock gates. The
whole lock was encased in steel sheet piles
driven in front of, through, and behind the old
walls, forming a watertight cut off in the London
Clay.

The rebuilding became a nightmare. The
outer walls started to move forward as soon as
the mud was removed in front of the toe. The
massive gate walls were founded 7 feet (2.13
metres) above the level shown on the original
drawings. (A little Victorian sharp practice?).
The levelling culverts behind the gate walls
were not constructed as shown on the drawings,
nor were they in the same place. Brickwork had
crushed due to differential settlement and there

13

14

*13 Royal Victoria Dock, the closed
Western entrance lock before
rebuilding, 1963. (Mowlem)*

*14 Royal Albert Dock, shipping
dressed for Queen's visit in 1963.*

*15 Rebuilding the Western
entrance lock 1963-5. Lime
concrete faced with cast-iron panels,
demolition of wall.*

15

16   Western entrance lock,
excavation for the outer section.
(Stanley J Coleman)

17   The Western entrance lock,
work nearing completion. (Stanley J
Coleman)

was no concrete foundation to them. However, all these troubles sent to try the engineers were overcome. The lock was opened in 1967 by Lord Simon the Chairman of the PLA, only to be closed a few years later due to the development of container traffic — it has now been filled in as redundant.

The emergency call-out

The dock Engineer is cursed by the telephone, especially when his name is at the top of the list of emergency numbers. About two o'clock in the morning appears to be the favourite time giving cause for the River Police to ring — "We have found one of your workboats adrift in the river, should there have been anyone in it?" Sleepily the decision is made — "No. It was tied up at Westminster Pier where repair work is being carried out. It has probably been cut adrift by youths for a lark. Thanks for recovering it. Arrangements will be made to collect it in the morning."

On arriving home from work one evening there is a frantic message waiting. A mobile crane has over-reached itself and fallen into the Connaught Road cutting. There are five ships trapped in Victoria Dock all waiting to sail at high tide in about two hours. Please will you come and see if it can be recovered in time?

Even birthday parties can be interrupted. One cold January evening in 1960 the CEGB "lost" Brunswick Wharf Power Station. Someone had been working in the cooling water culvert at low water and forgot to reseal the access cover. When the tide came in the basement and switchgear were being flooded. Could large capacity pumps be organised immediately to save further damage?

It sometimes has its humourous side. The West India Docks Police phoned after midnight. The mother of one of the Engineers was concerned that her son had not returned home. He said that he was working late, but surely not that late? Could he have fallen into the dock? After consideration, and knowing the young man, it was suggested to the police that it was more likely that he was in Epping Forest with his girl friend! When he was interviewed next morning he sheepishly agreed that indeed he had been in Epping Forest, but how did anyone know? He was warned that young Engineers must not get their love life entangled with their work, and most certainly should not waste the valuable time of the police.

Conclusions

This short sketch of the life of an Engineer in London's Docks only touches the surface of what has been acheived over the years. London became the centre of world trade and shipping. However, when container sizes were agreed at an international conference in 1965 the scene was set for the container revolution.

The new methods of container handling required about 20 areas of back-up land behind a quay length of 850 feet. One berth alone could handle about one million tons of cargo per year. Modern methods of handling packaged timber were so successful that the four timber berths at Tilbury could handle one and a half million tons in 1976, compared with a total pf 0.8 million tons for the whole of the 36 berths in the Surrey Commercial Docks.

To cope with the new methods of cargo handling the size of Container Ships grew enormously. It was neither possible nor necessary for them to come right up river to London. After 180 years striving to satisfy the demands of shipping companies, the Civil Engineer was no longer wanted. He had to see most of his efforts lost, but has been able to see Dockland being redeveloped for other uses.

A dockland community-
the Isle of Dogs

Eve Hostettler [1]

"Not what it was"

'The Isle of Dogs — An Alive Community': in the mid-1980s a visitor to the Island might have noticed this statement incorporated in a mural on a factory wall in West Ferry Road.[2] The visitor might then have wondered where the 'community' was, amongst the closed-down factories, blocks of post-war flats in various stages of delapidation, the half-built new homes and the occasional boarded-up shop, the litter and the graffiti. To the casual visitor, the Isle of Dogs in the 1980s had many of the characteristics of a run-down, neglected inner-city area — characteristics which were brought into sharp focus by their proximity to costly new developments. All traces of what is traditionally thought of as a 'community' had apparently vanished.

That 'The Island is not what it was', is a sentiment with which every Islander over 40 would agree in the 1980s, whilst recalling with affectionate regret the days when 'every door was open', and 'everyone knew everyone else'. Such phrases recall a neighbourliness, and sense of a local identity, both of which have been threatened with destruction by almost everything that has happened on the Isle of Dogs since 1939.

However, in spite of all appearances to the contrary, and against all odds, there *is* still a community of Islanders. Amidst the new buildings, the dereliction and the general upheavals of the 1980s, the visitor could easily overlook the significance of the blossoming parks and gardens, the footballers and dog-walkers, the One o'clock Club, and the pubs with their regular customers, the Saturday night music and Sunday dominoes. No passing tourist could know that down this side street or that, lay a bustling pensioners' club, a playgroup or youth club, or could know that the Mudchute is a District Park run by a committee of local people, or that the George Green Centre was built in response to local determination to have a secondary school for Island children, or that a vociferous local campaign led to the opening of the ASDA superstore. Today's Island community is necessarily a modern one, less

enclosed, less inward-looking, more critical and assertive, than the pre-war community; but its roots lie in that earlier period.[3]

A community recalled

In the first four decades of this century, the time recalled now with such affection, the Isle of Dogs was a solidly working-class district of the East End of London, with many of the characteristics traditionally associated with such communities.[4] One such characteristic is a strong sense of local identity, and in the case of the Island, this localism has always been heightened by its peculiar geography. Bounded on three sides by the river Thames, and with communications hindered (in those days) by the swing bridges at the entrances to the working docks, it had (and still has) a special feeling of isolation, which separates it from the rest of East London.

Local identity is one factor in shaping a community; another is a stable population, bound together by friendship, marriage and shared experience. Between 1901 and 1939, the population of the Island remained constant at around 21,000.[5] For the majority of these men, women and children, the daily round of family life, work, school and leisure could be accomplished without leaving their home district. In 1929, 75% of household heads on the Island worked locally,[6]; most island children attended local schools, and personal recollections suggest that almost all first jobs on leaving school were local, too. People tended to marry where they had grown up — finding a partner they had known at school, from a family known to their own family in some way, or through connections made at work, church, or social club. Local work and family connections encouraged newly-weds to find homes locally, even if this meant living in one upstairs front room in the parental house. Family ties were strong, and valued. In the days when hardly anyone had a telephone or a private car, a move 'over the water' to Greenwich or Lewisham, or out of London to Becontree or Dagenham, could weaken or break those important links, though in the interests of higher living

1 *Island schoolgirls, 1930s.*

2 *An Island family, 1916.*

standards or social betterment, such moves were sometimes made.[7]

Family ties were enhanced, and social customs ingrained, by close links between the generations. Working-class life expectancy in the early 20th century had improved by comparison with the previous century, so that Islanders could expect, with some degree of confidence, not only to see their children grow up, but also to know their grandchildren. Personal recollections reveal many instances of homes shared by three generations of the same family, and suggest a closeness, and a sharing of values between the generations which would have been impossible previously, and is unlikely today, though for different reasons.[8]

Two examples will help to illustrate this point about closeness of family and friends. Mrs H recalls her childhood in an 'airey' (ie, area) house in Manchester Road, where she lived with her sister, her parents, an aunt and uncle and two cousins, and her grandparents.

"I came home from school, I'd go into my aunt, just knock on the door, and she would say 'come in' and we'd sit there chatting. The garden was shared, we had a nice garden, 'cos my dad was a gardener, he put all the plants in . . . We weren't restricted in visiting. And if we didn't go upstairs to see grandmother! We never called her nanny, we had to call her grandmother, and she was an old Victorian — up till she died she wore long dresses and black hats. And my grandfather — do you remember Victory V Lozenges? Every morning we used to bring tea in before we went to school, and say, 'We are going to school, grandad, goodbye', and we had to have one of them put in our mouths. And when we came home he used to give us a peardrop. He was 85 when he died and I can remember his funeral."[9]

Mr B's memories illustrate the way in which one child and his family were part of an intricate network of friends and relations, both close and distant — a network which is still remembered with clarity over the space of half a century:

"I was born in 1920 at 332 Manchester Road, the 'Ivy House' as it was known then, a local landmark opposite Castalia Street and St John's Church, which I attended. (It) was occupied by my parents, Jack and Jessie Breen, and my sister Jessie and I, and my maternal grandparents, George and Emily Mantle. My grandfather was also a known local figure as he was coachman to Doctor Cardale and drove a large green and black Studebaker. Our neighbours to one side were the Radiczes, a stevedoring family of Scandanavian origin, and on the other side Mr and Mrs Collins, with Mrs Collins' mother, Mrs Hepworth, and her daughter and son-in-law, Marjorie and Jack Matthews and their son. Mrs Collins' sister, Mrs Easter, lived in 'The Terrace' near the bridge, and one of her sons, Harry, subsequently married my wife's sister. Among the near neighbours is the rising numbers towards the bridge, I recall the Devonshires, Clarkes, Cullens, Hooks and Whites. The Griffith family lived across the road, on the bridge side of Ferris's greengrocers shop. No 531, across the road, was once Dr Cardale's surgery, and relatives of mine lived in the house and acted as caretakers. At a slightly lower number lived another aunt of mine, Mercy Rickman and her family. They were also related to the Hook family. My mother's brother, Claude (a dock police officer) and his family, lived in East Ferry Road, and other relatives were scattered around."[10]

Neighbours, relatives and friends all shared the same environment — noisy with the sound of industry and the working docks, polluted with chemical fumes and the dust of manufacture. All families had similar housing conditions — privately rented nineteenth-century terraces, some with basements, most overcrowded and in multiple occupation — shared with relatives, with another family, or with lodgers. (Some new housing was built in the 1920s and 1930s, providing bathrooms, electric lighting and better space.) There was less privacy than there is now, more communal life. Poor housing conditions encouraged the use of the street and other outdoor places for social intercourse. 'Indoors' was crowded and hot in summer; the street was the place to play, for neighbourly chats, for arrivals and departures, for organised parties, for quarrels even, and it was the place to watch all these activities going on. Streets were served by local shops — often open till late and a focal point for the exchange of news (though almost everyone also went to the street market in Poplar).

There was a dominant culture which, although it could have been matched in many other similar communities throughout Britain, was essentially local in its provisions and its participants. The music hall, and later the movies, were less important in Island life than the pubs, of which there were over 30; the various chapels, churches and mission halls also had their following, and the year was punctuated by the processions of the Catholic church. The most popular sport was football; the Island had its own professional team until 1910 (Millwall, now based at New Cross), and there were dozens of amateur clubs. Fighting was a favourite pastime, either in the street or in the ring, and here again the Island produced its own professionals, such as Tammy (Ernie) Jarvis, bantam-weight champion.[11] The less agile kept dogs, rabbits, caged birds and racing pigeons,[12] and cultivated flowers and vegetables in their allotments and gardens. The North Greenwich Bowling Club, founded in 1901, produced an English International player in the 30s.

There was also a clear notion of 'men's work' and 'women's work', and the ideal preference was for married women not to work outside the home. There were accepted guidelines for behaviour in all life's stages — childhood, work, courtship, marriage and rearing a family, but also a tolerance and understanding for the widower who cooked for his children, and for the 'love-child' absorbed into the family circle without lasting scandal.

Politically, the Island, like the rest of Poplar, was almost solidly Labour. The influence of Conservative and Liberal employers had been considerable in the 19th century. Even when most had moved away to more affluent surroundings, they continued to control local politics through their support of local councillors who acquiesced in their views. This patronage was waning in the early 20th century with the extension of the franchise and the growth of the local Labour Party and increasing strength of the trade unions; it was wiped out completely in 1919, when Labour won a considerable majority on the local council — the beginning of a tradition still unbroken in the mid-1980s. Those first renowned councillors (some of whom were imprisoned over the rates issues) were for the most part local people who had put in years of work before being elected.[13]

Most occupations had their unions, and unions often met in rooms over public bars; some firms had football teams or cycling clubs, and organised annual outings, or children's parties — there was therefore a degree of shared leisure amongst those who worked together. In the trade unions, the experience of disputes and sometimes strikes added further dimension to community solidarity (though there was another side to this: disagreement over tactics and even basic principles could sometimes lead to open hostility, as in the division between the 'white' and the 'blue' unions of the dockers and stevedores).

The comradeship of work — sharing the same trade — formed close bonds within and between families. Some work in the docks was handed on from fathers to sons. Other trades also ran in families, and sometimes trades or occupations could be found grouped in a street. John S, recalls Launch Street, his childhood home:

"I was born at 79 Manchester Road in 1916. My father Ted worked at John Fraser's boiler shop in Wharf Road, practically all his life. Other fellows working there were three generations of Setch — old Harry, young Harry and his son 'Bronc', with whom I served in the Royal Navy. My mother's father was a boilermaker — he had four daughters and two sons, Bill (boilermaker) and Harry. In 1918 we moved to Launch Street — my brother Ted was serving his time at the London Graving Dock as a boilermaker, and in due course I followed him at the trade. Launch Street was a veritable bastion of the engineering and allied trades. There was Jack Anderson, foreman at the London Graving Dock; Bill Hunt, foreman at East Ferry Engineering, his brother Joe Hunt, foreman at the Aberdeen Steamship Company; Andrew Riley, sea-going boilermaker, Ernie Bowater, sea-going boilermaker, and Harold Phelvin, sea-going carpenter, later foreman joiner at the London Graving Dock; — so you see, we had the 'cream'."[14]

Whether employed in skilled or unskilled occupations, another aspect of life which most Islanders had in common in those days was a degree of poverty. This was not so much through lack of work (though there were times of high unemployment) as through the nature of the work itself. Thousands of Islanders, (and thousands of other people who came here daily), were employed in semi-skilled and unskilled work in the food-processing, paint, chemical, metal-working and manufacturing industries

3 *An outing from the local pub, 1920s.*

3

4 *Ernie Jarvis and friends, 1920s.*

5 *Neighbours celebrate the Coronation, 1937.*

which lay around the river's edge and alongside the docks; still more were employed on a range of jobs in the docks, and in civil and mechanical engineering workshops, and ship-repair yards; then there were the services — transport, communication, storage and catering. The majority of these workers were low-paid, especially the women in the food-processing factories — and all were subject to lay-offs, short-time, redundancies, or enforced unemployment through ill health or accident. Dockers, in particular, suffered through the notoriously casual nature of their trade. Even the relatively well-paid skilled workers were not immune from poverty — their jobs depended on the state of trade, like everyone else's; ship-repair work, for instance, flourished when the Port of London was busy, and declined whenever international trade declined.

From the standpoint of relative security and greater material comfort in the 1980s, people recall vividly the economic hardships of their childhood. Memory also reveals the ways in which poverty was off-set: the pawnbrokers, pawnshop runners, the local money lenders and Loan Clubs, the visits of the Relieving officer, the moonlight flits to avoid the rent man, the charitable help of church and chapel, the trade union membership, meetings and pay negotiations. No one weeps for the passing of the pawnbroker, but what is regretted today is the apparent absence of neighbourly caring, also so much a feature of pre-war life. The common insecurity and the close-knit life-style created many opportunities for mutual help and co-operation. Housewives supported each other in sickness and childbirth, shared food, including the produce of allotments and chicken runs, and passed on clothes. Neighbourliness also extended to shared joys and sorrows — parties with home-make music,

curtains closed all down the street for a funeral, children cared for in a mother's absence, even adopted. These acts of kindness and co-operation did not eliminate poverty, but they made it easier to bear, gave a vital meaning to the phrase 'looking after your own', and encouraged people to stay where they were known, rather than risk a move to live amongst perhaps uncaring 'strangers'.

It has to be said that Island life in those pre-war days was not necessarily as uniform or as caring as some memories suggest. 'The doors were never locked' because there was very little worth stealing, and because suspicion and blame would soon fall on anyone who did rob or cheat a neighbour. 'Knowing everyone' meant everyone in a street or block of streets, and life-long quarrels could divide relatives and neighbours as thoroughly as if they lived on separate continents. Today people identify with 'the Island', but memory recalls smaller communities within the large one; there was a distinct clannishness, especially during childhood, and people distinguished between 'this side' and 'that side' (the two districts of Millwall and Cubitt Town). Some sort of poverty was universal, but not all were equally poor; there were households with incomes of £4 or £5 a week, others with only ten shillings or a pound.[15] A few could afford holidays in Yarmouth, some had pianos in the front par-lour[16] whilst other families sent their children to school without boots, and a man was reported to have died of starvation in Samuda Street.[17]

Nevertheless, it is clearly true that large numbers of people were bound together in a community through the shared experience of the environment and living conditions, and through the friendship, neighbourliness, and the ties between the generations which arose from the common identity. Time and stability also played a part in the process. Between 1900 and 1939 there was no major change in the physical environment which had been shaped by earlier industrial development. The street lay-out, the shops, the pubs, the work places, looked much the same to the adult of the 1920s and 1930s as they had done to the child of Edwardian times. Familiar faces were seen every day, as people grew up and grew old together. There were changes — the First World War, the coming of the motor car and the cinema, some new housing, but these perhaps only served to emphasize the apparent stability of local conditions.

Yet it was not a community of any long-standing or deeply established tradition. It had emerged in the form in which it is remembered only just before the turn of the century, after almost a hundred years of growth and change.

The early industrial period
Until 1800 the population of the Isle of Dogs had numbered a mere handful of people. Although so close to the City and the busy Pool of London, it was still a windswept, open pasture and sheltered from the high tides by the encircling embankment. On the western bank stood the windmills which gave Millwall its name, and the only other buildings of note were the farmhouse in the centre, the Mast House on the south-west corner (see the modern *Mast House Terrace*), the Ferry House on the southern tip opposite Greenwich (today the *Ferry House* pub), and the *Folly House* tavern on the eastern side (near the modern *Folly Wall*).[18]

A great swathe of earthworks was cut across this peaceful scene in 1800, when the West India merchants built the West India Docks in order to enhance and protect their profitable foreign trade. (The lay-out of the docks, walls, locks and bridges can still be traced, and the dock basins and some of the original warehouses are a prominent feature of the modern landscape).[19] With the opening of these docks, the industrial era of the Island's history began. The expansion and mechanisation of industrial production in Britain, the demand for shipping, London's central importance for finance and trade, combined to make the open spaces of the Isle of Dogs an attractive target for development; industry and population soon followed the docks. By 1811 several new firms were established on Millwall, including a rope works, an iron works, and the chain cable works of Brown Lenox and Company. In 1812 the new Deptford and Greenwich Ferry Road (now West Ferry Road) was opened. By the 1830s a population of shipwrights, engineers, blacksmiths, coopers, ropemakers, stevedores, lock-keepers, drivers, stable boys, messengers, labourers and street traders, had arrived with their families to work in the new enterprises and live in the cottages which were erected here and there along the river bank and beside the new road.

These first industrial Islanders would have found themselves living in a damp and isolated place, with few amenities. The greater part of the Island was still an open pasture, and ships were built and anchor chains forged a stone's throw away from watery meadows and reed beds. In 1840 the Clerk to the Commissioners of Sewers for the Poplar District claimed in his evidence before a Government Inquiry into the Health of Towns that the Island was a healthy place, swept by cold fresh winds, and with the open drains sluiced out regularly by the tides. He stated that it was a place 'in the process of transition from a marsh to a manufacturing district', a phrase which nicely evokes an image of houses and factories rising out of the muddy earth, of chimneys beginning to smoke, of loaded carts coming and going along the unmade roads, carrying bricks for new cottages and raw materials for manufacturing.[20] A wave of developers was moving in then, much as they have done in the 1980s.

By 1851 the population had reached 5,000. It was concentrated in the Millwall district, where the embankment was by then built up with shipyards and factories and where, in the 1830s and 1840s, the first streets had been laid out — Alfred (now Manilla) Street, Robert (now Cuba) Street, and others — Tooke Street, Janet Street, Mellish Street. The Trade Directory lists butchers, grocers and linen drapers, and there was a Congregational chapel, a Catholic church and a post office, as well as half a dozen public houses.

The Islanders of the mid 19th century formed a very mixed society. They had come to live on the Island from all over the British Isles, and so brought many different customs and accents to the new street. They were strangers to each other, for the most part, and more 'strangers' arrived almost daily. Among the new arrivals were people of every class — ranging from the very poor, travelling on foot in search of work, perhaps from the famine-ridden districts of Ireland or the depressed textile areas of south-west and east of England — to owners of property and wealth, looking for new investments in manufacturing, land-owning or ship-building, some of whom came to live on the Island in comfortable houses built close to their factory or shipyard. Between these two extremes were other classes of people — tradespeople (shop-keepers, publicans, carriers); skilled workers (engineers, boilermakers, shipwrights), who earned good regular wages and regarded themselves as socially superior to the unskilled and semi-skilled labourers. Island society comprised a variety of classes, cultures and life-styles by 1850, and it was still growing, still on the move. It was also a predominantly young society, with large numbers of children, and very few 'senior citizens' in their fifties or over.[21]

The 1850s witnessed the building of Brunel's giant ship, *'The Great Eastern'*. This spectacular feat of engineering brought more new workers to the Isle of Dogs, amongst them the Scottish engineers who built their own church of St Paul's in West Ferry Road. In 1864, the new Millwall Dock was opened in the centre of the

Island and during the 1850s and 1860s, the whole of the southern and eastern banks and borders of the Island were developed under the direction of master builder William Cubitt, creating the new 'Cubitt Town', with its church, (Christ Church), its three-storeyed houses, and riverside wharves and industries.[22]

Arthur Joseph Hubbard, born in 1869, recalls the early Cubitt Town in his autobiography:

"(I was born) at 41 Marshfield Street, Cubitt town, a terraced house containing six rooms and not a very old building, for Cubitt Town was not developed to a great extent, there being large fields for the pasturage of cows

6

8

6 Back yard produce, 1930s.

8 A mother in mourning, 1919.

7 On holiday in Yarmouth, 1910.

7

9

9   *The Blitz — the morning after.*

10   *Christ Church Boys' Brigade, 1940s.*

10

and other animals. There was also a large piece of ground, near the Millwall Dock, which an estate agent called Bradshaw Brown used as a market garden and cultivated cabbages, mangolds and other market produce. I remember seeing market wagons, loaded with cabbage, going to the London markets. There were other vacant fields, one in the Glengall Road stretching from the Methodist chapel to a terrace near the docks, on which I have seen a flock of sheep, brought there for pasture, and which eventually became a place for building the first Glengall Road Board School for London in the year 1875. Not many of the streets and roads had foot paths; the main road, called Manchester Road, was paved, the side streets were mostly cinder paths. A toll gate existed at the *Queen Tavern* end of East Ferry Road, and vehicular traffic paid a toll for using the road."[23]

Late nineteenth-century changes

The building activity of the 1850s and 1860s represented a high level of capital investment, but this prosperity was more apparent than real for most Islanders. In 1866 the Thames ship-building industry suffered a financial collapse from which it was never to recover, throwing thousands of people out of work. This was a sign of the times. Ship-building and related trades, along with the heavy metal industries such as rolling mills, were moving out of London and the south-east to the north of England and Scotland. On the Island, their place was taken by light metal working and manufacturing industries, chemical works, and food processing firms, attracted by cheap labour and access to the river. McDougalls' Flour had been produced beside the Millwall Dock since the 1860s. The firm of C & E Morton, producing canned and processed foods, moved to Millwall in the mid 1870s. Mortons eventually employed over one thousand workers, the majority of them women, and operated the greatest private waterfront on all the Thames. In 1896 Maconochie Brothers acquired a site on the Island, and also expanded to have a workforce of a thousand, producing ninety-nine different varieties of processed food.

Although ship-repairing and civil engineering works survived the 1866 disaster, those skilled workers who chose to remain on the Island found themselves increasingly forced to live like the casual workers who they had regarded as their social inferiors, seeking work from day to day and even, in extremely, driven to take up labouring work. At the same time, many aspects of dock work, initially reasonably secure, had been casualised by the uncertain nature of trade and by the fierce competition which existed between the different dock companies. Dock work, however, because of its relatively unskilled nature, and seasonal peaks of employment, continued to attract into the Capital all sorts and conditions of the unemployed. Many newcomers came to the Island in the last quarter of the century,

attracted by dock work and the expanding new industries, driven out of their country villages by the low wages and lack of employment there. At the same time, the casual nature of much of the work that was available forced more women onto the labour market to supplement, or even wholly provide the family income. The low wages paid to women further depressed male rates.[24]

Whilst these changes were going on, employers and other middle class people were moving away from the Island, taking advantage of new forms of public and private transport to live in the cleaner and more luxurious realms of North Poplar, Blackheath, or even further afield.[25]

The last quarter of the nineteenth century was a time of mixed blessing as far as the Islanders were concerned. The population was still growing, but overall was getting poorer. Most of the land available for housing had been built on — but it was marshy, badly drained land, and many of the relatively new houses were in a poor state of repair. The sounds and smells of industry dominated the environment. Streets, wharves, factories, dust heaps, football pitches and rubbish tips were haphazardly intermingled. The air was filled with the odours of rubber, paint and chemical works, and the black smoke of dozens of chimneys. There were plenty of pubs and small shops, three parish churches and several chapels, and various social and political clubs — but no local market, music hall or other place of pleasure and entertainment. Transport off the Island was limited to horse-drawn trams, or the 'penny-puffer' railway (opened in 1876); the alternative was a long walk past 'the walls', which bounded the docks at the eastern and western approaches, or a ferry ride to Greenwich or Deptford.[26]

Several schools had been built in the 1870s, and by 1900, the majority of Island children went regularly to school. During the same period, the local Board of Health enforced some improvement to housing, and implemented measures to control epidemics of infectious diseases. Politically, Islanders found their own voice, as Conservative and Liberal employers moved away. The growth of trade unionism — exemplified locally in the dock strikes of the 1870s and 1880s, and the engineers' strike of 1897, together with the spread of co-operative and socialist movements created the conditions for the opening of the Isle of Dogs Progressive Club in 1897, with nearly 500 members. This contributed to the formation of Poplar Labour party which was to finance Will Crooks as a Member of Parliament and which was to produce George Lansbury and the other Poplar councillors renowned for their fight over the rates issue in 1921. Meanwhile, the Labour presence on the LCC helped to bring into being amenities such as public baths, parks and new lock bridges to speed communication.[27]

In Edwardian photographs of Islanders, we can look into their eyes and, fancifully perhaps, detect a gleam of determination there — a determination not only to survive their

11 Tower Blocks going up, 1966.

11

12 Publicity leaflet, 1984.

AT: 4 p.m

TODAY

IN SAUNDERS NESS GARDENS

We are asking all residents to a meeting TODAY in Saunders Ness Gardens to decide how we can unite together to maintain and improve the area.

In the past year there has been more than a dozen break-ins and burglaries, repairs and estate maintenance by the Council has virtually ceased — weeds are growing unchecked and threatening to break up paving stones, graffiti on seats, rails, and signs around the estate are left.

In the next few months major building work will commence on the Caledonian Wharf. This will mean pile driving work and heavy lorries daily — and, when the housing is finished, it could have a serious effect on our rents and rates (in Chelsea in a similar situation when luxery houses was built next to a council estate, rents went up to nearly £100 per week, and tenants were "invited" to move away from the riverside if they couldnt afford to pay the rent!

TOGETHER WE CAN DO SOMETHING ABOUT THIS. TOGETHER WE CAN DEMAND BETTER POLICEING IN THE AREA, WE CAN PUT PRESSURE ON THE COUNCIL AND THE LDDC TO ENSURE THAT OUR HOMES ARE NOT PUT AT RISK. WE CAN DO A GREAT DEAL OURSELVES TO KEEP THIS ESTATE AND THIS ARE PLEASANT PLACE TO LIVE IN.

12

unpromising conditions, but to flourish, and — if possible — to see their children and grandchildren survive and flourish, too. Ahead of them lay, still unknown, the agony of the First World War and the long grind of the Great Depression; years of damp housing, poor health and a struggle to make ends meet. From an outsider's point of view, their community life may have been narrow and constricting; from within, it was a buffer against hardship and insecurity. Life in that community provided its children with happy memories, and a clear set of values against which to measure succeeding generations.[28]

Modern times
Perhaps the dramatic events of 1939-45 helped to enshrine in memory the life that preceded them. The community seemed to be irrevocably shattered by the Second World War. Evacuation, casualties and mobilisation reduced the post-war population to 8,000. Whole streets were destroyed, public services put out of action, schools and churches laid waste, roads made impassable, factories and workshops reduced to rubble and ashes.

Further changes came in the post-war period. A new environment was created. Amidst the temporary prefabs erected to house those made homeless by the bombing, new blocks of flats rose up, and the ruins of the old terraces disappeared for ever in clouds of dust. The population changed — many Islanders left for ever during the war, and post-war housing policy moved people about relentlessly — from the Island to the suburbs, from other parts of London to the Island. Life-styles and values changed. There was still plenty of work, and some traditions of the pre-war community survived — pubs, clubs, football, outings, hop-picking, market shopping, trade unions — but post-war Britain was to be private, materialist, media-fed and motorised. A consumer society came into being, where ideally every household had its own front door, and behind every front door was a three-piece suite, a television set, radio, washing machine, fitted carpets and a gleaming new cooker. The Welfare State was created to take care of everyone in need. People retreated into the privacy of their new homes with the new possessions. Neighbourliness, street life, and mutual support dwindled. The telephone and the private car allowed family connections to be maintained over a distance. Trade Unions came to be run by a far-off bureaucracy, and rank-and-file activity became associated with the suspect red tinge of communism and subversion.

The local economy, prospered briefly in the 1950s — the docks were busy and industry still flourished. The early 1960s saw the onset of a long industrial decline, culminating with the closure of the docks in 1960's. The structure and problems of the post-war Island community were different from those of the pre-war period. Although the worse financial effects of unemployment were cushioned by redundancy agreements and welfare provisions, the industrial decline was accompanied by other aspects of social change which made the future seem bleak for many Islanders. The reality of the new housing soon proved to fall far short of the planners' dreams — there was not enough housing of the kind people wanted — houses with gardens, where they could see their children and grandchildren grow up. The dozens of small shops which had been a feature of the pre-war environment were replaced by only a handful of stores; there was no local secondary school; transport provision was inadequate. After the war-time dislocation of the community, a further stage of disintegration now seemed to be under way. Many Islanders began to feel that there was no future here for them or their families.

Looking back, older people remembered the poverty of pre-war times, and they also remembered the values of co-operation, mutual support and self-help which it engendered. Looking forward, some were determined that the Island should become a better place, and that Islanders should have a fair deal. Enough of the old values had survived to be passed on to new generations and to newcomers, and to find expression in ways of dealing with new circumstances. In the 1970s and 80s, local campaigns and organisations sprang up to meet the challenge of new collective needs. The thoughtful observer will still find a community spirit at work on the Isle of Dogs.

Notes

1   This chapter draws on two main sources:

a   The work done by the Island History Project workers and supporters, 1980-85. The Island History Project (now a charitable trust partly funded by the London Borough of Tower Hamlets (LBTH) and the Greater London Council) came into being in 1980 as part of a Community Education Project funded from the urban aid programme. The Project's aim is to collect and preserve the history of the Isle of Dogs, to make the results of its work publicly accessible and to involve local people in the process of collection, preservation and presentation. The Project now has an extensive collection of tape-recordings, local photographs and written reminiscence. More information about the work of the Project can be obtained by writing to 151 Manchester Road, London E14, Tel: 01–987 6041.

b   'Life and Labor in the Isle of Dogs: The Origins and Evolution of an East London Working-Class Community 1800-1980', a thesis submitted to the University of Oklahoma in 1984 by Thomas J Cole, as part of the requirements for the degree of Doctor of Philosophy. A copy of Dr Cole's thesis is deposited in the Local History Department, LBTH Central Library, Bancroft Road, Mile End, London E1 (henceforth: LBTH Central Library).

2   The mural referred to, on the south-facing wall of Blyth Burrell Colours, was still visible in 1985.

3   For a view of the Island community today, the interested reader is referred to *The Islander*, the newspaper of the Association of Island Communities, copies of which are deposited in LBTH Central Library.

4   See, for example, the work of E Hobsbawm or J Seabrook, on this subject.

5   Thomas Cole, Ph D thesis, LBTH Central Library, Chapter IV. (Henceforth: Cole).

6   Cole, Chapter IV.

7   Apart from the statistical references drawn from Cole, the observations in this paragraph are based on material collected by the Island History Project (henceforth: IHP).

8   This point about ties between the generations is based on Michael Anderson, 'The Emergence of the Modern Life Cycle in Britain', *Social History*, Vol 10: No 1, January 1985, pp 69-87.

9   IHP, interview, 1981.

10   IHP, correspondence, 1985.

11   IHP, photographic archive; see also: 'Ernie Beat Some of the World's Best', *Boxing News*, July 26 1985, pp 16-17.

12   Millwall United Homing Pigeon Society still flourishes in the 1980s.

13   Cole, Chapters III and IV. Noreen Branson, *Poplarism 1919-1925*, Lawrence and Wishart 1979.

14   IHP, correspondence, 1985.

15   New Survey of London, 1929, British Library of Political and Economic Science.

16   IHP, information from interviews and correspondence; advertisements in local church magazines.

17   *The News & Chronicle*, Friday April 15th, 1904.

18   For an interesting account of the pre-industrial Island and the first half of the nineteenth century, see W Cowper, *A History of Millwall*, 1853. (Available in LBTH Central Library)

19   John Pudney, *London's Docks*, one of the most readable accounts of dock history available.

20   Minutes of Evidence taken before the Select Committee on the Health of Towns; Mr William Baker, jnr, 1 April 1840. Parliamentary Papers, State Papers Room, British Library.

21   The local census returns for the years up to 1881 are available in LBTH Central Library. In Alfred Street (later Manilla Street) in 1851, only 10% of the population was over 50, and less than 1% was over 70. Analysis of the same street in 1881 gives a similar result. (IHP work)

22   Deeds and Plans of Cubitt Town Estates, LBTH Central Library.

23   A J Hubbard, unpublished autobiography, IHP (courtesy of his family).

24   This outline account of the changing economy and population structure of the Isle of Dogs in the last quarter of the 19th century is based on Cole, Chapter III.

25   For example, Joseph Cook, born in 1844, blacksmith, engineer and shipbuilder. He and Margaret Cook, with their children, moved to Cubitt Town from the north of England sometime between 1866 and 1875. By 1881 he had a house and works in Glengall Road, employing 20 men. Next door to him, employing 40 men, lived James Burdick. In the 1880s the two formed an engineering partnership, and together they financed the building of ships which were launched in the northern shipyards. In the 1890s the Cooks moved to Blackheath. Joseph Cook died there in 1934, leaving a furtune of a quarter of a million pounds. (IHP information, courtesy of Mrs M Sykes, descendant of J Cook)

26   Cole. See also R Free, *Seven Years Hard*, 1907, available in LBTH Central Library; also G H R Hames, written reminiscences, IHP.

27   Cole. See also clippings and publications of the Isle of Dogs Progressive Club, newspaper reports, etc, LBTH Central Library; also Branson, cited above.

28   'I could go on and on about the hard, sometimes bitter life, which somehow the Islanders' spirit, and sheet guts, overcame.' 'I was nearly 13 years old when we left the Island, but have never forgotten the places and the people — the salt of the earth.' 'My memories of life on the Island are my most treasured.' From IHP correspondence, 1985. See also Jeremy Seabrook, *What Went Wrong, Working People and the Ideals of the Labour Movement*, Golanz, 1978, for a detailed exploration of changes in working-class communities.

Photographs in this article are from the Island History Photograph Collection.

Dock labour history

Lord Howie

Although the history of the Port of London goes back for about 2,000 years the system of enclosed docks where ships could lie safely and unload straight on shore dates only from the late years of the 18th century or the early years of the 19th. The system was then one of privately owned and operated docks which were gradually merged into groups with the passage of time and the need to fend off competition. They were eventually replaced by the Port of London Authority, but that was not until 1909.

Until then, while the amalgamations sustained the viability of the dock companies in a period of ill-controlled economic individualism, they did little for the dock labourers. In the 1850s the average wage of the 20,000 labourers in London's seven main docks was 2s 4d a day in winter and 2s 6d a day in summer, or 4d an hour. And that was for work that was not only heavy and dangerous but was also precarious. The docker's life was one of casual labour at its grimmest.

A typical dock gate scene of the 1850s is described by the Victorian social investigator, Henry Mayhew, as follows:

'He who wishes to behold one of the most extraordinary and least-known scenes of this Metropolis should wend his way to the London Dock gates at half-past seven in the morning. There he will see congregated within the principal entrance masses of men of all grades, looks and kinds. Some in half-fashioned surtouts burst at the elbows, with the dirty shirts showing through. Others in greasy sporting jackets, with red pimpled faces. Others in the rags of their half-slang gentility, with the velvet collars of their paletots worn through to the canvas. Some in rusty black, with their waistcoats fastened tight up to the throat. Others, again, with the knowing thieves' curl on each side of the jaunty cap. . .

'Presently you know, by the stream pouring through the gates and the rush towards particular spots, that the 'calling foremen' have made their appearance. Then begins the scuffling and scrambling forth of

countless hands high in the air, to catch the eye of him whose voice may give them work. As the foreman calls from a book the names, some men jump up on the backs of the others, so as to lift themselves high above the rest, and attract the notice of him who hires

1 *Programme for a demonstration in favour of the extension of the vote to working men in 1866. The middle column gives a list of craftsmen who were in unions at the time. Marshal of the route was George Potter, Editor of the London Trades Council's Beehive and delegate to the first Trade Union Congress in 1868. (TUC Library)*

them. All are shouting. Some cry loud his surname, some his Christian name, others call out their own names, to remind him that they are there. Now the appeal is made in Irish blarney — now in broken English. Indeed, it is a sight to sadden the most callous. to see thousands of men struggling for only one day's hire; the scuffle being made the fiercer by the knowledge that hundreds out of the number there assembled must be left to idle the day out in want. To look in the faces of that hungry crowd is to see a sight that must be ever remembered. Some are smiling at the foreman to coax him into remembrance of them; others, with their protruding eyes, eager to snatch at the hoped-for pass. For weeks many have gone there, and gone through the same struggle — the same cries; and have gone away, after all, without the work they had screamed for . . .

Many of them, it was clear, came to the gate without the means of a day's meal, and being hired, were obliged to go on credit for the very food they worked upon'.

Little wonder then that the docks were centres of industrial unrest and they became targets for the union organisers and agitators who were then beginning to create the mass unions of the present day and fight for improved wages and conditions for their members. There were dock strikes in both 1871 and 1872, which resulted in a general wage rise of 1d an hour — that is from 4d to 5d. But the most famous and most passionate struggle came in 1889 in the battle for the 'dockers' tanner' — an increase to 6d an hour among other things — under the leadership of John Burns and Ben Tillett.

An insignificant dispute at the South West India Docks over plus rates which were additional to the hourly rate led to the men downing tools and marching to the nearby Victoria and London Docks where they were quickly joined by most of the dock and wharf employees including the lightermen and private wharfingers. Although the dispute might have appeared insignificant in itself, its effects were not. As Sidney and Beatrice Webb have said, '. . . the London dock labourers were marching to that brilliant victory over their employers which changed the whole face of the trade union world'.

The times were ripe for such a victory. The ideas of socialism had begun to gain a secure place in political discussion and action. The conditions of the poor and of the working class were becoming matters of concern to rulers and ruled alike. What is more, charismatic workers' leaders were arising to make their demands concrete. Throughout the 1880s, attempts were made to organise London's unskilled workers, the dockers among them. But little progress was made until 1888, when public opinion was

4 *Sweethearts and Wives: The Dock Labourers' Strike.* (The Illustrated London News, 7 September 1889)

aroused by the harsh conditions under which women worked making matches at Bryant & May's in Bow.

Annie Besant was then editor of an obscure weekly called *The Link,* and an editorial of hers deploring these conditions had the unexpected result of bringing 672 of these match girls out on strike. Their small number made their cause appear hopeless, but it turned out to be their strength. For their apparent weakness in the face of their powerful employers, who seemed unreasonable, struck a chord of public sympathy. After two weeks, the force of public opinion compelled the employers to make concessions. The lesson that it was possible to harness public opinion to defeat unwilling employers was not lost on the unions, and was to prove important in the dockers' struggle.

The dockers were helped too by the successes of John Burns, Ben Tillett, Tom Mann and Will Thorne in organising the gas workers, for many dockers turned to the gas works in the winter when the docks were slack. So they were greatly heartened when the gas workers won an eight hour day, then an important union aim, and a modest wage increase without a struggle.

Tillett was then a labourer in the tea warehouses and was trying to build up a union of tea workers and general labourers, but he had little to show for his efforts when the dockers struck work in August 1889. The men demanded 6d an hour, the abolition of piece and sub-contract work, overtime pay and a minimum engagement of four hours.

Tillett called Burns and Mann to his aid and appealed to all dock workers to join the strike. Within three days, 10,000 labourers were on strike and the better paid and trained stevedores came out as well. The strike paralysed the Port of London for five to six weeks, but again the general public and much of the press were sympathetic to the workers' demands.

Public disapproval prevented the employers from replacing the strikers by other unskilled labourers of which plenty were available. Funds were raised which, say the Webbs, '. . . allowed Mr Burns to organise an elaborate system of strike pay, which not only maintained the honest docker, but also bribed every East End loafer to withhold his labour'.

The strike ended in a great victory for the dockers and a far reaching one for trade unionism as a whole. The dock employers capitulated, and the dock labourers won virtually all they had asked for. The dockers union became firmly founded with Mann as its president and Tillett as its secretary. But more important, great encouragement had been given to trade unionists all over Britain.

Although the London docks were seldom entirely free from labour troubles from then on, the next important dispute came in 1920, and it

5 *A Quay at the East India Docks.* (The Illustrated London News, 14 September 1889)

brought into prominence another great figure in labour history, Ernest Bevin.

The cost of living rose sharply just after the first world war and there were widespread strikes in 1919. The importance of this dispute was that both sides agreed to accept arbitration under the Industrial Courts Act which had recently been passed. The dockers' case was

6   Half an hour for refreshment at the Docks. (The Illustrated London News, 14 September 1889)

argued by Bevin, then a 33-year-old national officer of the union. He made a great impression, especially by exhibiting the actual amount of food a docker's wages would buy. As a result of his advocacy, the union got most of its demands and Bevin became known as 'the dockers' K C'.

Later that year, the docks were again locked in dispute but this time with a difference, for the dispute was a political one. A ship called *The Jolly George* was to carry munitions from the East India Docks to help the Poles in their war against the new Soviet government in Russia. Encouraged by Bevin, the dockers refused to load the ship and prevented it from sailing. The British government, which had been backing the Poles, backed down and changed its policy. This is the only example of industrial action for political purposes being successful in Britain, apart from the strike in Northern Ireland some years ago.

Underlying the endemic industrial unrest, or at least uneasiness, in Dockland was the casual nature of dock labourers' employment. Stable industrial relations could scarcely be expected against a background of casual and uncertain employment. So the union's ambitions were aimed at complete decasualisation. A major step forward was taken in a dock labour scheme which was devised in 1947 under Mr Attlee's government. It was the brainchild of Ernest Bevin who had by then become Foreign Secretary after a spell as Minister of Labour in the wartime coalition government and many years as leader of the Transport and General Workers' Union.

The scheme was still, however, a long way short of the total decasualisation Bevin had dreamed of in his days as a dockers' leader. No more than a quarter of the labour force was in the pool of the permanently employed. Even this scheme did not bring peace to the docks which remained troublesome, not only in London but notably in Liverpool and Hull as well, and unofficial stoppages were rife. Potentially the most damaging of these occurred in mid-1948, when a small scale dispute in

7   The late strike of dock labourers in the Port of London: old dock hands. (The Illustrated London News, 28 September 1889)

London rapidly escalated to a major stoppage which threatened food supplies.

Unluckily for the strikers, the reputation of Prime Minister Attlee was at its highest at the time, and he was supported by public opinion when he took drastic measures. These included invoking the 1920 Emergency Powers Act for the first time since the general strike 20 years before. Attlee also spoke on the radio, and persuaded the strikers to return to work. The force of public opinion which had aided the dockers in 1889 was opposed to them this time. That and the hand of firm government quickly brought the dispute to an end.

But Attlee was not yet finished with the dockers — nor they with him — even then. In

8 Certificate of Membership of the Dock, Wharf, riverside and General Labourers' Union 1891. Note the signatures Tom Mann and Ben Tillett. (TUC Library)

9
10

11

May 1949, Britain's dockers struck in sympathy with the Canadian Seamen's Union. Since the seamen were communist-led, the government suspected communist influence in the docks too. Once again, Attlee's resolution was evident. Using defence regulations which were then still in force, he sent troops to unload ships in both Avonmouth and London.

But on this occasion, the dockers did not give up easily. In fact, the strike worsened. Attlee carefully prepared public opinion to counter it, attacking 'communist hypocrites' as he called them, and reminding the dockers of what had been done for them, particularly by Bevin. He showed a firm hand too by threatening a state of emergency and getting ready to draft 30,000 men to keep London's docks moving. In the face of that, the dockers caved in.

From then on, labour relations in Dockland were marked by a widening gulf between the

9 1911 Dock Strike. East End Boys imitating their fathers. (TUC Library)

10 1926 Dock Pickets. (TUC Library)

11 Veterans of the National Trade Unions meet at the Union Club in Oxford Street. Rt Hon George Lansbury, Mr James Sexton, Mr John Hodepe, Mr C W Bowerman and Mr Ben Tillett among others join in the music and merriment. Tom Mann (1856-1941) emphasises a point over James Sexton's head, 19 December 1930. (Hulton)

12 The London Dock Strike of 1931, Dockers gather outside the London Dock. (TUC Library)

13 Kitchen interior. (Museum of London)

12

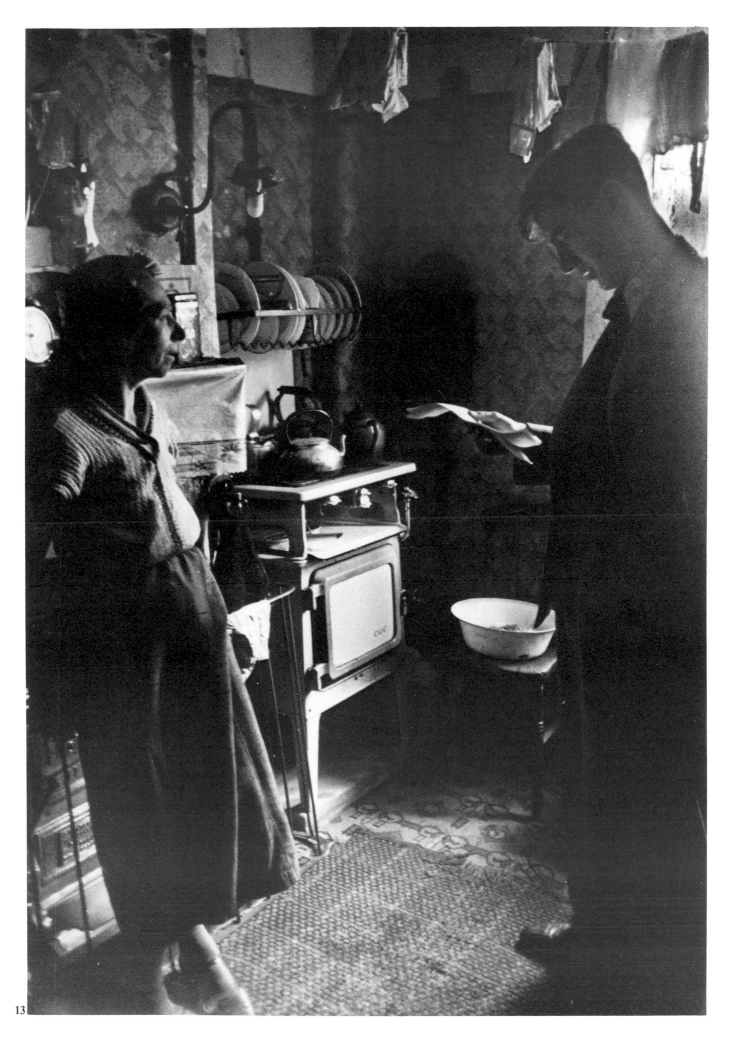

13

ROYAL GROUP OF DOCKS
SHOP STEWARDS
COMMITTEE
ARISE YE WORKERS

14

15

14 *Trade Unionists marching through the Billingsgate Fish Market area on their way from Tower Hill to Pentonville Prison to demand the release of jailed dockers, 25 July 1972. (TUC Library)*

15 *The Pentonville Five at the meeting on Tower Hill, 28 July 1972. Left to right, Anthony Merrick, Derek Watkins, Cornelius Clancy, Vic Turner and Bernie Steer. (TUC Library)*

dockers and their official union leaders. The dockers lived then in a world of their own, with their own traditions and their own loyalties, mainly local. Their sense of loyalty was similar to that of the mining communities. They would react instinctively as a body in defence of any one of their fellows threatened by injustice, as they saw it.

As one of the many reports on conditions in the docks put it, 'it appears to be incredibly easy to bring dock workers out on strike. We were given repeated instances of men stopping work almost automatically, with little or no idea why they were stopping. In the words of one witness, himself a dock worker, "All that was needed was for a man to go round the docks shouting 'All out' and waving the men off the ships and out they would come"'.

By the time Frank Cousins became general secretary of the TGWU, its dock section was virtually independent of the union's headquarters and the unofficial local leaders were virtually independent of it. The best known of these local leaders was Jack Dash, a colourful Cockney and a life long communist with a substantial following among his fellow dock workers.

In 1967, Dash succeeded in bringing out more than 5,000 dockers in protest against modernisation proposals which arose from the report of a committee of inquiry under the chairmanship of Lord Devlin. The strike was extremely damaging, and was said by the then Prime Minister, Harold Wilson (now Lord Wilson of Rievaulx), to have been a major factor in the devaluation of the pound later that year.

The Devlin committee had denounced Dash and his associates saying. 'In London the unofficial leadership is strong enough to amount to a rival power. No strong union can allow unofficial leadership to prevail in the way in which it has prevailed in London'. Maybe so,

but not even Cousins with all the authority of his left wing credentials and his prestige as a former cabinet minister could do anything about it. Nor could his successor, Jack Jones.

The next, and as it was to turn out, the last, important steps in the docks union's march into history followed the Industrial Relations Act of 1971 which was passed while Mr Heath was Prime Minister. As so often in recent years, the dispute hinged on a measure of modernisation which posed a threat to dockers' livelihoods. This time the dispute was over containerisation, and it started in Liverpool.

In the Spring of 1972, Liverpool dockers ignored a court order to stop blacking container lorries operated by Heatons Transport of St Helens. Their union, the TGWU now led by Jack Jones, was fined £5,000 but refused to pay. The court promptly added another £50,000 to the fine. This episode came to an end when the court of appeal ruled that the union could not be held responsible for the actions of its shop stewards.

The drama then moved to the Thames where three shop stewards were now faced with imprisonment for ignoring a similar court order to stop picketing lorries from the Chobham Farm depôt. This case had been brought against the dockers by workers at the depôt, but the shop stewards saw it as a struggle against the Court and, by implication, the Government.

In a defiant statement one of them declared,

> 'All three of us will not co-operate with the Industrial Relations Court. We do not recognise the Court and will have no dealings with it. I am not pleased about the thought of going to prison, but if that is what our struggle means, we will certainly go'.

London and Liverpool dockers immediately came out in their support, and the Government was said to be 'bewildered' by the chaos brought about by its industrial relations legislation. The Government's face was saved for the time being by the intervention of an obscure official called the Official Solicitor. One of his duties was to see that people sent to prison for contempt of court, as the three shop stewards were likely to be, were not left there to rot. On his interceding, the court of appeal set the court order aside, and the three went free. The Industrial Relations Act was now in ruins.

But the troubles were not yet over. In July the Court ordered dockers to stop blacking lorries at the Midland Cold Storage Company's terminal at Stratford in London's East End. Again shop stewards, this time five, were ordered to prison for contempt of court. As they went to jail, there to be immortalised as 'the Pentonville five', 170,000 workers came out on strike. It was, said the *Observer* newspaper, the 'most significant challenge to the authority of any Government since the general strike of 1926'.

Once again, the Official Solicitor came to the rescue, and five days later the shop stewards were released. He was not, said the president of the Industrial Court, Sir John Donaldson, 'a political or industrial fairy godmother armed with a magic key which unlocks prisons'. Nonetheless the prison doors opended at his approach and the stewards were held to have purged their contempt.

The dispute went on for some time, but the Industrial Relations Act was effectively dead. Thirteen years later, what is to be seen? A new framework of industrial relations law has been established, every bit as onerous as the laws the dockers fought against and much more likely to last. Containerisation is widespread. But London's up-river docks have gone.

The dockers' militancy was necessary in the early days when wages were poor and work was insecure. It arose from the intransigence of the employers and a slow recognition of the strength of organised labour. It improved wages and conditions, and had one great political triumph in *The Jolly George.* But in opposing modernisation, it is likely that the dockers' militancy was a factor in the decline and eventual death of London's docks.

Short Bibliography

There is a vast literature on industrial and labour relations much of which is applicable to the history of Dockland labour. The following books are particularly useful:

The History of Trade Unionism by Sidney and Beatrice Webb.

Attlee by Kenneth Harris.

Frank Cousins: a study by Margaret Stewart.

Tom Mann's memoirs.

A history of British trade unionism by Henry Pelling.

Victor Feather TUC by Eric Silver.

A museum in docklands

Chris Ellmers

In January 1982, the Museum of London proposed setting up a major new Museum — the Museum in Docklands — dealing with the story of the Capital as the Nation's greatest industrial and commercial centre. Notwithstanding the great national collections in the Science Museum and the National Maritime Museum, and the existence of specialised museums such as the London Transport Museum and Kew Bridge Engines Trust, it was felt that London's leading role in industrial development in world-wide trade and related activities, and in the creation of public utilities was nowhere fully portrayed. Within the main buildings of the Museum of London — where the galleries have to deal with the complex three-dimensional biography of the 620 square mile Metropolis over seven thousand years — it had proved possible only to evoke some of the most salient features of the recent past. The answer was seen to lay in the establishment of a new museum, closely associated with the Museum of London and drawing upon the substantial collections of relevant material which it has put together over recent years.

Whilst it was felt that such a museum would need to look at London's industrial and commercial history in its broadest context, the vital role played by the trading river and docks — once the largest in the world — quickly suggested that the most suitable location for it would be in Dockland. Within this vast area, which was only beginning to be redeveloped, there were surely dock buildings, stretches of adjacent quayside and areas of enclosed water that could merit both preservation and adaption to meet the need of a 'workplace' theme museum for London.

Such a museum, it was argued, would do much to redress the imbalance between London and most large provincial towns and cities which already had well-established and popular 'industrial', 'maritime' or 'open-air' museums. Indeed, given the phenomenal growth in the number of such museums over the past two decades, and the primary place of London in the industrial and commercial

history of the nation, it was remarkable that the Capital has not already achieved such a museum of its own. It would seem likely that the very size and complexity of London's workbase, which has resulted in the absence of any dominant staple industries — unlike most other cities — had worked against it in this respect. The nature of the land market in London, with property values and a rate of redevelopment far in excess of those encountered in the provinces undoubtedly also had an impact. In addition, perhaps the very presence of the Science Museum and the National Maritime Museum, with their wide-ranging collections, had drawn attention away from the need for a specialist industrial museum for London.

On the more local front, the proposed museum was seen as being able to provide part of the wider range of museum services which the population of the Dockland ought to enjoy. It was also clear that it had the potential, if developed to a realistic size, to create much needed new jobs, support a high level of visitors and generate income for the local community.

Even before 1982, the Museum of London had already been exploring the idea of a new museum to the extent of having looked seriously at a number of possible sites in Dockland. One of these had been the Skin Floor at the London Docks, Wapping, a building of considerable architectural potential and only a fifteen minute walk from Tower Hill Station. Unfortunately, the other early buildings of the London Docks had been demolished and most of the basins infilled leaving the site land-locked, thereby precluding the introduction of full-sized vessels capable of producing a major visitor attraction. Furthermore, the area was of relatively limited size and was felt to be incapable of the continued adaption which the museum would need.

Another potential site to be examined was Shad Thames in Bermondsey. Here two separate late nineteenth century buildings were looked at — one in Butler's Wharf itself and the other along St Saviour's Dock. Given that the St Saviour's Dock building was burnt out, serious consideration could only be given to the Butler's

Wharf building. Set in one of London's most evocative riverside streets this building had the added attraction of being only a few minutes walk from Tower Bridge. Sadly, the only external space was a narrow quay fronting the Thames, which would have effectively precluded any major outside displays. Any floating exhibits would have been subject to the tides and costly to maintain. Given the historic concentration of most of the enclosed docks on the north side of the river, its location was also seen as being somewhat eccentric.

The Museum of London finally selected the north-west corner of the West India Docks as offering the greatest number of attractions. These docks opened in 1802, were seen to be of unrivalled historic importance, having been the very first of London's new trading docks built in the first decade of the nineteenth century. Of these docks, they alone survived as a reminder of the entrepreneurial skill and engineering achievement that made them possible. Quite remarkably, after 180 years of use, a range of structures from the dock's working life were still to be found. The great importance of some of these surviving buildings, in particular the Gwilt Warehouses of 1802-03 (since listed Grade I), suggeseted that they should be retained and cherished at all costs. It was clear that the use of them, together with the dock itself, as part of a possible museum complex could help provide for their conservation and long-term retention for the enjoyment and enlightenment of our own and future generations.

The site was quickly seen as giving a unique opportunity to create a radically different sort of museum — one that would exploit the 'open-air' aspect of this historic and symbolic dock through the interactive presentation of the City's maritime, commercial and manufacturing past, with all the attendant social ramifications. The water area, for instance, could accommodate preserved Thames craft — trugs, lighters and barges — capable of being discharged and loaded by steam and electric quayside cranes. It was proposed that the warehouses behind would be used to explore the 'Port of London' theme — which would provide the visitor's initial springboard into the museum — ranging from dock construction to cargo handling techniques, to the lifestyle of stevedores and dockers, to the dubious delights of Ratcliffe Highway and Cable Street, and much more besides. They would also provide a space to display some of the museum's collection of small boats and working engines, besides telling the story of London as 'Workshop of the World' and centre of commerce.

It was also realised that the proposed location, within the newly created Enterprise Zone, would have other advantages. One of the most important was the planned Docklands Light Railway, (now to open in July 1987) which will provide a frequent and fast service to and from the City to Tower Hill. In addition, the regeneration of the area was already beginning with the development of both small workshops for local industries and larger units for more 'hi-tech' users from outside. The then newly opened Billingsgate Market, to the east of the museum site, was also seen as a potential attraction as well as serving as a timely reminder of the Port's origins on the historic City quays alongside the old Billingsgate Market. The future completion of such projects as the printing works for the Daily Telegraph, within the dock complex, was also seen as enhancing the Museum's 'workplace' theme and visitor potential. The museum was also seen as offering ongoing interpretation of changes in the area as well as an introduction to preserved sites in Dockland and to other local museums.

Even as these proposals for the future Museum in Docklands were being formulated, Museum of London staff, often fighting against what seemed overwhelming odds, were busy carrying out an extensive programme of collection. By then, this had become a major exercise in 'rescue archaeology' within the purpose of ensuring that important 'workaday' aspects of London's material culture would be saved for future generations to enjoy and study. Although the old London Museum had acquired the contents of the Port of London Authority's small Cutler Street Museum, together with some 25,000 photographs of the docks and river, in 1972, it had made no attempt to salvage material from the recently closed London Docks and Surrey Commercial Docks. The present writer rescued much valuable material at the London Docks, with the help of the Port of London Authority Librarian, in 1973, but it was some years before collecting work in the docks was to begin in earnest. Throughout the 1960s and 1970s, increased containerisation and the use of larger ships had seen the working port move progressively downstream, leaving in its wake empty docks and warehouses and vast areas of derelict land which proved to be a continuing challenge to the developers, planners and politicians. In 1979 it was decided that the Museum would have to act very fast if it were to save a representative collection of traditional cargo handling equipment and material from the many ancillary trades associated with the docks. It was then clear that the two remaining dock systems within the Greater London area — the West India and Millwall Docks and the Royal Group of Docks — had only a limited life expectancy (they closed in 1980 and 1981 respectively).

There then began — with the full co-operation and help of the PLA — a major exercise in the retrieval of many thousands of objects ranging from winches, trucks, trolleys, handling tools, weighing equipment and samples to the humble stevedores' hooks, guaging tools and signs (fig 1). A comprehensive collection of cranes has been assembled including a 1926 Stothert and Pitt electric quayside crane (fig 2), a small electric crane of 1915 and a number of 'runabout' cranes. The collection of PLA material has been supplemented by extensive donations from individuals and companies associated with the

1 Tea weighing and sampling station reconstructed in the Museum in Dockland's stores, 1985. Many cargoes — from silk to opium — were weighed and re-weighed in their passage through London's dock warehouses. Activities like this will be demonstrated in the new Museum's Cargo Handling Gallery. (Museum of London)

2 The Museum of London's 1926 Stothert and Pitt electric quayside crane being placed on the North Quay, West India Docks, by the PLA floating crane 'London Samson', June 1985. Having been moved from its original location at the North Quay of the King George V Dock, this crane — the oldest surviving in the enclosed docks — was the first arrival at the Museum in Docklands site. Once restored to full working order, this crane will be used to demonstrate the loading and unloading of barges. (Museum of London)

Port. Traditional Thames craft now in the collection include watermen's skiffs (fig 3), dumb barges (fig 4 and 5) and a tug (fig 6). Already in store, awaiting display, are a complete blacksmith's workshop, a co-operage (fig 7), riggers, workshop (fig 8) and chain testing shop (fig 9).

—Beyond the material from the working river, the Museum has been involved with the collection of a great variety of material relating to working London generally. This ranges from the equipment of some forty or so different London trades to a beam engine, the Museum's largest object to date, made by Easton and Anderson of Erith, in 1887. Whilst the Museum's record may sound impressive, a lack of resources, up until the early 1980s, has meant that we have lost much of importance. Over the past one hundred years London has continued to provide a rich source of industrial relics for museums in the provinces and overseas — in the late 1970s, alone, at least ten stationary steam engines, from a variety of locations left the Metropolis. It is clear that the historic absence of a local 'workplace' Museum for London was responsible for many of these losses.

The extensive proposals contained in the Museum of London's reports received encouraging and widespread support from many organisations and individuals. Productive meetings also took place with the PLA (owners of the proposed site until 1983) and the then newly created London Docklands Development Corporation (LDDC) to explore ways in which the Museum proposals could be developed. Whilst these two organisations enthusiastically supported the Museum in Docklands scheme in principle, initial discussions were complicated by existing negotiations between the PLA and a potential commercial developer. The LDDC, meanwhile, had no wish to pre-determine a longer-term strategy for the North Quay and directed the Museum's attention to other possible sites on Canary Wharf, South Dock (Shed 19) and Millwall Dock (the Olsen Terminal). The Museum found none of these alternatives entirely suitable and maintained its preference for the North Quay, where the General Office and Warehouses 1 and 2 formed what were arguably *the* most important artefacts in Dockland and of National importance.

In May 1983, however, the LDDC announced plans for a 'People-Draw Scheme', for the Western end of the Import Dock of the West India Docks, that specifically mentioned the Museum in Docklands as a centrepiece of a

3 The PLA waterman's skiff, 'MER 149', being turned in the South Dock, West India Docks, June 1985. Built at Cory's Bargeworks, Charlton, this boat ended its working life with the PLA as a wreck marker and has since been skillfully restored, with the aid of a grant from the LDDC, by a traditional boat builder. A distinctive type of Thames boat, the waterman's skiff had evolved by about 1800 and undertook a wide range of duties such as ferrying passengers to and fro on the river, carrying stevedores and lightermen out to craft moored in the Channel, supplying ships with provisions, carrying mooring cables, towing rafts of timber and policing the Thames. Now a rare survivor, the skiff will be displayed in the Museum in Dockland's Boat Hall, but will continue to take to the water for regular demonstrations and to attend special events. (Museum of London)

3

4

5

6

4 The Wey Navigation barge, 'Perseverance IV', fully loaded with grain at the Royal Victoria Dock, 1961. Built in 1936-37, to carry a wide variety of cargoes between the Wey and the Port, the 'Perseverance' continued to work to the Royals and Millwall Dock until 1969. Acquired by the Museum of London in 1982, this wooden barge, with its distinctive stern head and transom stern, represents one of the few survivors of the 'West Country' barges which traded westwards of the Port of London. (Patricia O'Driscoll)

5 George Fisher, skipper of the 'Perserverance', in the barge cabin, Royal Victoria Dock, 1981. Often away from home for few days or more, the cabins were fitted with stoves and bunks. This barge is now being restored by the Museum of London as a floating exhibit for the Museum in Docklands. (Patricia O'Driscoll)

6 The Museum of London's diesel tug 'Knocker White', approaching West India Pier, under tow by the PLA tug 'Plaudit', June 1985. Built as the London steam tug 'Cairnrock', in 1924, it spent many years towing Harrison's floating coal elevator 'Wotan' around the port. Used for general towage until 1982, it was saved from a scrapyard early in 1985, with the help of a grant from the LDDC. Restoration work on the vessel has already begun and it is hoped that a suitable steam engine can be found to replaced the original one removed in 1960. (Museum of London)

7 Dock cooperage, reconstructed in the Museum in Dockland's stores, 1985. In workshops like this dock coopers were kept busy repairing thousands of barrels of rum, whiskey, brandy, sherry, port, tobacco, ginger and other exotic products each year. When the Museum of Docklands opens, small casks and tubs will be made for sale in the cooperage. (Museum of London)

7

8 *Rigger's workshop, reconstructed in the Museum in Dockland's stores, 1985. In workshops like this, riggers were kept busy repairing rigging for ships and making cargo handling gear in rope and wire. Besides workshops collected from the docks and riverside, the Museum has some forty different craft workshops in store, which will form the basis of 'working' interpretive displays at the Museum in Docklands. (Museum of London)*

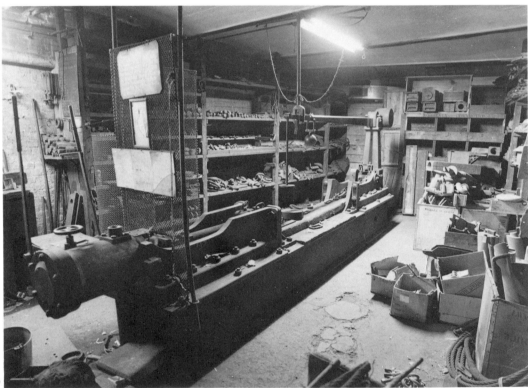

9 *Chain and gear testing shop, acquired from Davey's, shipchandlers, West India Dock Road in 1982. It is hoped to reconstruct this shop, with its splendid late Victorian testing machine, in the Museum in Docklands. (Museum of London)*

broad-based tourist and commercial development, many strands of which had been anticipated in the Museum of London's report on *Employment Generation* (November 1982).

For a number of reasons, the 'People-Draw Scheme' failed to materialise in 1983 and in September 1984, the Board of the LDDC decided to put together outline plans for a new 'West India Dock Scheme', now seen as occupying the whole of the North Quay as far as Billingsgate Market, that would include a major hotel, an indoor market, shops and the museum. As part of these preparations a Museum in

Docklands Working Party — consisting of representatives of the Museum of London, the LDDC and the PLA — was established and recommended a museum development with a minimum of 100,000 square feet (the 1982 reports had proposed an ideal of just under 150,000 square feet). 1984 also saw the museum project receive its first grant from the LDDC which has allowed a substantial increase in resources and the establishment of a working party base at Cannon Workshops, West India Docks. This base is shared with the PLA Library and Archive, which the Museum of

London jointly administers. The Museum's 'Docklands Team' has also retained its stores and workshop at the Royal Victoria Dock, which has generously been provided free of charge by the LDDC, since 1983, and before that by the PLA. Without this vital resource, collecting for the proposed museum could not have taken place on the scale that it has. In 1984, the museum also began a dialogue with the LDDC regarding the 'Museum of London in Docklands Trust' which is now being set up and will be the body primarily responsible for future developments and fundraising.

Early in January 1985, the LDDC published a two volume 'indicative study' of the West India Dock Scheme, aimed at eliciting reponses and schemes from selected developers. The study outlined the range of potential developments, including the Museum in Docklands with a proposed floorspace of only 50,000 square feet. At the same time the LDDC appointed A Y Grant Limited to carry out an independent feasibility study of the market and financial aspects of the new museum. Grant's *Museum in Docklands Feasibility Study* (March 1985) reported very favourably on the long-term financial viability of the proposed museum. It also forecast that, if the rest of the West India Dock Scheme was implemented according to plan, the Museum's visitors would grow from 476,000 in 1988 to 752,000 in 1998. Given these findings Grant was forced to conclude that:

> 'attendance projections suggest that a capacity of 50,000 square feet [brief from LDDC] will very soon be unable to accommodate likely visitor numbers . . . it is felt that more space will be needed to embrace all the above conceptual elements in the interests of visitor appeal, particularly as many of the artefacts are very large.'

Already concerned that the notional 50,000 square feet of floorspace would severely limit the nature and potential attractiveness of the new Museum, the Museum of London entered into further discussions with the LDDC and commissioned Feilden and Mawson, Architects, to produce detailed proposals for Shed 34 and Warehouse 1 at the North Quay. This work, together with some interpretative gallery designs by Michael Green Associates, appeared in April 1985. In essence, it attempted to show how a museum of around 100,000 square feet could be achieved on the site through a physical interlocking with the proposed commercial uses of the site.

Discussions are now taking place, with the LDDC, on this submission and on the future level of funding which will be necessary to establish the new museum. Whilst much more

10 *Some of the many thousands of objects saved from the docks, on display at the Museum of London, 1982-85. (Museum of London)*

11

11 The Museum in Docklands provided the basis for a small temporary exhibition at the Novag Commonwealth Chess Championships held at the North Quay. West India Docks, in April 1985. Many travelling exhibitions like this have been held in other parts of Dockland and elsewhere in London. (Museum of London)

remains to be resolved, regarding the West India Dock Scheme — not least the selection of the major developer for the North Quay — it is clear that raising the necessary capital for the conversion and fitting out of the museum will demand an enormous effort. Time is also short, with the expectation that much of the scheme including the first phase of the museum, will be ready to coincide with the opening of the Docklands Light Railway in July 1987.

Despite this, and the inevitable 'political' contests that the redevelopment of an area like London's Dockland has given rise to, the proposals for the Museum in Docklands continue to be well received. Over the past few years, somewhere in the region of 4,000 — 5,000 visitors have come to our stores in the docks, and thousands more have enjoyed the Museum's temporary exhibitions which formed part of the 1984 and 1985 East End Festivals, the 1985 GLC Living Memory Exhibition and the 1985 Novag Commonwealth Chess Championship (fig 11), actually held on the Museum site. These visitors are now attentively awaiting the start of the museum project proper. Special amongst these are portworkers, themselves, who have helped us add material to our collections and who attend the monthly meetings of the Docklands History Group held at the Museum of London.

London, and Dockland in particular, will continue to change and the patterns of life and work to alter. The new museum will help provide an understanding of these changes, make people more aware of their past and, above all, provide them with an enjoyable museum experience that cannot yet be gained South of the Severn-Wash line.

Museum ships and harbours in the United Kingdom

Vice-Admiral Sir Patrick Bayly KBE CB DSC

Introduction

In Britain, the inspiration to restore and display historic ships received its first great impetus from the success of *HMS Victory* at Portsmouth and the *Cutty Sark* at Greenwich. By the 1960s these static museum ships were, between them, attracting about 900,000 visitors a year and enthusiasts argued that if the public found these ships so interesting then there was a strong case for preserving other historic and traditional ships and craft which should then prove attractive enough to pay their way.

Some ship preservation societies were formed and there were also many individual enthusiasts. All could point out the ships and craft which, in their personal view, cried out for preservation as national relics and, although there was no possibility of a consensus, there was general agreement that something must be done. But there was no money to be had from government and little from established preservation organisations. It would therefore have to be sought from sponsors by fund raising and ultimately from the visiting public.

At this point it should be said that the *Victory* and the *Cutty Sark*, as well as being internationally famous names, are exceptional in several ways. Each ship has her own graving dock berth, rent-free, located in places well frequented by tourists and day visitors. The *Victory's* 220-year-old hull is maintained by the Ministry of Defence and direct costs do not fall on the ship management. The *Cutty Sark*, 115 years old, has to pay her way but her structure is simple and is easily maintained out of surplus earned from visitors' admission fees. Both ships are long past the possibility of going afloat again and liberties can be taken with their structures but, however desirable or necessary these alterations may be, they regrettably remove the ships further and further from their true seagoing form. Steel masts and yards in the *Victory* are one example. Others are the insertion of a deck in the lower hold of the *Cutty Sark* and an escape hatch in the ship's bottom. This is a museological problem common to the majority of preserved ships.

Formation of the Maritime Trust

In the mid 1960s Frank G G Carr, then the Director of the National Maritime Museum, and the driving force behind the preservation of the *Cutty Sark,* suggested the formation of a trust to attempt the preservation and restroration of some of the remaining but rapidly disappearing British traditional vessels. This was not a new enthusiasm for him. Thirty years earlier he had written an important book entitled 'Vanishing Craft', to which his new proposal was a natural sequel.

The time was ripe. In 1969 His Royal Highness The Duke of Edinburgh decided to found the Maritime Trust with the object of establishing a centrally placed organisation which could be the focus of information and proposals relating to possible ship preservation projects.

It was soon clear that if the Trust wished to carry influence it would not merely be a co-ordinating and advisory body but would have to own, restore and display ships itself — to get its hands dirty. Furthermore, appeals for support for the general idea of ship preservation evoked little response and it was necessary to identify particular ships as projects or targets. Most of the money raised by the Trust therefore went to its own projects, to the disappointment of a number of other hopeful organisations. But the Trust also sought to assist programmes already under way such as the SS Great Britain Project, the HMS Belfast Trust and several lesser projects without getting involved in their management. It was appreciated that the Trust cannot arbitrate between enthusiasts seeking to preserve this ship or that. It can give opinions culled from its own experience and sometimes give more tangible help but it has no right of veto over projects, however far-fetched they may seem to be.

1

2

There are now many ship preservation societies but almost all of them are occupied with a particular ship or perhaps a particular type of vessel. The Maritime Trust however has endeavoured to take a broad view and to promote active interest in all types of ship of British origin. It is no exaggeration to say that every ship or hulk in British waters more than about 40 years old has been looked at by someone with a view to preservation. New proposals are frequently being put forward by enthusiasts and, if approached, the Trust endeavours to advise them on the worthwhileness and the practicability of their favourite project, but the decision must be theirs.

Problems of ship preservation

Thirty years ago, at a time of stable currency, the *Cutty Sark* was restored and a dry dock berth built within the cost estimates. It is always difficult to produce accurate estimates for such work but in the severely inflationary period of the mid 1970s the actual costs were often more than double the best estimates. In a long drawn-out preservation project inflation is still a very serious and discouraging factor, particularly as there is often a human tendency to underestimate the costs.

It may prove possible to raise enough money to restore a ship but sponsors will view askance a project which cannot subsequently generate enough funds for its own subsequent maintanance. It is therefore necessary to adopt a practical attitude towards the purpose for which the ship is being restored. The idealist may wish to put her back to her original working role but except for small craft this is seldom sensible. Historic ships are, ipso facto, obsolete and modern regulations are likely to demand changes which conflict with the ship's original form. This is particularly so with passenger carrying vessels where safety considerations are, rightly, most stringent.

The resulting compromises can seriously affect the worthwhileness of any project. Too often the enthusiast will aver that a ship, or the remains of a ship, is of National importance but such a statement can rarely be accepted at its face value. Much effort and money may be needed to put a ship back to something like her form when she was a working vessel but this will be for nothing if she then cannot be kept in good repair for the indefinite future.

Ships as public attractions

The experience of the Maritime Trust with its own vessels and by observing others is that

1   Cutty Sark in her purpose-built dry dock at Greenwich — accessible for repairs.

2   The Thames sailing barge Cambria up river at the time of the public launching of the Maritime Trust in April 1971. (Central Press)

91

single small vessels, unless closely allied to larger attractions, cannot be expected to pay their own way, including maintenance costs, much less to recoup the capital expenditure of restoration. This applies whether the ships are in a mobile or a static role.

Projects which are dependent on paying visitors for their continued existence must be alert to changes in public taste. Now that the wonders of the world are shown nightly in colour on television, the possibility of showing off something new, different and exciting has dwindled. A survey shows that even in the *Cutty Sark* more than half her visitors come on board on impulse. They go to Greenwich for diverse reasons; they see the ships; they go on board, at an average rate of 345,000 per annum (her ten millionth visitor is expected to arrive in June 1986).

Few ship preservation organisations can afford to spend large sums on promotion and must content themselves with lesser sums, to be employed on public relations and making use of editorials, interviews and other media outlets. But the most widespread PR, positive or negative, comes from visitors and is expressed by the degree of visitor satisfaction which is a component of the cost of entry and opinion of the ship and her display. Preserved ships, unless under the wing of some major organisation, are small commercial businesses and must in the end observe the rule that the customer is always right. The *Great Britain*, at Bristol, berthed in an out-of-the-way place and only partially restored, achieves success in this respect to a remarkable degree, with a high proportion of her customers making repeat visits or coming on recommendation.

As most modern mass entertainments and diversions have a basis of movement, either by participation or in spectating, a static exhibition is now an unusual experience to the majority of the population and it requires a very special one to attract and hold a mass of visitors. Less special ones may not therefore be popular enough to remain viable.

A certain amount of life can be injected into a 'dead' ship by introducing simple bygone activities such as carpentering, splicing, sail-making, engines in steam and other ship-related activities. The Merseyside Maritime Museum is tackling this aspect with vigour and plans numerous activities to take place around static ship and boat exhibitions. It is significant that at the Ironbridge Gorge Museum with its multiple attractions, by far the greatest proportion of visitors goes to the Blists Hill site, a Victorian village under reconstruction where a number of appropriate activities take place.

Museum ports under development

The new Scottish Maritime Museum in the port of Irvine on the west coast will accommodate several static or mobile museum ships and a major quayside display of marine engineering. It has also taken over the famous test tank in the old Denny Shipyard at Dumbarton. This is all being done with massive help from the Scottish Development Agency in the expectation that it will increase the attractions of Irvine New Town. On the east coast, at Anstruther in Fife, the Scottish Fisheries Museum displays several fishing vessels of local types, restored to sailing condition, allied to a remarkably evocative museum on the quayside.

The development of the Merseyside Maritime Museum in the Albert Dock area of Liverpool is of National importance. It is being financed largely through government sources and with its extensive water area a major display of vessels, both mobile and static, is being planned. These will complement a museum in the Albert Dock buildings, and a museum of emigration will be housed in the vaults, made to represent the main deck of an emigrant ship.

At Ellesmere Port at the junction of the Shropshire Union Canal and the Manchester Ship Canal important buildings have been excellently restored and provide a most attractive setting for a display of inland water working craft and all that pertains to them.

At Bristol the success of the *Great Britain*, which achieves a steady 6% increase in visitor numbers each year, has inspired the City Council to make the Floating Harbour a major public attraction including a Maritime Centre situated adjacent to the *Great Britain's* dock.

The Exeter Maritime Museum is the only ship exhibition specialising in international craft — it possesses over a hundred and is still adding to them. With them goes the development of the quay and the restoration of eighteenth century warehouses and tunnels.

The developments at Portsmouth are the greatest projected for any ship orientated maritime museum complex in the world. *HMS Victory* remains the centre piece but around her are the Royal Naval Museum, the *Mary Rose* and the Mary Rose Museum, and in 1986 *HMS Warrior*. It is confidently expected that these combined exhibits will double the existing visitor intake to something over one million per annum. A complex organisation is being set up to market the heritage area which will include a number of the old naval buildings. The result will, in terms of visitor attraction, outshine anything else of this nature in this country and probably in the world.

The Chatham Historic Dockyard Trust is firstly concerned with the conservation and display of this largely unspoilt eighteenth century dockyard but there are three working dry docks and it is hoped that two will accommodate historic vessels. Discussions about this are proceeding with several organisations. It is intended to keep the third dock as a working commercial operation visible to the public.

In London the dock areas provide unlimited opportunities but also great challenges to ship preservationists. Compared with other ports the areas available are so vast that only small portions of them can be considered suitable for ship preservation.

3

4 *Captain Scott's Discovery (1901) with her new yards and rigging in the East Basin of the St Katharine Docks, June 1985. (National Maritime Museum)*

5 *The Merseyside Museum, Albert Dock, Liverpool. The West India Docks might look something like this. (Merseyside County Museums)*

In St Katharine's Docks the display of the Maritime Trust's ships including *RRS Discovery*, as the Historic Ship Collection, is attractive but has not been an unqualified success. Perhaps the difficulty is that redevelopment around the dock has continued for a number of years and is likely to go on for several more. This lessens the interest of the place and the average visitor seems to have difficulty in orientating himself. The fact that the Trust's ships are berthed within an area owned by a commercial enterprise whose main interests lie in other directions does not help, and the Trust has no premises ashore. The ships receive some 110,000 visitors a year but this is by no means sufficient to ensure a sound financial basis for the exhibition. The other central London attraction, *HMS Belfast*, is, perhaps fortunately, now funded by the Imperial War Museum.

The developments in the West India Docks offer great potential for the display of historic ships, both static and mobile, but this potential will only be realised when the area draws a sufficient volume of visitors to support ships in conjunction with the other attractions which are under consideration. The advent of the Dockland Light Railway gives considerable hope that this neglected area will flourish and it will also produce a beneficial effect for the *Cutty Sark* and the National Maritime Museum. One can visualise part of the docks becoming for mercantile shipping, a counterpart of the magnificent naval display at Portsmouth.

Conclusion

The often expressed ideal of general, central ship preservation being organised and controlled on the lines of the National Trust's

6

7

8

6 *The steam coaster Maria (formerly Robin, built 1890) at Bilbao in 1970.* [See the Gazetteer entry under Orchard House Yard] *(J Anderiesse)*

7 *The SS Maria steaming up the English Channel in July 1974 on repatriation from Spain. Now restored as the Robin. (The Maritime Trust)*

8 *The steam herring drifter Lydia Eva (YH89) leaving Great Yarmouth in the 1930s. The Lydia Eva, Robin and other vessels can be seen in the East Basin, St Katharine Docks.*

achievement with historic houses is probably unattainable. There are in all some thirty organisations in this country interested in historic vessels and although limited co-operation exists, their divergent interests deter any prospect of management concentration.

Most major historic ship preservation projects are both museological and commercial. They must be museological to justify their preservation and they must be commercial because of their need to earn the funds for their substantial annual running costs from the visiting public. Only exceptional individual ships can raise sufficient income to cover their direct costs. In England, a historic ship located by herself outside central London has a relatively weak potential in terms of attractiveness when competing with the large number of diverse and purpose-designed tourist attractions that have been developed in recent years. Enthusiasts will visit historic ships anywhere, but they are the few and, for viability, access to the mass market is usually necessary.

A co-location of historic ships of compatible types on the same site changes the nature of the attraction, provided that the complex is promoted as an entity. When the selected location is away from major urban centres and outside major resort areas, additional impact becomes even more essential. It seems therefore that the development of museum ship harbours, with a range of other activities and attractions nearby, is likely to be an essential feature in ensuring the longterm preservation of many historic ships.

Table of ship preservation organisations, maritime museums etc.

Key

N	Nationally funded
C	Charitable organisation
O	Open to public
M	Maritime Museum
L	Local Authority
MS	Museum Ship(s)
I	Independent
S	Actively sailing or steaming

Aberdeen Maritime Museum *LOM*
HMS Belfast *N (ex I) OMS*
The Boat Museum *ICOM + MS*
Bristol Industrial Museum *LOM + MS*
Bucklers Hard Maritime Museum *IOM*
HMS Cavalier Trust *IC (O) MS*
Cutty Sark Society *ICOMS*
Dolphin Sailing Barge Museum *ICOM + MS*
East Coast Sail Trust *ICS*
Exeter Maritime Museum *ICOM + MS*
East Kent Maritime Trust *I proposed*
Falmouth Maritime Museum *IOM + MS*
Foudroyant Trust *IC*
Grace Darling Museum *ICOM*
SS Great Britain Project *ICOMS*
Hartlepool Maritime Museum *LOM*
Historic Ship Collection *ICOMS*
Humber Keel and Sloop Preservation Society *ICS*
Island Cruising Club *IS*
Maritime Museum for East Anglia *LOM + MS*
Lowestoft and East Suffolk Maritime Museum *IOM*
The Maritime Trust *ICMS S*
The Mary Rose Trust *ICOMS*
Maryport Maritime Museum *LOM*
Merseyside Maritime Museum *LOM + MS*
National Maritime Museum *NOM*
Norfolk Wherry Trust *ICS*
North Devon Maritime Museum *ICOM*
Old Gaffers Association *IS*
Paddle Steamer Preservation Society *IS*

Porthmadog Maritime Museum *NOM + MS*
Portsmouth Royal Naval Museum *NOM*
Royal Navy Submarine Museum *N/I OM + MS*
Scottish Fisheries Museum *ICOM + MS*
Ships Preservation Trust *ICOMS*
Scottish Maritime Museum *LOM + MS*
Steam Boat Association of Great Britain *IS*
Steam Launch Restoration Group *IS*
Swansea Maritime and Industrial Museum *LOM + MS*
Thames Barge Sailing Club *IS*
Tyne and Wear Museums *LOM + MS*
Ulster folk and Transport Museum *NOM + MS*
Unicorn Preservation Society *ICOMS*
Valhalla Maritime Museum *NOM*
HMS Victory *NOMS*
Waverley Steam Navigation Co *IOS*
Welsh Industrial and Maritime Museum *NOM + MS*
Windermere Steamboat Museum *ICOM + MS*
World Ship Trust *IC*
The Yacht Trust *I (proposed)*
The Zetland Museum *LOM + MS*

Addenda
Brixham Museum *IOM*
Buckie Maritime Museum *OM*
Castletown: the Nautical Museum *OM*
Cowes Maritime Museum *LOM*
Hull: Town Docks Museum *LOM*
National Lifeboat Museum, Bristol *IOM*
Poole: Maritime Museum *LOM*
Southampton: Wool House Maritime Museum *LOM*
Massey Shaw and Marine Vessels Preservation Society *ICS*

Note
This list gives an impression of the number and variety of ship preservation organisations, maritime museums etc. in the UK but is by no means a complete list.

Cargo handling

George Adams

Introduction

Up to the middle of the last century sailing vessels predominated in the trade of the Port. They were small and their owners displayed no sense of urgency in their turnround.[1] Mechanical handling of cargoes was virtually unknown: goods were carried out of and into vessels or hoisted by means of a yardarm rig with a hand-operated winch. At some quays fixed jib cranes powered by a hand operated winch or by a treadmill were in use.[2]

From the 1850s onwards, with the increasing numbers of steam screw-propelled ships, mechanical power was introduced to cargo handling. Steamers grew steadily in size, carried a greater variety of cargo and increased tonnage and, more apposite, were costlier to build and operate than sail. Their rapid turn-round became imperative.[3] Steamers were equipped with derricks and steam powered winches (fig 1), some in the short sea trades even with steam cranes (fig 2); beginning in 1853, the enclosed docks and warehouses were progressively equipped with hydraulically powered cranes and hoists. Essentially, however, it was a speeding up of, and not a radical change in, methods which characterised the major part of cargo handling operations for the next hundred years.[4]

It was the bulk cargoes which adapted most easily to a mechanised system of handling: by the mid 1880s the majority of colliers were being discharged by machinery, by the early 1890s grain elevators (fig 3) were being employed on a considerable scale.[5] Commodities such as coal and grain, however, are homogeneous and submit to being flow processed whereas general (break-bulk) cargoes require batch processing. So, in the general cargo trades, the quick turn-round of vessels came to rely upon a large pliable labour force working at high speeds, often for long hours at a stretch,[6] making-up and breaking down discrete batches (sets/drafts) (fig 4) of general cargo to be hoisted up and down more rapidly than before.

Cargo handling

The spread of electric power to the Port around the turn of the century led to the introduction of

1   *Steam Winch Driver 1945. (PLA)*

2   *Ships' cranes in use, 1920s.*

1

2

3　Floating grain elevators discharging to craft. Millwall Inner Dock 1961.

4　Discharging a set of cargo by Union Purchase. Millwall Dock 1920s. (PLA)

5　Discharging tea by elevator conveyor. Tilbury Docks 1912. (Scruttons)

mechanical methods to some stages of general cargo operations: in 1908 an electrically operated system for transporting bales of jute was installed by Scruttons Ltd in the Clan Line sheds at Tilbury, followed by an elevator conveyor system for moving chests of tea from hold to shed (fig 5); other conveyor systems (figs 6 and 7) came close behind.[7] The Port of London Authority (PLA) introduced electric quay cranes to the Royal Docks in 1916. Scruttons Ltd, in 1920, designed a cargo carrying platform truck, powered by electric batteries, for use on shore (fig 8); this truck proved to be one of the most successful cargo handling appliances for many years, indeed, it rendered obsolescent almost all the shipside conveyor systems.[8]

Other innovations such as mobile cranes, electric winches and ship-board cranes helped forward the speeding-up process, but ultimately the pace was set by men making-up and breaking down sets, stowing and piling goods which, for the greater part, could be manhandled. Cargo handling methods could not evolve further without emulating the bulk trades. To effect this, miscellaneous general cargo had to have a homogeneity imposed upon it.

The first step was taken in the 1950s with the development of unitisation, ie the methodical assembling of small items of a like nature into a large unit for transport from point of assembly to final destination upon a pallet board or in a strapped bundle. The more definitive step was taken when, in the close of the 1960s, a new cargo handling *system*, containerisation, was instituted. General cargo could now pass through the Port pre-packed in containers of uniform dimensions and shape; the containers themselves, the documentation, the lifting equipment, land and sea vehicles, the changeover points, each specifically designed as an integral part of the flow process.

The first half of the 1950s, then, was the period when the methods of manual handling of cargoes evolved over centuries reached their zenith: it was in 1955 that the sanctioned strength of the dock worker register in London peaked at 32,000 registered dock workers (RDW).[9] In the thirty years since then, up to the first quarter of 1985, over 29,000 RDW[10] jobs have gone and along with them over 200 wharfingers, four dock systems and a way of life.

The registered dock workers

The dock worker register in London was sub-divided into docker, lighterman and overseas shipowners' tally clerk (OST). The docker sub-register contained the stevedores, the deal and corn porters; the lighterman sub-register encompassed, also, the bargeman and watchman who worked craft on non-tidal waters. The different categories could be identified by each man's registration number. The dockers and stevedores actually handled the cargoes, and worked under the same industrial agreements although demarcations did exist.[11] The lightermen operated the barges carrying the cargoes to and from the wharves and vessels within port limits. The OSTs checked and measured the ocean trades vessels' cargoes (fig 9) and also did varying amounts of the concomitant documentation; in the other trades the docker-checker checked the cargoes.

Organisation of work

The register contained weekly workers, the

6

7

"perms", contracted to a regular employer, and daily workers, the casual "poolmen", who would be engaged for as little as half a day by a registered employer. The docker and OST perm (the stevedore refused engagement as a perm) received overnight directions or reported to their employer's assembly or call-on point for orders: the casual could "shape-up" for the "free" call "on the stones", the recognised hiring places, at 7.45 am and 12.45 pm or go straight to the National Dock Labour Board (NDLB) control, "box/pen", at 8 am and 1 pm. On the stones, the hiring agent was at liberty to engage any man from amongst those shaping-up before him, but had to accept the last remaining man if he offered himself. The RDW, for his part, was free to accept or reject any job on offer. In practice, much manning was fixed-up before the call.

A man failing to engage for work on the free call had then to report to the control at 8 am and 1 pm. An employer with an unsatisfied labour requirement submitted his needs to the control where the NDLB sector manager attempted to fulfil the requirement from the RDWs reporting to his or other controls. If the sector manager had labour surplus to his requirements he would offer it to other controls. Pool men not required for work received a "fall back" payment.

Lighterage, also, had weekly and daily workers, but all engagements were conducted through the NDLB sector manager at the lighterage control. The daily worker not in work reported to the control at 4 pm each day and, if required, received orders for the next day collated from the lighterage firms by the manager. When at work, and his further services were required, the lighterman was given overnight orders direct from his employer.

Most dockers and stevedores formed themselves into gangs on a regular or ad hoc, "scratch", basis for the purpose of seeking work, the gang size being prescribed by industrial agreement. The basic ship discharging gang in the ocean trades was 10 to 12 men strong; the gang receiving from ship's side and the gang delivering imports were both 12 men. The basic ship loading gang consisted

8

of 13 men; the gang delivering to the ship's side 8 men; and the gang striking exports on the "back door" of the shed 6 men. All the gang strengths could, however, be increased for some operations or for untoward conditions.

Other men were employed individually on

9

6 Discharging frozen meat by electric conveyor. Tilbury Docks 1910. (Scruttons)

7 Discharging chilled beef by electric conveyor 1912. (Scruttons)

8 Battery operated platform truck 1920. Designed by Claud Scrutton. (Scruttons)

9 OSTs at work. One "on the stick" measuring, the other "on the pad" recording the measurements.

jobs such as the 'port-marker' who, using water based paint of several colours, distinguished one port from another amongst the consignments awaiting export; the 'bedder-out' who delineated the floor of a shed so that incoming cargo could be separated according to requirement; the 'needleman' who shovelled-up split bagwork cargo and rebagged it; the 'box knocker', who opened and re-nailed casework for the customs clearing clerk and repaired damaged packages; and the shedman who swept and secured the transit shed.

The RDWs in the Short Sea trades and the wharves had their own industrial agreements, but the variations in manning and payments was such that it was possible for wharves next door to each other to pay and work their men differently. Just as the employment conditions varied greatly at the wharves so, also, one found a greater variety of gear,[12] as wharves adapted or refined items to suit their local needs.

Cargo handling on shore
In the enclosed docks, imports would be discharged from ship direct to barge, or sometimes coaster (fig 10), or onto the shore for subsequent delivery to water, road or rail conveyance for onward transit or movement to warehouse. The cargo going into the transit shed would be piled to bill of lading or sub-mark as high as two men could lift the packages (fig 11), or higher if the shed permitted the operation of a mobile crane. Some goods were trucked along the quay into barges, in which case a mobile crane was used for swinging the sets into the barge or the cargo was slid down a shoot into the barge's hold (fig 12). Imported meat went straight over-side into insulated craft (fig 13) or straight through the shed to the loading bank and into vehicles (fig 14), or into cold store.

The wharves all handled barge traffic from the docks. Some wharves were large enough to accommodate ships the cargo from which was received into their own premises or delivered into barges for conveyance elsewhere according to the merchants' orders. Also, the wharves tended to specialise in particular commodities eg dairy produce, fruit, timber, etc. Those wharves handling timber and other commodities suitable for open stowage were equipped with a *scotch derrick* able to plumb over most of the yard, and/or mobile cranes for faster working or mobility; some of the larger timber

10 *Discharging bulk phosphates into coaster. Surrey Docks 1920s. (PLA)*

11 *Piling coffee. (PLA)*

12 *Shooting flour into barge. Royal Docks 1950s. (PLA)*

10

12

11

wharves had gantry cranes installed for their covered storage areas. The wharves handling dry goods were mostly equipped with multi-storied warehouses, and quay cranes and/or wall cranes able to plumb to the teagle openings, "bob hole/loop hole", servicing the floor on which the goods were to be housed. Resulting from the days when dock labour was cheap, many of the operations connected with the servicing of particular commodities were performed by the RDWs eg taring, sampling, bulking, blending, etc, in the tea trade (fig 15). Delivery was effected to the roadside by means of trucking off loading banks or by lowering sets direct onto the conveyance by crane or "whip" ie slacked down by a rope running through a pulley block, with the bight eased round a cleat. Where there was constant delivery to box vans eg at cold stores, elevators were the main means

13

of transport to and from the floors, especially on the landward side.

Export cargoes would be assembled in the dock transit shed or wharf warehouse preparatory to the ship's arrival and throughout the designated receiving period when she was alongside and working. In addition, the wharves loaded exports into craft for despatch alongside. Consignments would be bedded in the shed alongside according to port, convenient to the receiving hold, value and nature; eg whisky would be locked in the shed cage, dirty goods would be located well away from other beds. Heavy cargo and other cargo impervious to the weather would, if there was room, be placed outside within plumb of the purchase ready for when the ship opened-up, saving labour. The shed stowages would have to be trucked out to the pitch where two of the ship gang would

14

101

15 *Weighing tea. Cutler Street 1949. (PLA)*

make-up the sets for hoisting aboard (fig 16).

The tallying, measuring and documentation were undertaken in the coastal and Short Sea trades by docker-checkers and staff. In the ocean trades the "back door" tallying was done by PLA staff, except at berths where the ship acted as agent for the PLA. The tallying, measuring and, perhaps, the documentation of the cargo coming off and going onto the ship was performed by the OSTs.

Cargo handling on the ship

Work aboard ship was recognised as being more arduous and hazardous than that on shore: on the ship there was one mechanical aid only, the purchase, whose plumb was confined to the square of the hatch; the flooring down in the hold was poor in that after a certain stage men would be walking over broken stowages; and the portable lighting provided in the hold during the hours of darkness was at times inadequate. When in the docks, the PLA's quay cranes could be hired or the ship's own gear used, sometimes there was no choice when the quay crane would not plumb out over the ship's far side. On the river, the wharfingers' cranes could be used, but afloat at the buoys or tiers the ship's gear had to be used.

The most common rig used with the ship's gear, both discharging and loading was the *union purchase* employing two winches and two fixed derricks (fig 20). One derrick is positioned over the hatchway, the other over the ship's side. The runner or fall from each winch is led up through the heel block at the foot of the derrick, through the derrick head block and down to be shackled with the other runner into the union piece, an assembly of swivel shackles, ring and cargo hook. The set is hooked on, and the runner plumbing the load is winched up whilst the other runner is hauled in without strain (fig 18, see also fig 4). When the set is clear of obstructions, the runner first activated is stopped as the other runner takes more of the strain. Just before the set begins to rise into the air as it is traversing, the first runner is paid out until the set is above where it is to be landed, when both runners then lower the load.

16 *Making-up a set of general cargo for export. Royal Docks 1953. (PLA)*

102

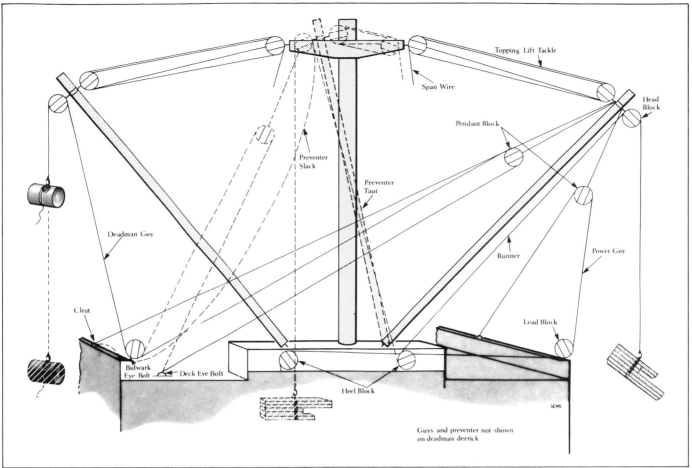

Topping Lift Tackle

Span Wire

Head Block

Pendant Block

Preventer Slack

Preventer Taut

Power Guy

Runner

Deadman Guy

Lead Block

Cleat

Bulwark Eye Bolt

Deck Eye Bolt

Heel Block

Guys and preventer not shown on deadman derrick

GEMS

17

Another rig using a fixed derrick for discharging was the *"jumper"*. The derrick was fixed overside. A gob rope was attached to the runner above the hook by means of a shackle or traveller, but still allowing the runner free movement up and down. The gob rope was led to a cruciform dolly clamped to the coaming opposite the derrick, hauled in and secured to the dolly whilst the runner was lowered. The set was hoisted until clear of the hold, when the gob rope was slacked away to allow the load to swing over the side. This rig was much used on weighing jobs, such as bales of esparto grass, when the runner was slacked first to the scale on deck, then again, permitting the bale to swing overside.

The other rigs in use employed a swinging derrick, one such was known as the *"swinging tit"* (fig 17). It was usually used for discharging commodities which could suffer being dragged along in the hold eg timber, logs and some bagwork. The swinging derrick was dressed each side of its head with a block suspended from a pendant. The runner from the inboard winch was taken up through its heel block, across to and through a block on the outboard bulwark, then fed through the pendant block on the outboard side of the derrick and its end secured on the bulwark. The other derrick was plumbed and fixed in a position just outside the inboard bulwark. One end of a wire rope was fastened to the deck and the other end led through the inboard pendant block on the swinging derrick, back down and through a block shackled on the inboard deck. It was then

18

led up through the head block on the fixed derrick and fastened to a counterbalance, the *"deadman"* (fig 21). The set was hoisted from the hold on the swinger's runner until clear, when the inboard winch heaved the swinger round over the outboard side. After the load was disengaged and the hook clear of the bulwark, the inboard winch paid out allowing the deadman to pull the light (empty) swinger back over the hold.

17 "Swinging Tit" rig.

18 Export steel being lifted aboard by Union Purchase. The overside runner has the strain, whilst the other runner is just taut. Royal Docks 1961.

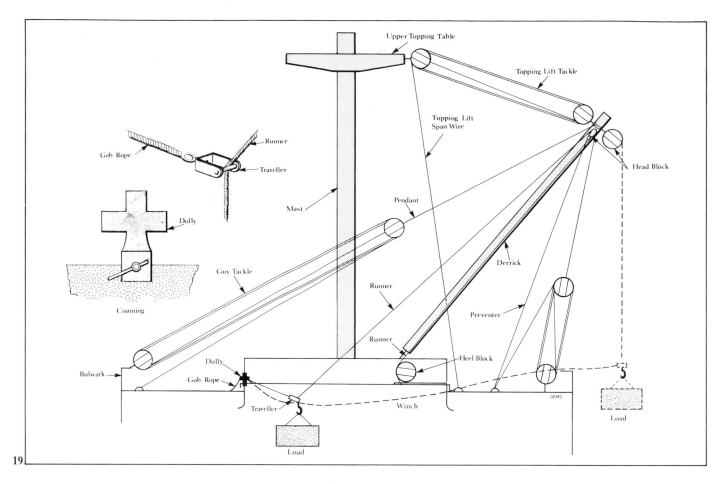

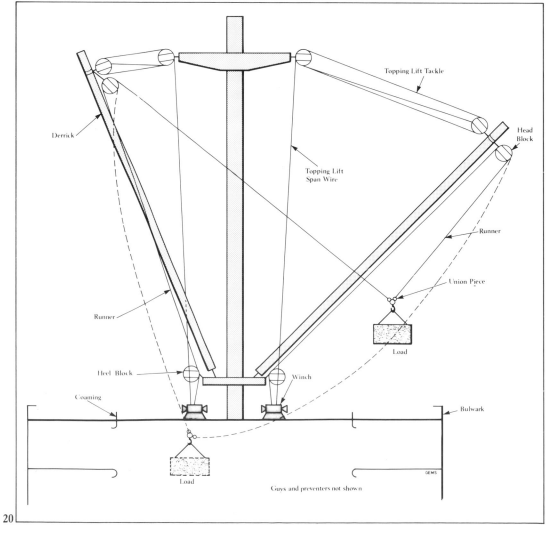

19 "Jumper" rig.

20 Union Purchase rig diagram.

21

The swinging derrick used for *heavy lift* (fig 22) work acted more like a crane, because it was rigged to top and luff in addition to hoist and slew. The cargo runner from the winch under the derrick employed acted as the hoist wire and was rigged as a gun tackle, "doubling block", ie it was rigged with a second block on the runner below the derrick head block to double the pull of the winch. The span wire from the topping lift of the swinging derrick was led through the

lead block on the deck, across to and up through the heel block on the adjacent derrick and made fast to the barrel of the adjacent winch. This winch became responsible for the topping and luffing motions. The head of the swinger was dressed each side with a block suspended from a pendant. The runner from each winch of the hold backing onto the operation was led through the heel block, down through a block secured to the deck abreast of the winch, then up through the pendant block and down to be secured to the bulwark. These runners constituted the power guys and acted to slew the swinger as one paid out and the other heaved in. Because the power guy winches faced away from the focal point of operations, a man called the "crow" or "call-boy" was employed to relay the signals of the hatchwayman to the guy winchmen.

The *wing lead* "flyaway" rig (fig 23) was fierce in operation. It was used for discharging, and then mainly in the discharge of bales of wood pulp. The preventer was left fastened to the outboard side of the swinging derrick's head and given enough slack to permit the derrick to plumb over the hatchway before being checked. The runner was led through the heel block, across to and through a block on the bulwark and then up through the derrick head block and down to its cargo hook. The inboard guy was left shackled to the derrick. The derrick was hauled manually over the hold by means of the guy as the winch slacked off; the guy was then secured. The load was hoisted, with the strain of the purchase trying to pull the derrick towards the bulwark block until, when clear of the coaming,

21 The "deadman" in use. The lead block is high because when rigged it had to clear the much higher deck load at the commencement of discharge. Surrey Docks 1961.

22 Heavy lift rig.

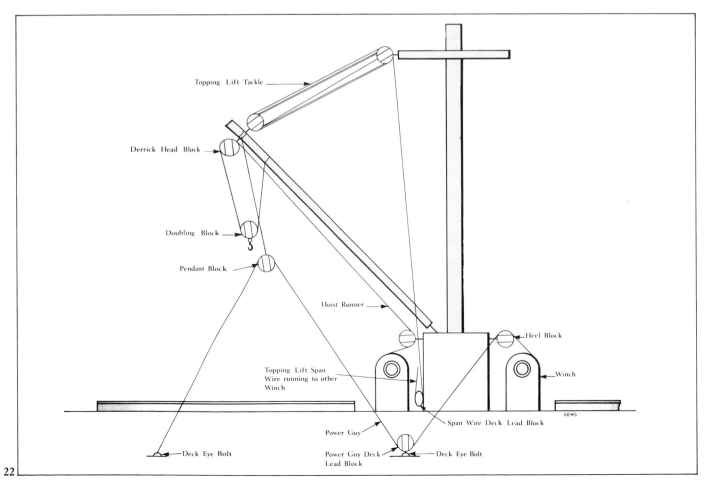

22

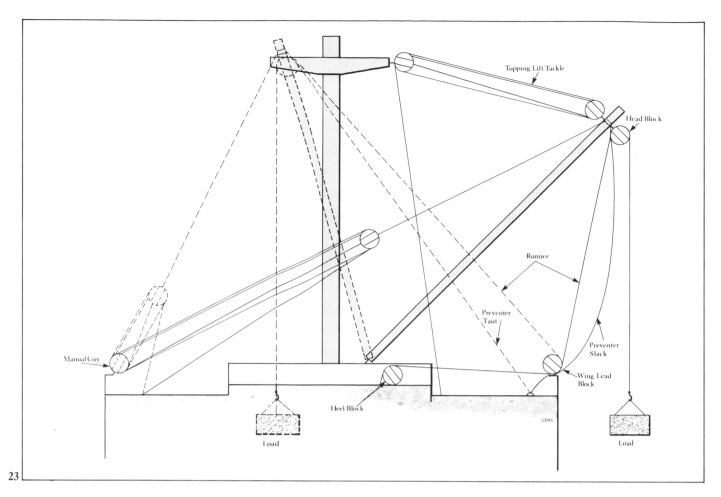

Topping Lift Tackle

Head Block

Runner

Preventer
Taut

Preventer
Slack

Wing Lead
Block

Manual Guy

Heel Block

Load

GEMS

Load

23

23 Wing lead "flyaway" rig.

23   *Wing lead "flyaway" rig.*

the inboard guy was smartly slacked off and the derrick flew outboard. As the set was clearing the bulwark the winch was put into reverse and the load swung out and down.

The shipboard gang disposed itself according to the function required and the work in hand. In a twelve handed overside discharging gang there would be the hatchwayman, the crane driver, six down holders and four barge hands.

The down holders, when using slings for making-up sets, would work in (fig 24) pairs, and similarly the barge hands for throwing away, but when employing boards or nets the down holders would work two sides and the barge hands all round the one board or net (see fig 13). The down holders would "break down" into the cargo in the square until they had worked out an ample hole of about shoulder

24   *Down holders making-up sets of ammonium phosphate. Third pair's sling can be seen beyond the ladder. Greenland Dock 1946. (PLA)*

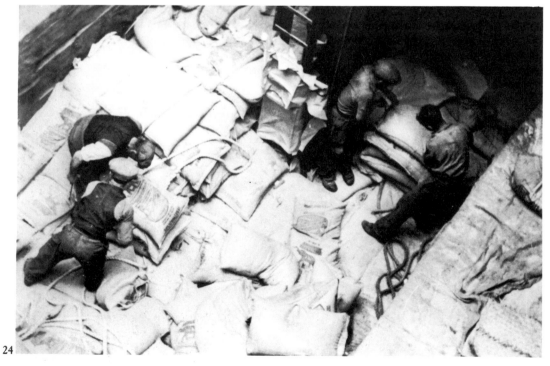

24

25 Down holders digging down on timber. Note bolster under the set, and the marking of ther next bill of lading showing. Surrey Docks 1961.

25

height, permitting them to work "bottoms-to-bottoms, tops-to-tops" ie reducing lifting to the irreducible minimum. Then they would work away from the square, one pair towards the port wing, the second to the starboard wing and the remaining pair for'ard or aft into the "long end" until the level being worked was cleared. The sequence would be repeated until the stowage was exhausted. Cargo which could be slung in a choke sling would be hooked on to the purchase and dragged out into the square for hoisting, but commodities which had to be slung on boards were carried out near to the square for slinging unless the employer was of such substance as to provide gravity rollers. Cargo in the tween deck cupboards (compartments with doors) had to be humped out or passed and repassed into the square for slinging, unless gravity rollers were to hand.

Softwood discharge was a job on its own. The bulk of it came into the Surrey Commercial Docks, but 80% of it went out again in craft to the wharves.[13] The stevedore gang discharging timber was organised in a different manner: nine men were called off as inside men and four as outside men. The inside men worked on the ship under a different piecework rate from the outside men who received the sets into the barge or onto the shore. If the size of timber permitted, the down holders worked singly, digging down within the designated bill of lading stow (fig 25). They would make-up a set by putting single lengths of timber on a bolster, binding the set as they piled, and when the purchase brought the chain sling to them they would hook it around the set on the fore side of the middle, so that the nose would lift as it dragged (fig 26). Meanwhile, except when handling baulks, the outside men would have erected a horse (a form of trestle) standing above the coaming of the lighter (fig 27). The sets would be landed leaning on the horizontal of the horse, alternately either side. After releasing the chain sling, each man would take away as much as he could carry under arm and drop his load neatly into the stow. As they worked their way up, the horizontal would be raised until it gave no further advantage then the horse would be dismantled and further sets landed on bearers until the lighter's freight was

26 Set of timber slung and being dragged under plumb prior to hoisting. The two stevedores are guiding the set so as to prevent knocking over the set being made up in the foreground. Surrey Docks 1961.

26

27 Loading to barge using the horse. Note the timber piled on shore by the far ship and awaiting the deal porters' attention. Surrey Docks, pre-war. (PLA)

27

28 Deal porters carrying timber.
Millwall Dock 1939. (PLA)

complete. When discharging to shore, the
outside men would safely, but not too fussily,
pile the timber close to the ship's side. After the
ship had finished landing, the deal porters
would move the piles to stowages in the sheds
and there stack it very neatly (figs 28 and 29).[14]

Ship loading was seldom a straight forward
operation. Theoretically, the cargo was to be
stowed in port rotation, ie "last port out, first
port in"; incompatible commodities had to be
kept separate, and the ship had to be loaded so
that whatever she met and whatever the
intermediate discharge she would remain trim
and stable with safe stowages. However, the
right cargo was not always available when
required and expensive labour could not be
allowed to stand about waiting for it, so much
chopping and changing could take place in the
stowages in order to keep the ship working and
trim and stable and safe.

The complement of down holders split up,
half port side and half starboard side and
worked alternate sets. They took the cargo into
the corners of the long end and worked across to
meet one another in the middle, tier by tier,
stowing tightly up to about shoulder height with
miscellaneous general cargo, keeping the top as
level as possible for working over on the next
run-in. The most skilful part of this stage lay in
"taking the bilge out", ie fitting rectangular
cargo into the deep curve of the bilge so as to
give a solid level top to stow cargo on when
working the next height. The stowage was
extended into the square sufficient to allow sets
to be landed on the next height for working in,
and the men worked the cargo in as their
forbears had, carrying, passing, dragging,
bowling, rolling, skidding and levering —
except that for the heavy items the power of the
purchase could be used.

Using the power of the purchase in
conjunction with the positioning of blocks to
alter or increase the direction and power of the
pull to heave cargo in, was called bull-roping, an
art in itself. The blocks would be placed so as to
lead the wire rope from the winch down into the
hold and into the wing or long end, where it
would return through a block to heave or
"switch" in the heavy item. With a straight
heave, the load would be dragged over prepared
ground whereas with the switch the load would
be lifted as it slid in. There were many other
variations used, but for really heavy lifts the
ship's jumbo derrick or the PLA's floating crane
would be employed and the lift placed down
once in the square or on deck.

The big consignments of bagwork were
usually refined sugar or fertiliser in 2 cwt
(101 kg) hessian sacks, and cement in 1 cwt
(50 kg) paper bags. The quickest and easiest
way to work the 2 cwt sacks was by "backing".
In this method, the men made a block-stow,
taking-up all the square of the hatch, and
landed the sets on to a specially assembled pitch
on each edge of the block-stow in succession.
Each man then carried a sack on his back into
the stow. The 1 cwt paper bags were carried in
by hand from a pitch made about four bags high,

28

29 Timber neatly stacked by deal
porters. Mobile cranes introduced by
the PLA obviated the need for the
deal porters to carry the wood up the
"ways". Surrey Docks 1961.

29

one deep and one bag wider than the set, with
the pitch one bag higher each end so that the set
would be prevented from spewing. In practice,
for all commodities which could be carried, a
raised pitch of one sort or another was built to
minimise lifting and thus conserve energy and
speed the job.

It was usual when the ship was taking a full
freight, which included unpacked cars, to leave
height between the top of the stow and the deck
head (the ceiling on shore) in the lower hold
sufficient to allow cars to be stowed (fig 30).
Under the cars the stow would consist of
thousands of different items; cases, cartons,
bags, bales, drums, even buses knitted together
safely into a whole like the pieces of a gigantic
three-dimensional jigsaw.

30 *Stowing cargo in the lower hold, leaving height for a stow of unpacked cars. Royal Docks 1961.*

Effects of the new cargo handling methods

Over the two decades after the war much cargo was still handled by conventional methods, but all the time pressure was on to convert the break-bulk to bulk cargo. From 1949 onwards the import of sugar changed from bagged to bulk cargo to be grabbed out; sulphur, which had come in a dry form suitable for grabbing and shovelling, by-passed the Port in specialised tankers carrying sulphur as a heated liquid ready for pumping-out; wine which had been imported in casks came in 500 gallon (2,272 litre) tanks of stainless steel or plastic, and finally in tankers; timber was packaged into bundles of a ton or more, obviating each individual piece being picked up. These commodities yielded to innovatory methods, but miscellaneous general cargo was more stubborn.

In the general cargo trades, shippers began strapping their goods into larger units, eg bundling lightweight cartons into, say, units of three; hardboard, which had come over as single sheets, began to be shipped in bundles; similarly asbestos corrugated sheeting; lead pigs of up to 70 lbs (32 kg) converted into one and two ton ingots; aluminium ingots were strapped into one ton bundles. Many of these innovations were made possible because at the place of manufacture fork lift trucks had come into use. Fork lift trucks were insinuated on to the PLA's quays from 1951, enabling the shore operators to handle unit loads and pallets effectively. The most noticeable effect on ships was the widening of the hatchways on new building, and the introduction of twin and triple hatchways abreast on ships of other lines (fig 31), all permitting the placing of a greater volume of cargo once down. On the older conventional ships, cargo still had to be worked in from out of the square, using the old methods when loading, which meant more thoughtful planning

31 *Triple-hatchway vessel.*

of the stow or more damage. It meant, also, that the stevedore's pallet coming onto the ship had to be discharged and returned. Eventually fork lift trucks were put aboard ships, but the shape of the hold, the obstruction of ladders and columns, tween deck coamings, the point loading capacity of flooring, etc, on most conventional ships militated against the effective employment of the machine. Not until purpose-built vessels were introduced were the docks away, and that in more than one sense of the word.

Notes

1 Jeffery, The History of Scruttons p 25.

2 Jackson, The History and Archaeology of Ports pp 96-98.

3 Lovell, Stevedores and Dockers p 26.

4 Ibid, p 39.

5 Ibid, p 28.

6 Ibid, p 29.

7 Jeffery, The History of Scruttons p 46.

8 Ibid, p 48.

9 National Dock Labour Board Annual Report 1955.

10 National Dock Labour Board.

11 Cmnd 3146, S 2.

12 The term "gear" as commonly used encompasses all the cargo handling apparatus used by the docker for making-up or assisting in the making-up of sets for hoisting, as distinct from ship's gear which consists of its winches, derricks and their attachments.

13 Bird, The Geography of the Port of London.

14 Oram, The Dockers' Tragedy pp 162-3 pp 167-8.

Short Bibliography

Jackson, G,
'The History and Archaeology of Ports'.

Jeffery, A E,
'The History of Scruttons'.

Lovell, J,
'Stevedores and Dockers' National Dock Labour Board, Annual Reports.

Oram, R B,
'The Dockers' Tragedy' Report of a Court of Inquiry into the causes and circumstances of a Strike by members of the National Amalgamated Stevedores and Dockers in the Port of London, and into practices relevant thereto. Cmnd 3146 November 1966.

The Royal Dockyards of Woolwich and Deptford

Philip MacDougall

The yards of Deptford and of Woolwich are noble sights, and give us a just idea of the great perfection to which we are arrived in building those float-castles and the figure which we may always make in Europe among the other maritime powers.

Henry Fielding, 1754

For the former Kentish townships of Woolwich and Deptford, 1869 was to mark the beginning of a very real period of suffering and decline. In that year, the government finally decided that the two local royal dockyards should be closed, so annihilating a 350-year tradition of shipbuilding and repair. It was, in fact, an administrative act that ripped the heart out of these two communities, forcing thousands of long term residents to seek employment elsewhere. Not surprisingly, a great many families found themselves hopelessly split, with fathers, sons and daughters each having to go their separate ways. It was a recipe for social chaos and mass disorder, with a large number of those involved eventually putting down new roots at Chatham and Sheerness.

It was during the reign of King Henry VIII that the two dockyards were first established. A time of naval expansion, much thought was being given to the ideal location for a number of new dockyards and repair centres. The nation already had one other royal dockyard, that of Portsmouth, but this not only lacked facilities, it was isolated as a result of its great distance from London. This created the problem of forcing newly completed vessels to first undertake the long sea journey to the Thames, where they could eventually anchor off the Tower for purposes of taking on stores and ordnance. Far more sensible therefore, would be to have at least one dockyard situated on the Thames itself, capable of both repairing and building the very largest warships. Portsmouth would continue to be of use, but only as a naval base, necessary for the protection of the south coast.

In 1513 Woolwich first appears to have been established as a royal dockyard. In December of that year construction started on a new flagship for the Tudor navy. This was *Henry Grace a Dieu*, a massive ship for its day, being of an estimated 1,500 tons burden. At the time however, Woolwich could offer very few facilities, everything being of a rather temporary nature. A few storehouses had certainly been rented, whilst there is evidence of an actual smithery being brought into existence. As for the vessel itself, this was being constructed in a dry dock made of nothing more than impacted mud which was reinforced with brushwood and planking. The idea was that once *Henry Grace a Dieu* was built, the dock would be more or less demolished, allowing the vessel to be floated out upon the next convenient high tide.

At about this point in time, consideration seems to have been given to the location of a further yard at Erith. Since the reign of Henry VII it had been normal for this part of the river to be used as a naval anchorage, whilst it is possible that a number of smaller vessels were under construction in the same year as *Henry Grace a Dieu* was being built at Woolwich. Even more important however, was the purchase in 1514 of four acres of land upon which a new storehouse was to be constructed. With this, and a nearby dock for the mooring of vessels, Erith might well have become a major dockyard. That it did not was almost certainly due to the unsuitable nature of the surrounding land, the storehouse being liable to inundation during both exceptional and ordinary tides.

As a possible replacement for Erith, it was decided that expansion of already existing facilities at Deptford should now be undertaken. For a number of years this part of the Thames had also served as a mooring point for warships, with storehouses being rented to serve their occasional needs. One further storehouse was certainly erected in 1513, whilst in 1517 an agreement was reached for the construction of a basin or wet dock. To be sited on land that once made up a meadow, and which was close to the previously mentioned storehouses, it was designed to accommodate five large vessels. Probably completed sometime in the year 1520 it meant that waiting warships

Half plans of Woolwich and Deptford dockyards as executed by Thomas Milton in 1753

1 Woolwich. *At this time the dockyard was then the fifth largest in the country (only Sheerness was smaller) and employed just over 700 artisans and labourers. Specialising in heavy repair and building work the large number of slipways (marked x) and the single (l) and double dock (m) were essential features around which the whole of the yard was organised. Recent expansion at the western end of the yard, consisting of 20 acres purchased in 1743, was yet to be fully incorporated into the dockyard. Future building work, to be carried out over the next twenty years, would include additional slips, seasoning sheds and an anchor stand. (National Maritime Museum)*

112

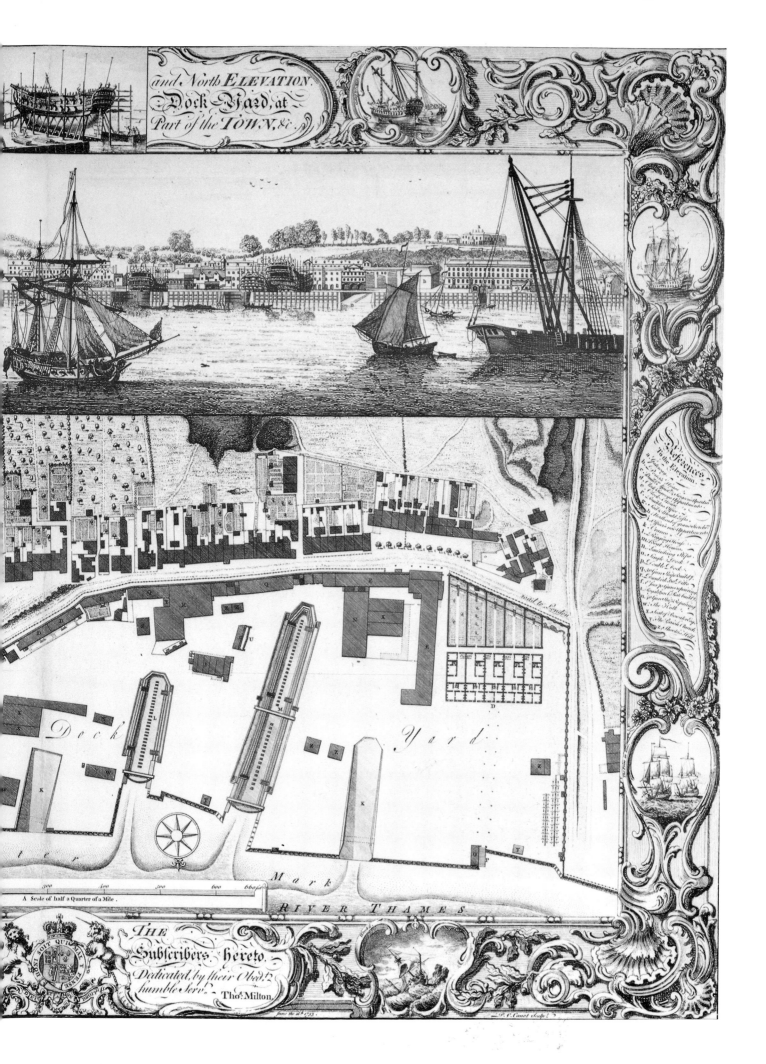

and North ELEVATION.
Dock Yard, at
Part of the TOWN, &c.

References
To the Elevation.

Dock   Yard.

A Scale of half a Quarter of a Mile.

Mark

RIVER THAMES

THE
Subscribers hereto
Dedicated by their Obed.t
humble Serv.t Tho.s Milton.

113

2 Deptford. *Employing at that time just over 800 men, this was the fourth largest yard in the country (being exceeded in size by Portsmouth, Chatham and Plymouth). The obvious features of this yard are an extensive wet dock (q) that was originally established during the reign of King Henry VIII, together with a double dock (x) and the great storehouse (m). Future work is yet to include a large group of mast houses, a further slip, offices and store sheds. All this was to be completed by 1774. (National Maritime Museum)*

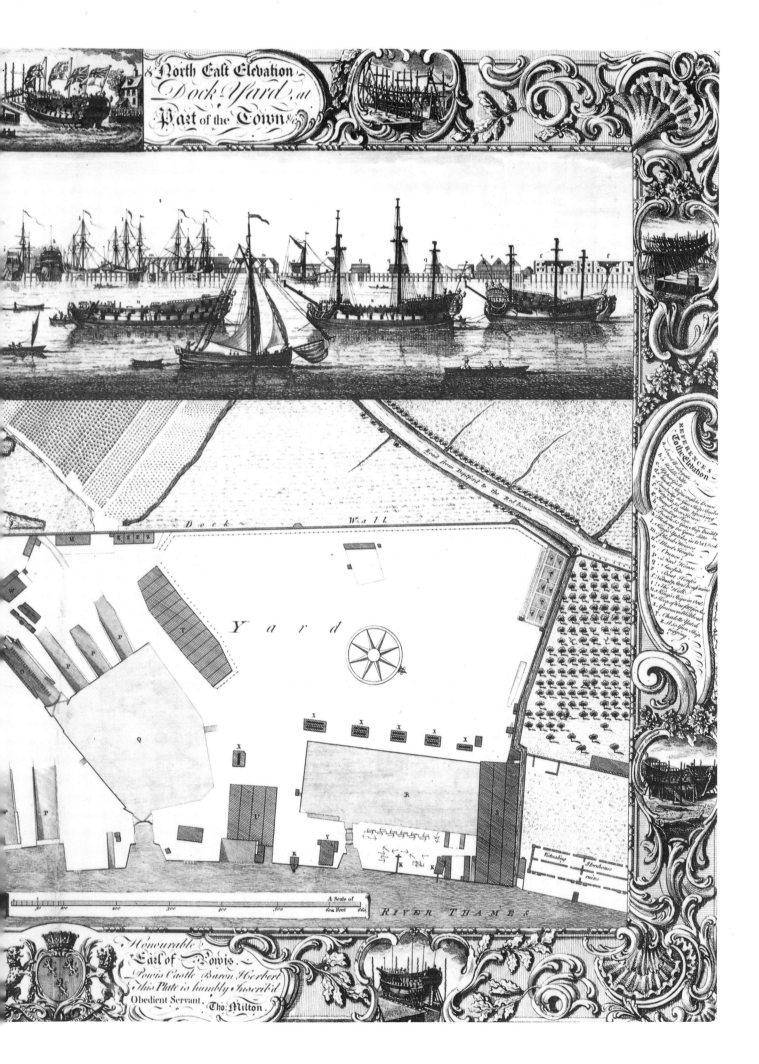

North East Elevation & Dock-Yard, at Part of the Town &c.

Yard

Dock Wall

Road from Deptford to the Red House

A Scale of 600 Feet

RIVER THAMES

Honourable Earl of Powis, Powis Castle, Baron Herbert. This Plate is humbly Inscrib'd Obedient Servant, Tho. Milton

REFERENCES To the Elevation

115

could be more easily fitted out, no longer having to remain moored in a mid-river position while a mass of small boats ferried back and forth with numerous items of equipment.

Over the next few decades Woolwich and Deptford continued to develop, acquiring a level of importance that was never to be equalled in later years. With few other royal dockyards then in existence virtually all warships were either built or repaired on the Thames, whilst Deptford became increasingly associated with the generalised distribution of stores and naval equipment. For this particular reason therefore, and the fact that it was also much closer to London, Deptford witnessed a much more intensive period of expansion. Already the fitting out dock has been noted, whilst this same yard was soon to receive a permanent dry dock. Taking the form of a double dock, and completed in timber, it allowed for the repair or construction of two vessels simultaneously, giving this one yard facilities that no other dockyard was to share until the early seventeenth century.

The undoubted supremacy of the two Thameside royal dockyards was however, to be remarkably short lived. The advantage of being so close to London was to prove of only limited importance in future years, a greater emphasis soon being placed on strategic needs. The late sixteenth, and much of the seventeenth century, were to see a whole series of maritime wars that involved such diverse enemies as Spain, France and Holland. In each case, dockyards were required that could not only maintain vessels, but would be so positioned that ships in their care might quickly enter the Channel or North Sea. For this reason Portsmouth was once more expanded, whilst an even larger dockyard was established at Chatham. This latter yard was to have a real influence upon Woolwich and Deptford, undertaking much of the repair work that would otherwise have gone to the Thames. Indeed, so important did Chatham become, that in the year 1618 it was even suggested that Deptford should be closed, with all work undertaken at this yard being transferred to the Medway. The first of many such proposals, effecting as they did either Woolwich or Deptford, it was a factor constantly militating against any massive expenditure upon the general re-planning of the two yards.

Despite this change in fortune, the early seventeenth century did see a few improvements undertaken. Both Woolwich and Deptford were enclosed at this time, whilst Woolwich also saw construction of a government ropery[1] and conversion of an earlier single dock into a double dock. Additionally, a sudden flurry of activity during the 1650s brought to Woolwich a second dry dock and several storehouses. Deptford, on the other hand, received little in the way of large-scale rebuilding, but attention was given to renovating many existing facilities whilst wharves and a mast pond were certainly added. Thus, an overall tendency towards general expansion is still to be discerned, but compared with Portsmouth and Chatham, it was now somewhat limited. Indeed, this point is admirably brought out by a survey conducted in 1688 that shows the total value of all royal dockyards during this period to have been as follows:

Chatham	£44,940
Portsmouth	35,045
Deptford	15,760
Woolwich	9,669
Sheerness	5,393[2]

The situation in the eighteenth century was to remain virtually unchanged. Certain improvements were carried out towards the beginning of the century, mostly at Deptford, although the double dock at Woolwich was rebuilt in 1720. Again, the reasons for this comparative neglect were more or less as stated, with the authorities increasingly concerned about the length of time necessary for navigating a ship this far up the Thames. Indeed, without favourable winds, it might take as long as eight weeks for a ship to pass from the great fleet anchorage of the Nore to one or other of these two dockyards. For anything less than a major repair this was a quite uneconomic use of time, with Woolwich and Deptford rarely considered for fleet maintenance work. An additional problem had now also emerged, the Thames having insufficient depth for larger ships to take up moorings off Deptford. This was partly through shoaling, but also because vessels were continually growing in size. The outcome therefore, was that first rates were rarely to be built or repaired at Deptford, whilst most ships bound for Woolwich had their guns and stores previously removed at Northfleet.

Yet, despite such problems, the yards at Deptford and Woolwich were quite indispensable when it came to the construction of new warships. Here was a very real specialism, with both yards producing a large number of third, fourth and fifth rates throughout the entire century. To facilitate such work, a number of building slips were eventually added to already existing dry docks, giving both yards a much enhanced ability. By 1772 therefore, Deptford had acquired six of these slipways, with Woolwich having four. The size of these slips varied considerably, but generally allowed the two yards to produce ships not only of any size, but also in greater numbers than all other yards except Chatham.

A further area of specialism was that of supplying general naval equipment to other royal dockyards both at home and abroad. The wholesale purchase of materials through the commercial markets in London meant that a huge quantity of items was constantly being delivered to Deptford for storage or immediate redistribution. Nor, as it happens, was this supplying of other yards restricted only to purchased material. Both Woolwich and Deptford had the ability to manufacture a wide range of commodities and these, once again, might be exported. Most important was the

Woolwich ropery which had originally been established in 1614. Greatly enlarged during the mid-eighteenth century it was capable of supplying not only local needs but also, when required, those of Sheerness and Chatham.[3] As for Deptford, such items as anchors and pumps were capable of being produced in vast quantities, and were most often supplied to those merchant yards that had been contracted by the Navy board to build warships.

Finally, due to its proximity to the Navy Board offices in Seething Lane, Deptford was also the yard most frequently chosen for any new or experimental construction work. For this reason, a number of more senior shipwrights were appointed to the yard, able to give their immediate attention to any problems that might arise. Because of this, a number of projects were begun at Deptford, some of them having a considerable influence upon the future development of the warship. Amongst these was the building of *Culloden*, a 74-gun third rate. Launched in 1747, she was the first, and also the smallest, of a whole series of such vessels, with this type of ship going on to dominate the line of battle. A further experiment, also involving the 74-gun warship, was the laying down of *Brunswick* in 1785. Built with a shallow draught, it was hoped that such a vessel would overcome the numerous problems created by the constant shoaling of the Thames. The experiment, on this occasion however, proved a failure. Finally, the yard was involved in early experiments that eventually led to the successful coppering of timber-hulled warships. It was a complex and difficult task, and one that took some twenty or thirty years to complete but, once solved, gave the Royal Navy a distinct edge in the protection of their hulls from the attacks of 'ship worm'.

Perhaps the real value of Deptford can be seen by reference to a contemporary report upon all royal dockyards produced in 1774. At that time an extension to the north-east had just been completed, allowing construction of a mast pond, mast houses and the already mentioned sixth building slip. According to the report, Deptford:

> . . . is conveniently situated for receiving timber from the interior part of the kingdom by the River Thames, therefore is useful for building both large and small ships there being a sufficient flow of water for launching them although not a sufficient depth at low water to lay the large ships on float, therefore after such are launched they are moved the first opportunity that offers for sailing them down the river to be laid up at other ports. But it admits of laying up frigates and other small ships which may also be repaired here and more expeditiously equip't on urgent occasions than at any other place by contract Riggers to be hired in the River, as was practiced in the later part of the last war when this method was found to be far more expeditious than by their own officers and men.[4]

3 A view of Deptford dockyard engraved by Richard Paton of Wardour Street, Soho. An artist noted for his accuracy and detail, Paton shows the eastern part of the yard dominated, as it was, by the Great Storehouse. This is the building immediately beyond the slipway (foreground) and behind the swing crane. Noted on maps since the late seventeenth century, the storehouse was greatly enlarged and improved over the years. (National Maritime Museum)

3

Also, as this same report noted, 'it is not advisable to keep many ships here that are in good condition any length of time' indicating that the fresh water of the Thames at this point would lead to their decay. Instead, such vessels were usually transferred to the Medway.

As for Woolwich, which also received a number of new stores and work sheds, this same report briefly summarised its basic advantages and disadvantages:

The conveniencys and inconveniencys belonging to this yard are much the same as those at Deptford, except the inconveniencys of getting large ships down the river after they are launched, is not as great as at Deptford.

This yard is much smaller than Deptford and will not contain a proper quantity of timber suitable to the works that otherwise might be carried on for building and repair of ships.

At about half a mile distant from the dockyard is a very good Ropeyard where is made all the cordage for the use of this and Deptford yard also for the supply of all the foreign yards.[5]

Moving towards the end of the century, it is impossible to discuss further developments at Woolwich and Deptford without reference to the long drawn out wars with revolutionary France and the Empire (1793-1815). For both dockyards it was an extremely difficult period, placing a considerable burden upon their comparatively meagre resources. In order to keep pace with naval demands, the size of the work-force was greatly expanded, with that of Woolwich increasing by 97% and that of Deptford by 74%.[6] Of course, the other dockyards rose by very similar proportions, but it does show that the two Thames yards were extremely useful, continuing to perform the essential building and heavy repair work for which they were so ideally suited. Of ships built during this period, the third rate was most common, with Deptford launching twelve and Woolwich eight. In addition, Woolwich also launched a first and a second rate together with several smaller vessels, whilst Deptford also launched a second rate and a number of smaller vessels.

Despite this constant activity, characterised by the large-scale increase in work-force, neither yard was completely safe from the continuing threats of closure. In 1800, Sir Samuel Bentham, Inspector General of Naval Works, proposed a radical scheme in which both Woolwich and Deptford, together with the dockyards at Chatham and Sheerness, would have been completely replaced by a new yard built on the Isle of Grain. The reasons for this proposal were contained in a detailed letter that was submitted to the Admiralty in April 1800:

. . . considering their great distance from the sea, the unavoidable delays attending the navigation of the Rivers in which they are situated, the want of a sufficient depth of water for ships of war when in a state fit for sea, and the want of accommodation for ships to lie to fit within the precincts of either of these dockyards, it has appeared to me that however great might be the sum which should be appropriated to their improvement, still the sending a ship to either of these yards for the purpose of refitting or repair must occasion a much greater expense for the performing a given quantity of work than at an Out Port.[7]

The scheme for an Isle of Grain dockyard was never pursued beyond that of an inspection of the site by members of the Board of Admiralty.[8]

Other schemes for the closure of Deptford and Woolwich were also put forward in this same period[9] but, as much as anything, the two yards were probably saved by the successful introduction of new dredging procedures. At the beginning of the century Sir Samuel Bentham had successfully pioneered a steam operated river dredger that had the ability to raise 1,000 tons of soil every twelve hours. First introduced at Portsmouth, a second machine was actually built at Deptford and was being used in the Thames off Woolwich by October 1802. This proved an immediate success, allowing the deepening of channels and the safer movement of larger warships. By 1807, a second dredger was in use off Deptford, whilst an even larger one was eventually operating at Woolwich.

An eventual conclusion to the wars with France resulted in further thought being given to the future of the two yards. Whilst most dockyards had been merely returned to a peace time footing, Deptford was now faced with the very real possibility of closure. Hopelessly organised, badly positioned and comparatively disadvantaged when it came to handling the very largest of ships, the dockyard gates were first sealed in 1832. This, however, proved only temporary, the yard being re-opened five years later as a 'depôt for receipt and issue of naval stores for foreign stations'. During this period of resuscitation the yard was also responsible for the construction of several new warships.

At Woolwich the story was quite different. Progress in technology meant that the Royal Navy was soon experimenting with small steam powered ships, many of them built on the Thames. For this reason Woolwich was chosen as the most suitable yard for co-ordinating their work, soon going on to specialise in the servicing of such vessels. To undertake these new duties Woolwich, in 1831, was given a purpose-built steam basin and additional building slips, the whole being designed by John Rennie (the younger), and completed at a cost of £34,000. Ten years later, even more elaborate facilities were added in the form of a seven acre steam yard that included a massive graving dock (the largest built in any royal dockyard up to that date), a mast house and various work sheds together with a factory building that housed a large vertical boring machine. Completed in 1843, and allowing the work force at Woolwich

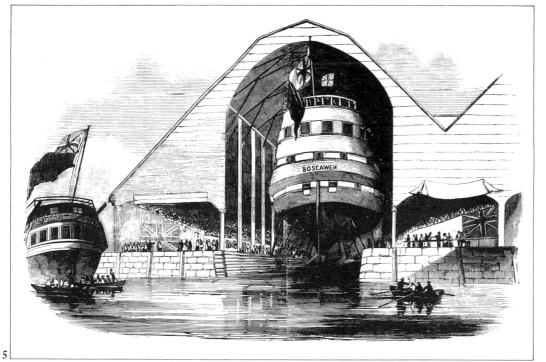

to be increased by a further thousand, the whole extension was built by Messrs Grissel and Peto at a cost of £80,000.

Acquiring therefore a growing expertise in steam, it looked as if Woolwich might well have a secure future. This, however, was not to be. The dockyard, despite the employment of dredgers, had not fully solved the problem of access, mud accumulating almost as fast as it was removed. Needless to say, all this was proving extremely expensive, and had cost £125,692 in the first ten years of dredging. To this cost must also be added the charge for a new wharf, constructed in 1818, and mainly designed to check the constant presence of mud which, once more, had been threatening to bring the yard to a standstill. Specifically, during those immediate post-war years, and on towards the middle of the century, the problem was partly concealed by the limited size of many early steamships. From the 1860s onwards however, there was a considerable leap in the overall size of such vessels, the emphasis soon being placed upon the much heavier ironclads with their greater draught. The eventual outcome therefore, was a series of renewed

119

6 *A further view of the covered slips at Woolwich. The earliest of these were timber roofed, with metal coverings being used for the later slips. (Greenwich Local History Library)*

7 *The launch of the screw frigate Ariadne, built at Deptford in 1859. The covered slipways, also introduced at this yard, should be noted. Deptford had been building steamships for a number of years, but lacked facilities, many ships built here having later to proceed to Woolwich for fitting out. (Greenwich Local History Library)*

6

7

threats to the future prosperity of Woolwich dockyard.

As much as anything, it was an eventually agreed extension to Chatham dockyard that really sounded the death knell for both Woolwich and Deptford. Consisting of numerous dry docks and basins, it gave Chatham facilities far in advance of those to be found elsewhere, and allowed this particular dockyard to take on work that might otherwise have gone to Woolwich. Furthermore, Chatham could actually build the ironclads, and had gained considerable expertise in this field. Woolwich, on the other hand, was very much in decline, with the government reluctant to update facilities that were not only duplicated at

Chatham, but were now being put to much better use.

Of the two yards, it was Deptford that was the first to close. The last vessel built here was the *Druid,* a steam powered corvette that was launched on 13 March 1869. Eighteen days later, on 31 March, the yard officially closed. During that period much of the work force was made redundant, with only a small number eligible for pensions. The vast majority were forced to seek alternative employment, with some being offered work at the newly expanded Chatham yard. As for Deptford itself, this was

initially sold to a Mr T P Austin for £70,000. He appears to have made a very quick profit on the deal, soon selling 21 acres of the yard to the City of London for £94,640. They transformed the area into a foreign cattle market, helping at that time to supply the nearby Royal Victoria Victualling Yard.

Woolwich remained in operation for a further six months. Here the running down process was a lot more complicated, with some of the sheds and machinery also being transferred to Chatham. The final launching was on 13 July 1869, that of the screw corvette *Thalia,* with the

8   A mid-nineteenth century view of Woolwich dockyard showing the mast pond and boat house. Situated at the eastern end of the yard they were originally constructed during the early part of the preceding century. (Greenwich Local History Library)

9   The Woolwich steam basin as completed in 1831. The vessel being fitted out or repaired is the steam warship Terrible *which had originally been launched at Deptford in February 1845. (Greenwich Local History Library)*

10-12 *In the dockyard at Deptford shortly before its closure in 1869. For many years the yard had been greatly under-utilised with only a few improvements being made to its basic facilities.*

10 *General storesheds with one of the large covered slipways in the background. (Author's Collection)* **10**

11 *Storage area showing obvious age and dilapidation of dockyard buildings. (Author's Collection)* **11**

12 *The pension office from where elderly retired dockyard workers collected a regular pension. The royal dockyards were one of the first organisations in the country to introduce such a scheme. (Author's Collection)* **12**

gates of the yard finally closed on 1 October. Already a large number of lay-offs had been effected, with only a small proportion being offered work at Chatham. In many respects, the situation at Woolwich was far more serious, for not only were the numbers involved much greater, but the nearby Arsenal had also been involved in the reduction of its work force. Subsequently a relief fund was set up which was to realise £3,000, allowing some 2,300 to emigrate to Canada. As for the dockyard itself, this was handed over to the War Office, being used for a number of years as a store depôt. Although no longer in use as a dockyard, it is interesting to note that one of the docks was lengthened in 1876, being used to receive the Brazilian ironclad *Independencia* prior to her purchase for the Royal Navy as the *Neptune.*

As for the later history of the two former dockyards this becomes increasingly complicated with the continual sale and renting of increasingly smaller parcels of land. At Deptford the foreign cattle market was closed in 1913 and has since become a site for numerous industrial units and high rise flats, the former area of the dockyard being difficult to discern. Woolwich, on the other hand, is still fairly easy to locate, the yard having now fallen into the hands of three separate owners who have not totally destroyed all links with earlier dockyard days. At the eastern end of the area once occupied by the dockyard is a four acre site, originally sold by the War Office in 1872, and formerly occupied by Cubow, a small shipbuilding firm that at one time made use of some of the original slips. A further 15 acres, sold off in 1926, is owned by the Royal Arsenal Co-operative Society, being originally acquired for laundry, warehousing and garage space. Much clearance work has been undertaken since the RACS came into occupation of the site, with part of this area now designated 'The Woolwich Dockyard Industrial Estate'.

A final section of Woolwich dockyard, and certainly the most interesting, was purchased by the London Borough of Greenwich in 1969. Consisting of 22 acres to the west it has since been developed into an imaginative blend of housing and leisure facilities. More important, from the point of view of this article, is that once again former dockyard buildings have been retained with some fully incorporated into the development scheme. Clearly worth a visit, remaining features include the admiral-superintendant's house, colonnaded entrance lobby and two graving docks.

For purposes of concluding this survey of the yards, it is of value also to record two former Woolwich structures that are no longer 'in situ', having been removed to other sites. The first of these is the covering to a slipway and taken to Chatham dockyard at the time the Woolwich yard was closed. Subsequently re-erected, it was converted for use as a machine shop and is still to be found in position. A second structure, of greater historic importance, is that of the cast iron columns and trusses to an anchor forge and smithery that was originally erected in 1810, and

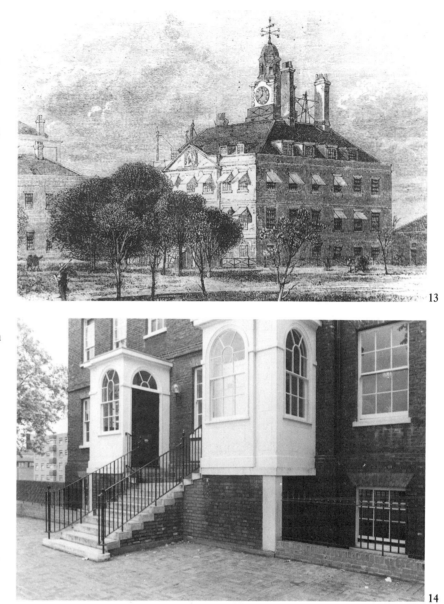

13

14

15

13 *The Admiral-Superintendent's office at Woolwich, 1869. Admiral-Superintendents were appointed to each of the yards to ensure that Admiralty instructions were effectively carried out. In earlier years this task had been carried out by a resident commissioner, although for a long period both Woolwich and Deptford were directly controlled by the Navy Board in London. Only in times of emergency were resident commissioners appointed at these two yards. (Author's Collection)*

14 *A detailed view of the Admiral-Superintendent's house, now known as the clocktower house, as it appears today. Still standing, it serves as a community centre within the Greenwich council leisure scheme. (Author's Collection)*

15 *Another Woolwich survivor is the colonnaded entrance lobby which is to be found just off Woolwich Road/Church Street. (Author's Collection)*

16

16 *Part of the former dockyard area at Deptford with the two surviving slipway coverings. (Greater London Council)*

17 *The Master Shipwright's apartment at Deptford as seen in 1982. (Greater London Council)*

18 *A clocktower from one of the storehouses at Deptford. Removed from the site in 1982 it is eventually to be incorporated as a feature in the Thamesmead shopping centre. (Greater London Council)* 16

17

18

since taken to the Iron Bridge Gorge Museum for re-assembly and display. The original building was designed by John Rennie (1761-1821) and, with the machinery it once housed, represents the first use of steam power within that dockyard. Finally, it is worth noting that at Plumstead library there is a small exhibition of items taken from the central portion of Woolwich dockyard during an archaeological excavation led by Terry Courtney in 1972 and 1973.

Notes

1 Unlike the other royal dockyards with a ropery, the ropeyard at Woolwich was not actually contained within the area of the dockyard, being situated about half a mile away. Approximately aligning with present day Beresford Street, it was to be disestablished in 1835.

2 BM (British Museum) Kings 43. In mentioning valuations of the various dockyards it should be noted that a sixth royal yard, that of Plymouth, was yet to be established. In operation prior to the end of the seventeenth century it was to rapidly expand, quickly exceeding Woolwich and Deptford, and eventually becoming the nation's second dockyard.

3 Although Chatham had its own ropery, situated at the southern end of that yard, its output frequently fell short of demand. On such occasions Woolwich ropery would make up the difference.

4 BM Kings 44.

5 ibid.

6 National Maritime Museum ADM/B series. From the regular documentation sent from the Navy Board to the Admiralty it is possible to accurately trace numbers employed at these two dockyards for the entire eighteenth century. A few of these have been extracted to produce the following table:

Year	Nos employed at Woolwich	Nos employed at Deptford
1756 (Jun)	1,101	1,232
1770 (Sep)	834	788
1775 (Sep)	875	931
1780 (Dec)	1,079	1,209
1785 (Dec)	969	1,105
1792 (Dec)	1,023	1,080
1799 (Dec)	1,357	1,382
1814 (Mar)	2,026	1,886

The fluctuation in numbers was very much a reflection of whether the country was in a state of war or in the midst of a period of peace. The year 1756, for instance, marked the beginning of the Seven Years War, whilst 1780 was towards the end of the American War of Independence.

7 Public Record Office (PRO) ADM1/3526. 19 April 1800.

8 The inspection of the Isle of Grain was made in September 1802.

9 In May 1807 John Rennie put forward a similar scheme to that which had been previously proposed by Bentham. Instead of the Isle of Grain however, he suggested a new dockyard at Northfleet. Once more the plan was not pursued, although sufficient land was actually purchased. Of Deptford, Rennie was to write:

> 'I have heard many instances of its ineligibility stated; ships of the line that are built there, cannot, as I am informed, with propriety be docked and coppered: jury masts are put into them, and they are taken to Woolwich, where they are docked, coppered and rigged; and I have been told of an instance where many weeks elapsed before a favourable wind and tide capable of floating a large ship of the line to Woolwich, without risk, occurred.'

Short Bibliography

Banbury, P
Shipbuilders of the Thames and Medway.

Baugh, D A
British Naval Administration in the Age of Walpole.

Baugh, D A
Naval Administration 1715-1750.

Coad, J
Historic Architecture of the Royal Navy.

Courtney, T
'Excavations at the Royal Dockyard Woolwich' in Transactions of the Greenwich and Lewisham Antiquarian Society, Vol VIII nos 1 and 2.

Dews, N
The History of Deptford.

Ehrman, J
The Navy in the War of William III.

Grinling, W H
A Survey and Record of Woolwich and West Kent.

Jefferson, E F E
The Woolwich Story.

Morriss, R
The Royal Dockyards during the Revolutionary and Napoleonic Wars.

Perrin, W G
The Autobiography of Phineas Pett.

Oppenheim, M
A History of the Administration of the Royal Navy.

Oppenheim, M
'Maritime History' in Victoria County History of Kent 2p 336f.

Remaining buildings

Deptford Royal Dockyard
The site of the original dockyard is now covered by domestic accommodation and warehousing. Within this area survive only the three buildings that are listed below.

Slipway coverings
Now used for storage, two slipway coverings remain, these originally supplying shelter to those slips once attached to the wet dock (see Thomas Milton's map of 1755). The coverings were completed with iron roofs and seem to date from the mid- to late-1840s. Present owners are Convoy Wharves Ltd of London.

Master Shipwright's apartment
Situated in the SE corner of the former

dockyard and shown on Thomas Milton's map of 1755, is the one-time accommodation of the yard's Master Shipwright. Possibly dating to the seventeenth century, it was originally completed with a gabled roof that has since been re-shaped and shortened. To be found immediately off Prince Street, it is a grade 2 listed building.

Principal dockyard offices
Early eighteenth century building attached to the Master Shipwright's apartment (above). Again to be seen on Milton's map it is a two storey building that has a gently mansarded, slate covered, roof. Much altered, it is a grade 2 listed building.

Deptford. The Royal Victoria victualling yard

Apart from the dockyard, Deptford also had one further long term association with the Royal Navy. From 1742, the headquarters of the Victualling Board was established in the area, being situated immediately adjacent to the dockyard. Responsible for the purchase of various food stocks, the victualling yard at Deptford had not only numerous offices but a considerable array of warehouses. Supplies, usually purchased from the London food markets, were temporarily stored at Deptford prior to later transfer to various out stations at Woolwich, Chatham, Harwich and Sheerness.

Today the former Victualling Yard has been largely replaced by a council housing estate, although some buildings remain. Amongst these are the eighteenth-century rum warehouses which now house a public library, facing Deptford Strand. The former gateway to the Victualling Yard still stands to one side of Grove Street. Apart from the gateway and rum storehouse there is also a fine set of terraced houses, built for the accommodation of officers.

The development of the ship

Alan Pearsall

Londoners accepted the existence of their great docks and the well-known shipping lines which used them, but both are quite recent creations. The need for such docks is not universal in ports, and reflects the large rise and fall of tide round the British Isles, and the consequent difficulties it creates for berthing large ships. As one of the largest ports in the world, the growth of London's dock system was both a response to and a governing factor in the development of ship design during the nineteenth century, a development which itself both arose from and gave impulse to a wider range of trades and to new commercial practices. This chapter will therefore survey the crucial factor of ship design, both for its intrinsic interest and for its relation to developments in the docks.

The nature of the shipping world in the days of sail was very different to what it became by, say, 1914. Small ownerships, small ships and small scale of business were the general, but not invariable, rule. This world, a highly personal one, survived in the operation of tramp steamers and small coasters. The great shipping lines, whether passenger or cargo, were creations of 1840 onwards, often arising from the old type of owner, it is true, but increasingly they became large scale businesses.

The ships owned by such firms were often large and famous, but we must always, in dealing in such general terms as does this chapter, remember the vast range of shipping in existence at any one time. Ships last for many years, so that even if one size is being generally built at one period, old and smaller vessels are still active, while some trades only require ships of particular sizes. Moreover, the most famous ships are frequently the largest, and may in numbers be only one, two or perhaps half-a-dozen. Yet, to take a well-known example, the Thames sailing barge — well able to make coasting and short sea voyages — existed in thousands, tramp steamers certainly in hundreds. London, as a port, handled the largest sailing ships, but never the largest steamships, for the great Atlantic liners always used Liverpool or Southampton. The Port did, however, attract large numbers of very

considerable steamships of above average tonnage as new facilities and commercial developments allowed larger cargoes and more passengers to be conveniently handled, and these did include the largest ships in the Australian and Eastern trades.

At the beginning of our period, in 1815, the optimum size of ship was probably about 200-250 tons. During the next forty years, while timber remained the principal building material, its limitations continued to control the size and general increase in quantity but only small increases in ship size. The largest ships of all, the East Indiamen, were found uneconomic after the Company's monopoly ended, and from 1,400 tons, Indian traders in the form of the famous "Blackwall frigates" became 800-1,000 tons for a time. In general, however, the rise of more long-distance trades, and some requiring passenger facilities, which were little needed prior to 1815, did result in rather larger vessels, and by 1850 the Blackwallers were again in the 1,200 to 1,400 tons class, and many more 400-600 tons ships were to be found. But the coastal and near-European trades employed many far smaller craft.

The changes had begun by 1850 and they may be summarised:

1 Paddle steamers.

2 Improved hull forms.

3 Iron hulls and, later, steel.

4 Screw propellers.

5 Composite hulls.

6 Iron/steel rigging.

7 Larger size.

8 Specialised design.

in approximate order of appearance. In oceanic shipping (which affected the docks most) little had changed by 1850. The contract mail services of the Cunard, P & O and Royal Mail companies did not use London. There was already a large system of coastal and short sea steamers dependent on paddle propulsion, but they mostly berthed in the River.

It was the combination of iron hulls and the screw propeller which really accelerated the use of steam. At the same time, the use of "clipper" hulls was improving the sailing ship, whilst on the coast, the schooner rig was showing its advantages over the previous brigs.

Of all the above improvements, the iron hull was perhaps initially the most far-reaching. Iron, and steel later on, gave greater strength, permitting the construction of larger ships with clear holds free of obstructions and with watertight bulkheads for greater safety. Sailing

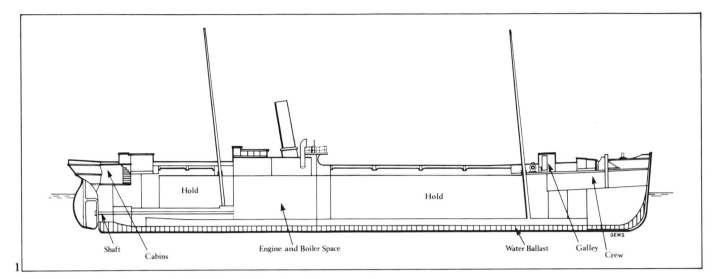

Hold · Hold

Shaft · Cabins · Engine and Boiler Space · Water Ballast · Galley · Crew

GEMS

1

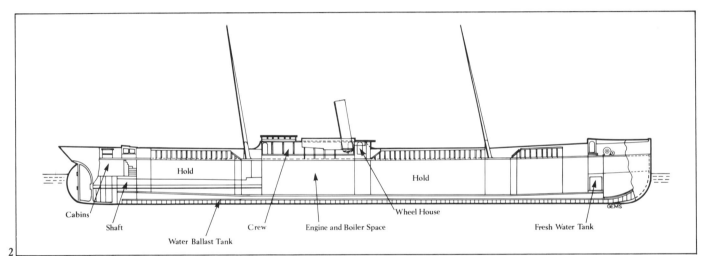

Hold · Hold

Cabins · Shaft · Water Ballast Tank · Crew · Engine and Boiler Space · Wheel House · Fresh Water Tank

GEMS

2

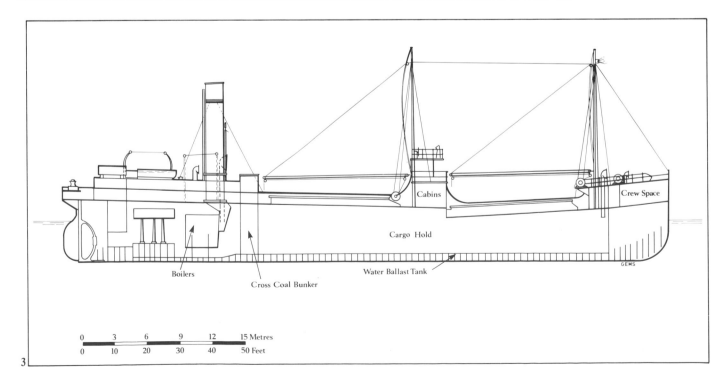

Cabins · Crew Space

Cargo Hold

Boilers · Cross Coal Bunker · Water Ballast Tank

GEMS

0	3	6	9	12	15 Metres
0	10	20	30	40	50 Feet

3

vessels could and did take advantage of it to provide a final chapter of commercial sail, but steamers fitted with screw propellers made, in the long run, a greater impression. Paddle steamers had shown their worth for reliability in short-distance passenger and high-class cargo services, but the more compact design possible with a screw engine produced a satisfactory bulk carrier, first of all in that trade most associated with London, the east-coast coal trade, but soon extending to many of the coastal and near-European trades and to the Mediterranean, often ousting paddle steamers. These early screw vessels were not greatly larger than existing ships, but the usual process of detail development of hull, engines and other elements of design ensured that a perpetual slow increase in size was maintained, as well as producing greater economy of operation. Once again, average size certainly increased, imposing new demands on the docks, particularly as the box section of steamships made many of the older locks difficult for them to use.

It will now be most convenient to take sailing ships and steamships separately, as their course of development diverges. Sailing ship owners met the new conditions by either going over to iron or by adopting composite construction, ie an iron frame planked with timber, a mode of construction much used in the 1860s, and a size of 230 ft x 35-40 ft became usual. Few wooden deep-sea ships were built after 1860 or so. While basic layout of ships remained much the same, finer lines became more common and with the new materials the detailing produced very different looking vessels.

Although from 1870 onwards, the sailing vessel steadily lost ground, especially in quality trades, for long ocean voyages, owing to the steamer's need for coal, it held a strong position until the 1890s, and for bulk cargoes, even longer. Many improvements were made. Iron or steel rigging was stronger, and could supplement iron or steel hulls to propel bigger ships. Various methods were used to reduce crews. With the loss of the good trades, speed was not so important and the era of the big carrier had arrived. During the 1870s four-masted ships and barques, at first of about 250-260 ft appeared and later going up to over 300 ft, although the 250 ft size remained popular for new construction until the end. Such vessels could earn money well until a general collapse began after 1900 and the sailing ship eventually became confined to bulk cargoes from out of the way ports, where steamers could not afford the lengthy loading times, to the big European ports, of which London was only one. However, though the sailing ship developed considerably, their increase in size had been outstripped by that of steamers.

The screw steamer had a more complex development. The early colliers were simple enough — single decked vessels, with their engines well apt, a feature which, despite early reaction against it, was eventually to become almost normal in our own time. But when they appeared, iron was already showing its value in the larger mail vessels, albeit paddle propelled, where greater internal subdivision was necessary, to provide passenger accommodation on various decks and separate cargo, engine and boiler spaces, and these advantages were adopted for screw vessels. From the mid-fifties onwards dock companies were faced with the inexorable pressure of larger and larger ships. Extra size rarely meant a proportionate increase in running expenses, more often in fact it was cheaper per ton or per passenger.

Economies of size thus favoured larger shipments. Developments in commercial practice also encouraged the more complex layout of ships, for more bulkheads apart from being safer, could reliably separate mixed cargoes. Additional decks below the upper gave more accommodation, or more separate stowage for cargoes of different commodities or for different destinations, whilst both added to the strength of the structure. The hull form also took on new layouts to suit specific trades, for cargoes varied in weight and bulk — some put the ship down to her capacity without filling her, others could fill her without being heavy enough to load her deeply. Thus one found types such as well-deckers, three island ships, shelter deckers, and others without mentioning more bizarre types produced by the growing complexity of the tonnage rules and their many exemptions of various spaces in a ship, through which owners and builders naturally attempted to drive the proverbial "coach and four".

All this inventiveness affected all types of ship. The tramp steamer remained a fairly simple craft, for she was essentially a bulk carrier of one commodity cargoes, though these could be varied enough. As markets adapted to larger quantities, the ships grew too. Typical tramps might be about 1,000 gross tons in the early 1870s, 1,500-1,800, 2,600 in 1890 and 3,600 in 1900. After the first World War, 5,200 was a general size, increasing to about 5,700 by 1939, but one could find among them many different layouts. Once again, the average size increase in a type of ship which the docks had to cater for.

At first, the high class steamers were combined passenger and cargo vessels, usually with passengers in the tween decks and cargo below. However, the course of trade tended to make the longer-distance routes which depended purely on commercial factors, ie without a mail subsidy, separate passengers from cargo to a certain extent, partly to allow better passenger accommodation, but partly to eliminate from the passenger ships some of the uncertainties of the cargo business and partly because there was more cargo to be carried than the passenger ships could take. Thus although all passenger ships continued to carry cargo in large quantities, many of their owners also developed large and fast pure cargo carriers. In both passenger and cargo ships of these types, increase in size was rapid. The old principle of

1 **New Pelton,** steam collier of the 1870s. Clear holds, large hatches. Length overall about 250 ft.

2 **Lambeth,** early up-river collier, similarly clear holds and large hatches, but lowering masts and funnel. Length overall about 250 ft.

3 **Typical Coaster** 1900-30, steam engine aft, large clear holds without lower decks, suitable for bulk cargoes. Length overall 250 ft.

E

129

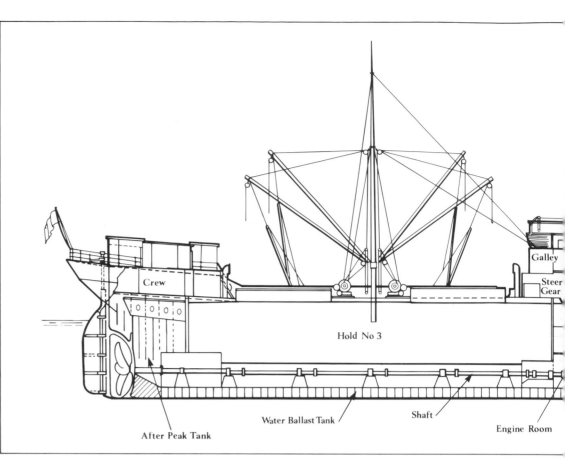

4 Sunbank, *tramp steamer of the 1920s, no tween-decks, large holds. Overall length 331 ft.*

5 Beaverdale, *large cargo liner of the late 1920s for Atlantic service, many holds, all with many derricks, two tween decks, steam turbines. Length overall 520 ft.*

4

Galley

Steer Gear

Crew

Hold No 3

Water Ballast Tank

Shaft

After Peak Tank

Engine Room

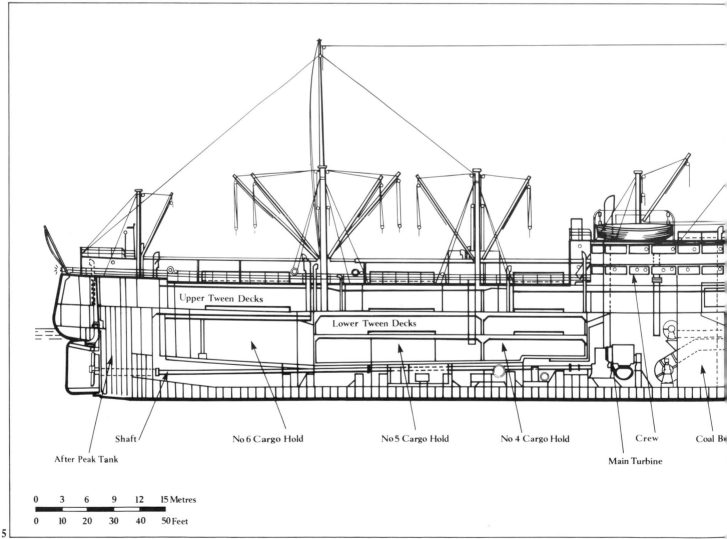

Upper Tween Decks

Lower Tween Decks

Shaft

After Peak Tank

No 6 Cargo Hold

No 5 Cargo Hold

No 4 Cargo Hold

Crew

Coal B

Main Turbine

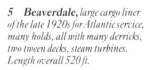

0	3	6	9	12	15 Metres
0	10	20	30	40	50 Feet

5

130

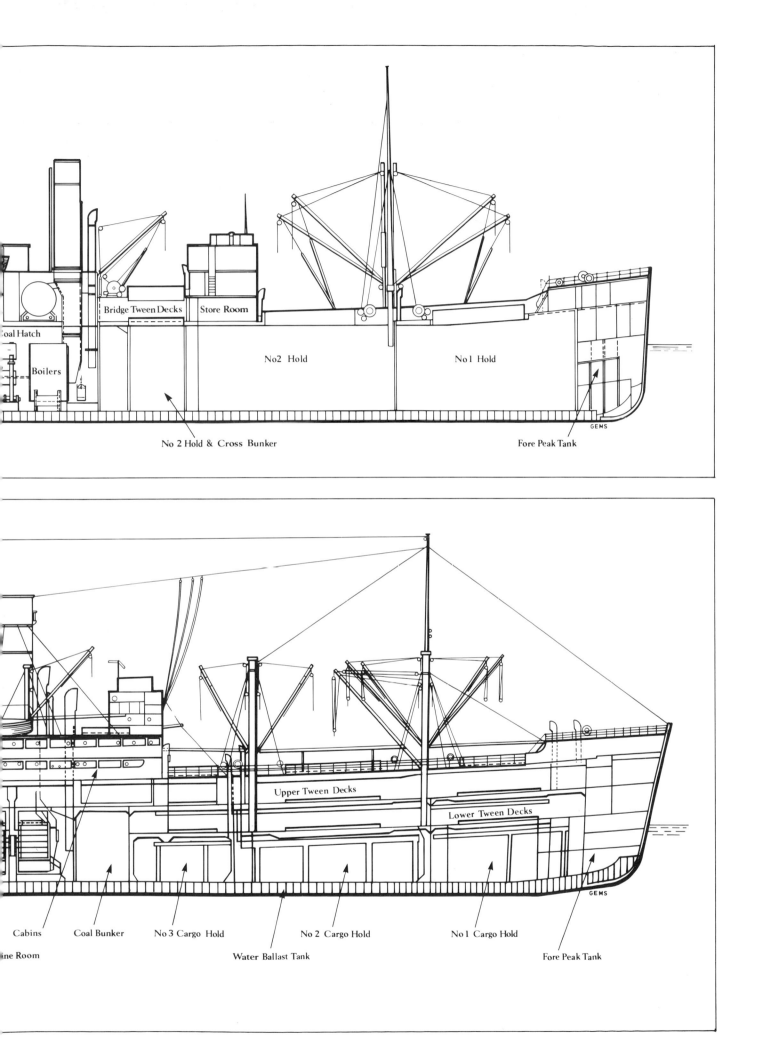

Coal Hatch

Boilers

Bridge Tween Decks   Store Room

No2 Hold   No1 Hold

GEMS

No 2 Hold & Cross Bunker   Fore Peak Tank

Upper Tween Decks

Lower Tween Decks

GEMS

Cabins   Coal Bunker   No 3 Cargo Hold   No 2 Cargo Hold   No 1 Cargo Hold

ine Room   Water Ballast Tank   Fore Peak Tank

131

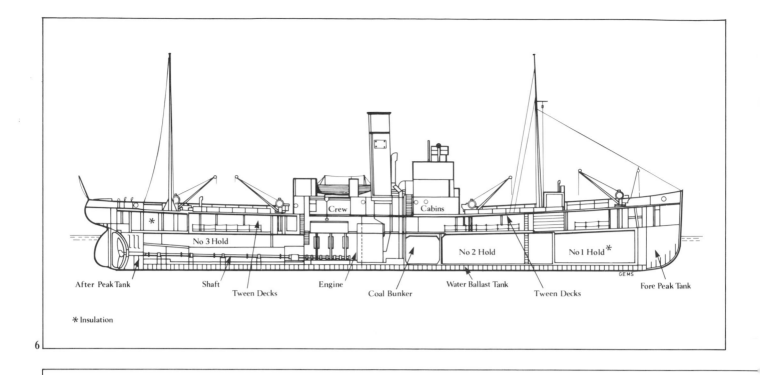

After Peak Tank   Shaft   Tween Decks   Engine   Coal Bunker   Water Ballast Tank   Tween Decks   Fore Peak Tank

No 3 Hold   Crew   Cabins   No 2 Hold   No 1 Hold *

GEMS

* Insulation

6

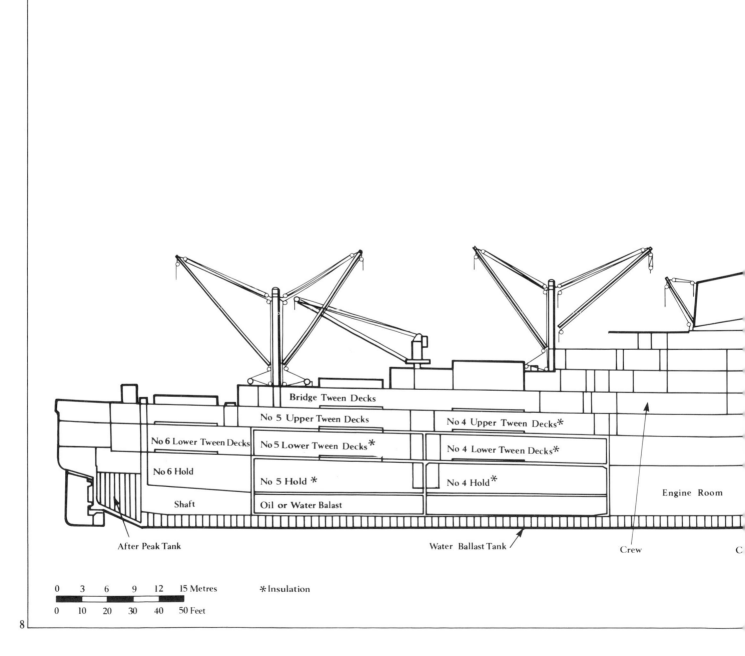

Bridge Tween Decks

No 5 Upper Tween Decks   No 4 Upper Tween Decks *

No 6 Lower Tween Decks   No 5 Lower Tween Decks *   No 4 Lower Tween Decks *

No 6 Hold   No 5 Hold *   No 4 Hold *   Engine Room

Shaft   Oil or Water Balast

After Peak Tank   Water Ballast Tank   Crew   C

0	3	6	9	12	15 Metres
0	10	20	30	40	50 Feet

* Insulation

8

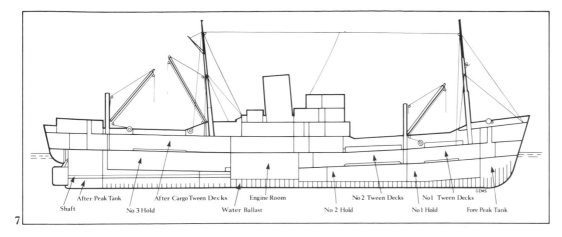

6 *Groningen, short-sea regular trader of the 1920s, steam, some insulated space, deck cranes. Length overall 256 ft 6 ins.*

7 *Copeland, short sea or coastal regular trader of 1948, motorship, not dissimilar to Groningen. Overall length 235 ft.*

After Peak Tank
Shaft
No 3 Hold
After Cargo Tween Decks
Engine Room
Water Ballast
No 2 Tween Decks
No 2 Hold
No 1 Tween Decks
No 1 Hold
Fore Peak Tank

loading a ship for one destination was replaced by regular sailings along a route with several intermediate and terminal ports, the ships sailing on time full or not. Such ships were known as liners. It was here that big ships with several tween decks and many holds were advantageous in carrying many types of cargo, and needing to separate many different lots for various ports. The evolving commercial system of the world could handle larger cargoes. New needs arose, of which the rise of refrigeration in particular developed a highly important trade and specialised ships. Competition in service, speed and luxury drove owners to provide

8 *Port Brisbane, large cargo liner of the 1950s for Australian trade, practically all insulated cargo space. Diesel powered. Overall length 524 ft.*

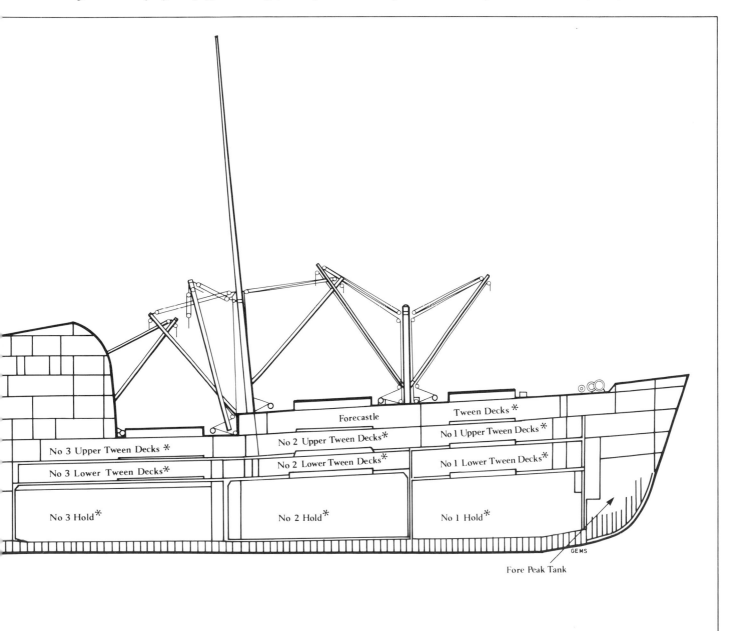

No 3 Upper Tween Decks *
Forecastle
No 2 Upper Tween Decks *
Tween Decks *
No 1 Upper Tween Decks *
No 3 Lower Tween Decks *
No 2 Lower Tween Decks *
No 1 Lower Tween Decks *
No 3 Hold *
No 2 Hold *
No 1 Hold *
Fore Peak Tank

bigger ships. Moreover, the 1870s idea of long narrow ships gave place to beamier vessels, particularly as passenger ships began to put much of their accommodation on top of rather than in the hull. Thus in 1870 the first 400 ft ships were appearing, by 1890 this was up to 450 or 470 ft, but the 42 ft beam might then be up to 50 or over, and by 1900 a 600 ft ship with 65 ft beam was perplexing port authorities. These ships were, of course, also proportion- ately deeper, and drew over 30 ft of water compared with 20 or so of the 1870s. The extent of this pressure on existing channels and locks will be obvious. The opening of the Royal Albert and then Tilbury Docks in fact only enabled the Port on dock the ships then coming into service, and permitted the P & O, for example, to transfer their main services to London. The 600 ft ships could only use Tilbury.

As a result of these trends, and the fundamental importance of London in the economy, the port came to handle a very large number of big ships, notably the passenger-cargo ships for India, Australia and New Zealand, and the large cargo ships running to the same places and also to the Far East a and to South America. It may be useful to categorise the types of vessel using the port from 1900 on. [NOTE: Where only one tonnage or range of tonnage is given, the ships remained over the period much the same size, though the average might well be higher. In other cases, tonnages are given for typical ships of 1900 and 1960, but it must be made clear that these are figures to guide the reader only; exceptions can easily be found and variations of type and size were legion].

	1900	1960	Usual berth
Passenger Liners	5,000-8,000	15,000-29,000	Royals, Tilbury
Cargo Liners	4,000-7,000	7,000-11,000	Royals, Tilbury, West India Docks
Refrigerated Cargo Liners	5,000-7,000	8,000-12,000	Royals
Tramp Steamers	3,000-6,000		All docks
Mediterranean Cargo Liners	1,000-2,000	1,500-4,000	West India, London Docks
North Sea Passenger Ships	1,500-2,500	2,500-7,000	Millwall Dock
North Sea Regular Cargo Ships	800-1,500		River, Millwall Dock
Coastal Passenger Ships	1,000-2,500		River
Coastal Regular Cargo Ships	800-2,500		River, London Docks
Coastal Tramps	500-1,500		Anywhere
Colliers	1,000-4,500		River, up-River
Tankers	All sizes		Estuary, Purfleet

Notes

The largest liners in practice used Tilbury, despite the well-documented visit of the MAURETANIA to the Royals. The North Sea passenger category was not a large one, though they were well-known vessels. The coastal passenger ships ended in 1939. Tankers, apart from small refuelling and distribution barges, did not come beyond Gravesend as a rule. The use of "river" in the list of berths normally indicates wharves, but there were some places where deep-sea ships could work cargo into barges while lying at buoys.

The "London River" produced several distinctive types of vessel of its own. River passenger steamers and lighters are dealt with separately, there were tugs, floating cranes and grain and coal elevators which had equivalents elsewhere, but the collier, the sailing barge, the hospital steamers and the "sludge boats" were all concerned with features mentioned elsewhere in this book, and deserve mention.

The "coal trade" goes back to mediaeval times, and the first screw cargo ships, as we have seen, were built for this trade. Vessels continued to be specially built for the trade, though often used on other routes, and were larger than colliers elsewhere, though of similar layouts, as sea coal became increasingly used for gasworks and electric power stations and other riverside industries. The original ships brought 900-1,000 tons, but this rose to 3,000 by 1900 and to 4-5,000 tons by 1950.

The most specialised colliers were the "up-river" ships often called "flat-irons" from their low upperworks. These vessels were much circumscribed in dimensions by depth of water, width of channel and height of bridges. The originals, in 1878 carried about 1,000 tons, but careful design brought this to 2,800 tons for the last ones built in 1958-9.

The Thames sailing barge was a characteristic and important element of the river scene, offering a valuable water distribution system to the Thames estuary and further afield, bringing all kinds of goods to meet the needs of the city.

The "hospital steamers" were a few small passenger steamer type vessels, owned by the Metropolitan Asylums Board to communicate with the isolation hospital ships in Long Reach and later with Joyce Green Hospital nearby, conveying patients, staff and visitors both ways, from North and South Wharves (qv) and West Wharf in Fulham from 1883 until 1932.

The "sludge boats" belonged at first to the Metropolitan Board of Works, then to the LCC, the GLC and now the Thames Water Authority. They convey the residue of sludge from the Crossness and Beckton sewage outfalls to dumping areas in the Thames estuary. the first was built in 1887 and four still run.

Short Bibliography

Bowen, F C
London Ship Types

Bonsor, N R P
North Atlantic Seaway

Duckworth, C L D and Langmuir, G E
Clyde and Other Coastal Steamers

Gibbs, C R Vernon
British Passenger Liners of the Five Oceans

Lubbock, Basil
The Blackwall Brigates
The Colonial Clippers
The Last of the Windjammers (2 vols)

Maber, J M
North Star to Southern Cross

Macgregor, David
The Merchant Sailing Ship (3 vols)

Shipbuilding and related industries on the Isle of Dogs

Eve Hostettler

The Isle of Dogs is best known to Londoners of the 1980s for its deserted docks and their redevelopment. 'The heart of London's Docklands' is how many will have heard it described by estate agents. The West India and Millwall Docks occupy the centre of the Island peninsula, and their vast stretches of water make a stunning visual impact on the visitor. It is impossible to deny their existence and their history, impossible not to be stirred by the images of trade and trouble, central to the story of British Imperialism, which they evoke.

Less well known, and today scarcely apparent any longer, is the industrial heritage of the Isle of Dogs. The docks and all their associations are only a part of the Island's history. In the nineteenth century, thousands of tons of small ships were launched from the foreshore here, as well as great iron-clads like the *Northumberland,* and merchantmen destined for the West India trade. After the Thames shipbuilding industry had collapsed in the 1860s, ship-repair yards and small boat builders survived and flourished on the island. Alongside these industries, and complementing them, were civil and mechanical engineering works and metal-working firms, some of which grew from small beginnings early in the nineteenth century to achieve world-wide recognition. On a lesser scale there were boiler-makers and repairers, drum manufacturers, pipe-work engineers, pump makers, tank makers, firms making valves, tubes, tarpaulins, sacks and ropes; firms making and stocking steel sections, plates, drums and doors, dealing in hardwoods and softwoods, specialising in lifting gear, in metal polishing and in power-station repairs. The larger engineering firms undertook contracts all over the world from Welwyn Garden City to the West African coast, erecting gas holders, building bridges, replacing engine parts and repairing ships in dry dock. These big firms supported a network of services and subsidiaries on the Island — wharfingers and lorry drivers, scrap metal dealers and young lads who collected nuts and bolts on the foreshore for a penny a bucketful.

The working docks, with their ships and sheds and lorry-loads of cargo, were closed to visitors and even to most Islanders, behind high walls and guarded gates. It was the industrial activity of the perimeter which gave the Island its notable character — the noise and fumes of manufacture, the crowds of engineers and machinists leaving the factory at the end of a shift; the order books, the typists and telephonists, the loaded barges alongside the wharves and the narrow roads crowded with carts and lorries.[1]

In 1800, London's predominance as the ship-building centre of Britain was already on the wane, giving way to the growing ports of the north and west.[2] However, this trend was hardly discernible in the face of demand for shipping caused by the Napoleonic Wars and later by Britain's expanding world trade. On both banks of the Thames, eastwards to Blackwall and Woolwich, there were thriving shipyards and dry docks; within this area only the windswept pastures of the Isle of Dogs remained undeveloped. The opening of the West India Docks in 1802, and the building of the new Deptford and Greenwich Ferry Road (now West Ferry Road) in 1812, coinciding with a time of experiment with new methods and materials for ship-building, brought the first wave of industrial investment to Millwall, the western side of the Island. By 1810 a rope maker, an oil works, an iron works, a mast and block maker and a chain-cable manufacturer, were all established there.[3]

The chain-cable makers were Brown, Lenox & Co, a firm which was to be associated with the Isle of Dogs for almost the full span of its industrial history. They chose their site in West Ferry Road because it was opposite the naval dockyard at Deptford, their largest customer. Commander Samuel Brown, one of the founders, had patented the stud link chain whilst serving in the navy under Nelson. The chain cable was adopted for naval use, replacing the traditional hemp ropes, in 1810; Brown, Lenox & Co Ltd remained the sole manufacturers of chain cable for the Navy until 1916 — the longest-ever unbroken Admiralty contract. The firm also supplied chain cables

1 The Great Eastern *at*
Millwall, Isle of Dogs, London E14,
c1857.

2 The Great Eastern *under*
construction, Millwall, Isle of Dogs,
London E14, 1857.

for many foreign governments, and for the largest ships of the time, including the *Great Eastern*, the *Mauretania*, and the *Acquitania;* they earned an international reputation as manufacturers of chain cables and berth moorings for the harbours and rivers of the world. Thousands of tons of chain cables, anchors and mooring buoys were manufactured at the Millwall works until the 1970s. The company also has a site at Pontypridd, next to the Glamorgan Canal, which is still operating.[4]

Industrial growth on the Island was relatively slow in the first three decades of the nineteenth century owing to the recession in ship-building which followed the ending of the French Wars, though in 1824 John Seaward founded the Canal Ironworks (near the present-day *City Arms*) to build engines for ships; he is credited with many advances in marine engineering, such as the direct-acting paddle engine.[5] The 1830s and 1840s were a period of expansion, as the shipbuilding industry recovered nationally, and the open foreshore of the Isle of Dogs provided an opportunity for new firms to be set up, close to the Port and the City. The Trade Directory of 1837 lists 25 businesses in Millwall, of which 13 were directly connected with ship- and boat-building. In 1848, ship-building and related trades still dominated the expanded list, which included the names of some well-known experimental engineers.

One of these was David Napier. He was brought up in Scotland, where, working with his father, he experienced the difficulties of building the first engines for wooden ships, notably the *Comet*. By the 1830s, Napier had a sizeable boat-building business on the Clyde, but in 1839 he acquired a site on Millwall. Here his two sons ran the business, while he devoted himself to experiments in improving the speed and efficiency of the steamboat. In 1854 the Napiers realised that iron ship-building would never become a major Thames-side industry, and they closed the Millwall yard, which was then sold to the builders of the *Great Eastern*.[6]

Another famous Millwall name of the 1830s was William Fairbairn, also a Scot, once described as 'one of the most eminent engineers and cultivators of mechanical science'. During his apprenticeship as a millwright he became friends with George Stephenson, the great railway engineer — a friendship which lasted a lifetime. Fairbairn established a shipyard on Millwall in 1835. The works were sold again in 1848, but it was here that Fairbairn tested and proved the idea of the tubular iron bridge, leading to the rectangular cellular construction used in the Conway and Britannia bridges and about 1,000 others built by his firm.[7]

Another name in the 1848 Trade Directory was that of Henry Wimshurst, patent steamship builder. It was in his yard that the *Archimedes* was built — designed by Sir Francis Pettit Smith and destined to go down in history as the first screw steamship.[8]

Ship-building and related industries flourished on Millwall in the first 50 years of the nineteenth century — a period when the demand for shipping was rising worldwide, and when the possibility of building faster, stronger and bigger ships was being explored. The Isle of Dogs was not particularly remarkable in seeing experiment and innovation in the industry — shipwrights and engineers all round the coast of Britain were doing the same thing. In the gradual transition from sail to steam, and in the change-over from ships of wood to ships of iron and steel, London's role was a declining one, even as expansion was taking place. This decline, however, was not apparent to the investor. So confident was the market, and so well-established was London's reputation for skill and quality in ship-building, that when the engineer Isambard Kingdom Brunel required a ship-yard to build his *Great Eastern*, which was to be the largest and most powerful ship afloat, using all the most advanced techniques, it was to the London yards that he turned, and to the Millwall yard of John Scott Russell in particular. Russell occupied the sites previously owned by Napier and Fairbairn (modern location: West Ferry Road, opposite Cahir Street and Harbinger Road).

The story of the ill-fated vessel, of the disagreements between the engineer and the ship-builder, of the difficulties of the launching in 1858 and the mishaps of the early voyages, has been told elsewhere.[9] Brunel's vision of a large, fast, economic ship was beyond the capacity of marine engineering at the time. It was not until the 1880s that the compound and triple expansion marine engines and the high tensile steel hull enabled steam ships to compete successfully against the fastest clippers over long voyages.

In 1984, when the site of Scott Russell's former yard was being prepared for a new housing estate, the contractors uncovered what turned out to be one of the two slipways from which the *Great Eastern* was launched, with massive timbers laid out on piles and crosspieces sloping down to the river. This discovery may be preserved on the site as a memorial to the ship and those who built her.

The unhappy experience of the *Great Eastern* did not deter ship-owners from placing further orders with Island firms. London was thought to have the lead for quality, even though costs were lower in the yards of the north and west. Many major ship owners had their head offices in London and preferred to place their orders locally. This was still the great age of sail. (British sailing tonnage reached its peak of just under five million in 1865, while steam, though more effective, comprised well under one million).[10] Steam ships were in demand for the shorter sea routes, and Island firms were well placed to build these, as well as sailing ships and large armour-plated ships for the Royal Navy and foreign governments.[11]

New companies were set up. Dudgeons, of Cubitt Town (on the eastern side of the Island) began work in 1862, on a site now renamed Compass Point and used for housing. Dudgeons employed up to 1500 men and specialised in building blockade runners for the

American Civil War. James Ash, previously employed as a naval architect by C J Mare and also by Millwall Ironworks, started his business at the end of Pier Street in Cubitt Town, with the most impressive offices and works of any of the Thames private ship-yards, in 1863. This firm built screw ships and paddle steamers and yachts; one of their customers was the famous P & O Line.[12]

In 1864 Barry counted 13 ships being built at the Millwall Iron Works (formerly Scott Russell's yard), from the armour-plated *Northumberland* to small screw traders, and including sailing ships. Of Samuda's ship-yard in Cubitt Town (commemorated in the modern Samuda Estate) he wrote that it was one of the best-known on the Thames, and usually had in hand as much as 16,000 tons of shipping.[13]

In the mid-1860s, just before the industry collapsed, Thomas Wright described the Isle of Dogs as the centre of iron ship-building and marine engineering on the Thames. 'There are more than a dozen ship and marine engineering establishments, among them being the gigantic one in which the operations of the Millwall Iron Works are carried on . . . The work of this company alone employs on an average 4,000 men and boys, and the other ship and marine engine works on the Island employ from 2,000 to 100 men each'. Wright estimated that altogether the Island industry provided work for 15,000 men and boys.[14]

The sudden collapse of all this apparent prosperity, with bankruptcies, closures and widespread unemployment, in the financial crisis of 1866, had several causes. Samuda, in his evidence to the Government Commission on Trades Unions in the following year, put it down to 'over-confidence, too much investment, wage increases given on the basis of

full order books, anbd losses made on contracts'. The demise of Ash's company after three years' trading he attributed to 'reckless speculations', and in fact it emerged that Ash's expenses had exceeded his income by the whole amount of wages paid out.[15]

By January 1867 it was estimated that there were 30,000 people on relief in Poplar, and journalists described the 'grass-grown wastes' of the former busy yards, and the near-starvation of the workers and children. 'No-one looks for a revival of business' wrote the *New York Times*, and indeed the London ship-yards never did recover. The 1860s were the age of sail still, but the new technologies of steam and steel were rapidly overtaking tradition. The ship-yards of the north were blossoming with their advantages of cheap coal and iron, and by the mid-1870s the Clyde alone, with 40,000 workers, was estimated to have the capacity to replace the entire British Navy in two years.[16] (Wages were lower in the north, but rose to comparable levels after the collapse of the London yards.)[17]

On the Island, those firms which did not go bankrupt (the fate of James Ash, and Millwall Iron Works), adapted and survived. All over the world, governments and traders were recognising the efficiency of the small steam-powered boat, and Samuda and Dudgeon continued to produce for this market. A new firm, Yarrows, set up on Folly Wall in Cubitt Town in 1865, and made an international reputation from building and fitting-out specialised steam boats. Yarrow had the enterprise and good fortune to be the right man for his times. The last quarter of the nineteenth century was a time of world-wide conflict and of great developments in the technology of water-borne armaments as

3   Torpedo boats built by Yarrows, Isle of Dogs, London E14, c1890.

governments struggled to extend their areas of influence or fend-off aggressors from their territories. The warring nations, and the practice of 'gun-boat diplomacy', created a demand for the fast and deadly torpedo boats which became a speciality of the Yarrow yard. He and his engineers improved the design of these weapons, adopting the high-tensile steel hull for lightness and strength and the water tube boiler for maximum fuel efficiency. Besides the Royal Navy Yarrow supplied the governments of Argentina, Spain, France, Holland, Greece, Australia, Russia, Italy, Chile and Japan. It is not too fanciful to suppose that some of those boats, built on the Isle of Dogs up to a hundred years ago, are still in use on remote lakes and rivers in distant continents. Yarrow moved his work to Scotstoun, on the Clyde, in 1906; his yard is commemorated in Yarrow House in Stewart Street, Cubitt Town.[18]

Ship-building left behind a legacy of skills — knowledge of wood and metal, of engines and of the ships themselves. Wooden sailing ships needed repairs after most long voyages, and the skills of joiners, carpenters, rope and sail makers, boiler makers and engineers, were in demand to work on the hundreds of ships which passed regularly through the Port of London. Until the 1930s the sight of a ship's prow stretched across the road, nearly touching the houses opposite as it lay in dry dock, was a familiar one to Islanders. London's largest ship-repair yard, Green and Silley Weir Ltd, came into being in 1911 through the amalgamation of two companies, one of which, the Green's, had been at Blackwall for several generations. Many Islanders worked in this yard and at others on the Island — the London Graving Dock, Fletcher's Dry Dock, Regent's Dry Dock, Badger's and Rye Arc's.[19]

Britain had been the first country to industrialise, but other countries followed in the nineteenth century, and manufacturers combed the earth's surface for supplies of raw materials. The engineering industries of the Island won their share of the market created by this expansion — supplying sections of bridges to cross African rivers, engines to pump out South American mines, machinery for new factories in the Russian steppes and even the workers to operate and maintain it all.

The names of the large employers, the civil and mechanical engineers, echo across the years — Westwoods, Matthew T Shaw, Samuel Cutlers. The remembered skills of the workers have been absorbed into the traditions of hard work and hard times which are the heritage of every pre-war Islander. Joseph Westwoods, in West Ferry Road (on Scott Russell's site), supplied and built steel structures all over the South-East and abroad. In his autobiography, A J Hubbard, born on the Island in 1869, recalls:

"... I obtained employment at the firm of Westwood, Bailee & Co, engineers and bridge builders, where my father was foreman over the erecting department. Bridges, girders and roofing were made and built at the works, and when completed were examined by the inspector. After being passed by the inspector the various sections were distinctly marked, unbolted and shipped off to the company or railway from which the order came. Many orders came from the home and foreign railways. Large contracts came from the Indian State Railways. A fine bridge for over the River Indus, at a town named Sukkur, was made by this firm on the cantilever principle. The bridge opened up trade with Afghanistan in textiles, sugar, opium, saltpetre and other commodities. It was named the Sukkur bridge, and was partly built at the works. To carry the weight of the steelwork and staging, piles were driven into the ground, and extended with cross bracings to a height of 150 feet."

Another family which worked at Westwoods was the Smiths, father and sons, of Ship Street. Of young George Smith it was said that he 'could do anything with steel'. There were also generations of skilled workers in the Thomson

4   Sailing vessel built by Yarrows, Isle of Dogs, London E14, date unknown, late 19th century.

5   Workers in the yard of Cargo Fleet Limited, steel stockholders, West Ferry Road, Isle of Dogs, London E14, 1930s.

6 *The Smith family of Ship Street, Isle of Dogs, London E14, 1916; father and sons were all steelworkers.*

7 *Sophie Anderson (nee Thomson — her father and brothers were boiler makers) and Harry Anderson of West Ferry Road, Isle of Dogs, London E14, 1899. Harry came from Warwickshire, where his father was a railway wagon inspector; Harry was a boiler maker by trade and later worked in the docks as a stevedore.*

8 *The Thomson family, boiler-makers and engineers, Isle of Dogs, London E14, 1930s.*

family. David Thomson senior, born in Scotland in 1852, came to Millwall as a young man, and married a local girl. He worked as a boiler-maker, 'wherever there was work'. His sons in turn became engineers, one of them, David Thomson, being outside manager for Samuel Cutlers, steel erectors, for many years. At the age of 70 he was still climbing gas holders to inspect the results of his work.

George Hames also worked for Cutlers in his youth and he says of the firm: 'For the greater part of 130 years that name was on the gates of Providence Iron Works . . . during that time, the name spread all over the globe — Shanghai, Hong Kong, Ismailia, Karachi, Ceylon, Jamaica, South America, Australia, South Africa and of course, Europe. Cutlers were gas works specialists, and built the largest gas holders in the UK: nos 1 and 2 at East Greenwich. They also constructed all sorts of tanks for oil storage, and sewage farms, and refrigeration plant, coal conveyors, hangars, mooring masts for the R101 and the Crystal Palace aerial mast. During World War Two they worked on landing craft, gun turrets, and did work for the RAF and other contracts'.

Meanwhile anchor chains and mooring buoys were still being made at Brown, Lenox & Co. At Manganese and Bronze,, the ponderous shining propellors were made which drove such giants of the sea as the *Mauretania* and the Cunard liners. The firm of Ebners specialised in wooden flooring and provided the dance floor for the *Queen Mary* and other ships. East Ferry Road Engineering Co made hydraulic cranes and factory machinery.

Another metal-working industry with long associations with the Isle of Dogs was lead refining and processing. Locke Lancaster & Co Ltd (later Associated Lead) had two sites on the Island, one in Bridge Road (now the northern end of West Ferry Road) and one at the southern end of West Ferry Road, opposite Millwall Fire Station. Lead bullion was imported from Australia, Canada, Greece, Spain, Burma and South America and brought to the works by barge for sampling and analysis in the firm's laboratory. It was then re-sold on the London market or used in the firm's own manufacturing departments. Hundreds of local people worked there, making lead oxide for use in the batteries that powered submarines; lead cases to house cobalt isotopes used in X-ray machines; white lead the basic ingredient in paint making and lead foil for damp courses. Another major product, until it was replaced by aluminium, was lead sheeting, covered with an alloy of tin used to line tea chests in India, Assam, Burma and Ceylon.

In the 1830s and 1840s, and for up to a hundred years after that, it had been profitable to invest in British ship-building, manufacturing and related industries. In a favoured position, close to the finance houses of the City and the transport facilities of the busy Port, Island industries had survived and even flourished through booms, depressions and the upheavals of two world wars. But by the 1960s

9 *Friends and relations from Millwall visiting men from Cutler's steel works at Welwyn Garden City where they were erecting gas holders. The men lived in wooden huts on the site. This work was done in the 1920s and Cutler's also put up two big gas holders at Beckton. In the photograph from left to right: Mrs Till Cox, Mrs Lizzie Thomson (whose husband David was outside manager for Cutler's), Mrs Sophie Anderson, Harry Anderson (behind the flowers), Kate Camm and her husband and Fred Cox, wearing school cap. Cox boys in front. These families lived in West Ferry Road near the Scotch Church, or in Crews Street.*

10 *Lead Works and Isle of Dogs waterfront, London E14. View from Stowage Power Station chimney, probably 1930s.*

11 *Associated Lead, firm's dinner, 1930s. Isle of Dogs, London E14.*

143

times were already changing again, and this time more radically than ever before in the Island's industrial history. Britain was no longer the Workshop of the World, nor was London the heart of an Empire. Traffic in the Port and on the river, which for centuries had grown as London had grown, gradually came to a standstill. Island companies, housed in their nineteenth-century factories and warehouses round the crowded river's edge, could not easily adapt to the late-twentieth-century conditions of world-wide competition, new manufacturing techniques and increasing dependence on road and air transport. By the late 1960s, many local firms had closed, moved away or were being run down. Private housing and high-technology industries are the attractive investments of the 1980s, and developers are rapidly overlaying the sites of former dry docks and engineering sheds with bright new buildings and modern transport systems. It will still be some time before all evidence of the Island's industrial past is eradicated. In the 1980s the visitor with discerning eye can still identify the site of C J Mare's works, of Yarrow's yard and the Folly House pub which caused him so much irritation; can still pick out traces of the railway lines which crossed the road from one factory to another and may still notice, abondoned and decaying, the peeling signboards of once-bustling wharves and workshops.

Notes

1   The information dealing with engineering and related industries on the Isle of Dogs in the late nineteenth and early twentieth centuries is based on material accumulated by the Island History Project from trade directories, newspapers and other publications, mainly in the Local History Department of Tower Hamlets Central Library; another major source was the written and recorded recollections of Islanders themselves. Apart from the individuals named in the text, particular thanks are due to Mr L Jones for his assistance with the story of Locke Lancaster's lead works. Research for the history of ship-building and associated industries on the Isle of Dogs (Notes 2-18) has been carried out for the Island History Project by Dr A P Wailey.

2   *Artisans and Politics in Early Nineteenth Century London: John Gast and His Times,* I Prothero, 1979.

3   *The Environs of London,* Lyson, 1811.

4   *Romance of a Welsh Industry, South Wales News,* 19 January 1924.
A link with the past: The History of the Newbridge Works of Brown Lenox & Co Pontypridd, Stephen K Jones, Glamorgan Historian, 12, pp 27-46.

5   *Shipbuilders of the Thames and Medway,* P Banbury, p 260.

6   *The Story of David Napier, Shipbuilder of Millwall,* Ian W Muir, Institute of Marine and Naval Engineers, c 1970.
David Napier, Engineer, 1790-1869, D D Napier.

7   *William Fairbairn, Experimental Engineer, A I Smith, The Chartered Mechanical Engineer,* June 1963.
The Life of Sir William Fairbairn (Bart.), (Ed William Cole)

8   *The Pioneer of Screw Propulsion, J Clifton, The Port of London,* October 1974, pp 321-323.

9   Eg, *The Great Iron Ship,* James Dugan, and many contemporary accounts.
I K Brunel, L T C Rolt.
John Scott Russell, George S Emmerson.

10   *The Rise of Industrial Society in England, 1815-1885,* S G Checkland.

11   Banbury, *cited above*
The Decline of Shipbuilding on the Thames, S Pollard, *Economic History Review,* 2nd series, 1950.

12   Banbury, cited above
Dockyard Economy and Naval Power, J Barry.
Royal Commission on Trade Unions, 1867: Reports of Commissioners.

13   As note 12.

14   *Some Habits and Customs of the Working Classes,* Thomas Wright.

15   *R C on Trade Unions,* cited above.
Banbury, cited above.

16   *Clyde Shipbuilders in 1876, Economist Newspaper Commercial History and Review of 1876,* 1877, p 24 quoted in Checkland, cited above.

17   *Workers on Their Industries,* 'Shipbuilding' by W C Steadman.

18   *The Life of Sir Alfred Yarrow,* Lady E C Yarrow.
One Hundred Years on, Yarrows 1865-1965, A Borthwick.

Photographs in this article are from the Island History Photograph Collection.

Dockland transport

Alan Pearsall

River Steamers

The success of Henry Bell's *Comet* on the Clyde in 1812 soon brought paddle steamers as the first improvement to the transport facilities of our area. At first, the steamers provided a better service only to places in the Thames estuary and to Woolwich and Gravesend. A local service, running more often than the one or two daily trips usual with the longer distance vessels, only began in the mid-1830s, from the City to Greenwich and Woolwich, calling at intermediate piers, whose number increased as the banks of the river were developed. Originally, there was a Greenwich company and a Woolwich one and the opening of the Blackwall Railway in 1841 found that company adding to rival the Star Diamond and Watermans' Companies, with Blackwall-Woolwich trips, and on to Gravesend, and through fares from Fenchurch Street. The local services, once a degree of co-operation was introduced, proved very popular. The steamers sailed frequently, often every quarter of an hour, and supplied links for a variety of places, with some speed and comfort as compared with other contemporary forms of transport. The vessels had cabins for first and second class, and usually refreshments were obtainable.

The passage of time and the further expansion of the railway system, and later the underground, began, however, to erode the traffic of the steamers, an effect made worse by the advent of trams. The steamers could not cater for very short distance traffic, like the tram could, whilst the train could now run, say, from Greenwich right through to Charing Cross much more quickly. The frequent winter fogs probably disrupted river traffic more than it did the railway. Despite amalgamation of all the steamers under one management from 1865 onwards, and the institution of a service from Woolwich right through to Kew, the fortunes of the river service steadily declined, and several reconstructions of the company took place. By the same token, there was little or no capital to build new steamers. Finally, in 1902, the then company announced that it could no longer continue.

All was not yet lost, for there was sufficient public disquiet to justify the London County Council taking action, although it must be admitted that its action was probably too ambitious. It ordered thirty new steamers and inaugurated a new service in June 1905. The Council rapidly found, however, like its predecessors, that the service had, in effect, become a tourist service, for the winter of 1905-6 brought heavy losses. The Council continued for the summers only of 1906 and 1907, before a change of party control led to the abandonment of the service, probably rather prematurely, and the sale of the steamers.

Another company purchased some of them and carried on a summer service up to 1914. Since then, although various efforts have been made to re-start the service, none have really succeeded. Since 1945 the service to Greenwich has improved, and even runs for much of the year, but it makes no intermediate calls, cannot compete in speed with land transport, and cannot therefore be regarded as an effective part of the Dockland transport system. Whilst it is to be hoped that more use can eventually be made of the river, the disadvantages of the circuitousness of its route, and the effect of tides need a fast craft to overcome them, and experiments with new

*1   The Lower Pool, 1914.
(National Maritime Museum)*

1

145

types of vessel have not so far produced an economic answer.

Railways in Dockland

Second in the improvements of transport came the railway. Whilst the railways of Dockland were not a coherent system, just as Dockland itself is an artificial concept, enough of them owed their existence to the presence of the docks and the Port generally, to justify a separate examination.

The first railway in our area was indeed the first railway in London — the London and Greenwich, but this was a line "in" but not "of" Dockland, for it was passenger only with no connection to the riverside. It was a pioneer, however, of the frequent service and of urban railways built on a viaduct. Although its terminus and its route caused other railways to use it, these were even less concerned with our district.

Its north bank counterpart had several similarities but, in contrast, became the Dockland railway *par excellence*. The Blackwall and Poplar area already had a good omnibus service. In 1834 the Brunswick Wharf was opened, a calling place for river steamers and, it was hoped, also a terminus for seagoing vessels. The prospects were fair for a direct railway to the City, avoiding the detour round the Isle of Dogs, and so appeared the London and Blackwall Railway, another short line on a viaduct, but with the additional peculiarities of a 5 ft gauge and cable haulage. Although quite successful, its full potential was not realised until it abandoned these features, after which it too made links with other lines and brought to itself much traffic, both passenger and goods, for the true Dockland railway carried much of both. While the branch to Bow, connecting to the Eastern Counties Railway, did not at first divert much traffic from still rural inner Essex, the opening of the North London line meant links to the main lines.

The original title of the North London well described its purpose, ie the East and West India Docks and Birmingham Junction Railway. By the 1940s, the potentiality of goods traffic was being recognised by the large railways, and the new line was to sweep round the northern outskirts of London to gain access for what soon became the London and North Western Railway to the goods traffic of the Docks and to the City, the latter via a short connection to the Blackwall Railway at Bow. Although intended for goods, the possibilities for passengers were soon recognised, and the line rapidly contributed to the northerly spread of buildings.

Concurrently, on the other side of the Lea, the other principal dock line was being built, from Stratford, where the two routes into East Anglia diverged, to the long-established ferry at Woolwich, through a somewhat unpromising district of market gardens or marsh. To complete the activities of the late 1840s, the North Kent line along the Southern bank to Woolwich and beyond was also opened.

While useful passenger services followed these main routes, there followed the construction of many short branches for goods purposes. Some of these served the industries of the City itself, such as Haydon Square goods station, whilst others were aimed at dock or river traffic, some of them moreover by railways without their own line to Dockland, who obtained running powers to a depôt built off the existing lines. The Great Northern and Midland both took advantage of this method. The railways south of the river had very few actual connections with the northern lines in these early days, and they also built short branches to river wharves so that shipment traffic could be lightered out to ships in the river or docks. Only the Great Western, with its broad gauge, could not send its own trains, and had to lighter in traffic from Brentford Dock.

Subsequent developments responded to the increase in traffic in the port, the construction of new docks and the rise of industries. When the North London built its "City extension" to Broad Street, it reorganised its passenger services and the dock line service there after ran from that station to Poplar and later Blackwall, a rather circuitous route, with a connecting service from Bow to Fenchurch Street. The building of Millwall Dock and of Cubitt Town led to the building of a branch from the Blackwall line through the Isle of Dogs to North Greenwich and the railway also took over the ferry to Greenwich itself. More radical changes occurred east of Bow Creek, where the Victoria and later the Royal Albert Docks were built. The North Woolwich line had to be diverted in order to serve the former, and then it acquired two branches, one to serve the new gasworks at Beckton and the other to serve the Royal Albert Dock. Its route to London was also shortened by using the new direct line of the London Tilbury and Southend Railway (which at this stage had little effect on our area) and then a short connection north of Canning Town. For goods traffic, the use of lighters was increasingly supplemented by direct lines into the new docks, and large sidings were laid out in the Poplar anbd Canning Town-Custom House areas, while the North London improved Poplar Dock on its own account. The two areas mentioned became, in fact, almost full of sidings and depôts of one or another company. The dock companies also developed their own internal lines. The only new route in the latter part of the nineteenth century was not connected to any existing line. The East London Railway was laid through the original Brunel Thames Tunnel to make a route from Shoreditch to New Cross, thus being one of the few cross-river links. Jointly owned, it provided a service beyond its southern termini to Croydon and elsewhere.

Activity on all these lines had the same character, peculiar to them, saving perhaps the North London in general. There were closely spaced stations, frequent passenger trains hauled by smallish tank engines and composed of close-coupled sets usually of four-wheeled

2

vehicles, most of which provided rather spartan third class accommodation. Between the passenger trains would often come a goods train, also hauled by a small tank engine, very probably of another company. Signal boxes occurred as often as stations or even more so, as there were many points for junctions or goods yards. The semaphore signals were sometimes lofty, at other times crowded under bridges. Stations were mostly well built and roofed, though some were cramped like Silvertown, or lightly built such as those on the Blackwall viaduct.

For many years the two principal services, the Blackwall and the North London, were quarter-hourly, as was the North Greenwich in connection, and a half-hourly train ran from Bow (North London) to Fenchurch Street. The North Woolwich line service was more complex, as there was an hourly train on each of three routes, ie Liverpool Street to North Woolwich via Stratford, Fenchurch Street to North Woolwich similarly, and Fenchurch Street to Gallions via the London Tilbury and Southend line. Additional trains ran in connection between Custom House and Gallions, a line incidentally which served very little habitation and existed solely for users of the docks. Local trains also ran between Victoria Park (North London) and Canning Town. The East London line had a variety of services, operated by the partners in its joint ownership.

Goods services were obviously far less systematic, but usually ran from each company's depôts in Dockland to their main marshalling yards, in most cases using their own engines over North London or Great Eastern lines, though some traffic might be local, like coal brought by sea for stations in the London area. Main line engines were rarely seen in Dockland.

The passenger services began to suffer, even before 1914, from electric tram and later, bus, competition and the extension in 1908 of District electric trains from the West End to East Ham over the Whitechapel and Bow line of 1902. After 1918 the situation became worse. Little renewal of rolling stock took place, expenses were rising and receipts falling. The Blackwall was the first casualty. Its closure and that of its Greenwich connection had already been announced, but the General Strike brought about an earlier cessation. The North Woolwich trains were severely reduced after 1939, and the service ran mostly to Stratford only, so that the docks rather curiously had no through service to the City. The North London line, after gradual reductions in service over the years, finally closed in 1944. Goods traffic, however, continued to be heavy — indeed, during both wars, it caused delays and cancellations so that the passenger services found little favour — and remained an important justification for the lines until the great decline in railway goods traffic during the

2 *Wapping Station, East London Railway, looking south about 1870. (London Transport)*

147

1960s and the closure of the PLA railway system. Even then, Poplar Dock continued to be quite busy until around 1981.

The need to rehabilitate Dockland with the cessation of most port activity has, however, begun to reverse this decline. In 1985 work began to revive the Blackwall line for most of its route, using light tram-type cars, and it is to be extended once again to North Greenwich, with a second stage using the old North London line runing from Poplar to Stratford. The North Woolwich line has been electrified, and the Richmond — Broad Street service diverted over it. Both measures recognise the importance of either through running or good connections to overcome the drawbacks and isolation of the past.

Road Transport

The revival of road transport brought about decline in the railways. For our area, it is sufficient to deal with trams, trolleybuses and buses in one section, as, with few exceptions, their routes were all confined to main roads east and west.

These two routes, the East India Dock Road on the north and the Lower Road — Jamaica Road in the south, were both busy in horse bus days, and, by virtue of running beyond the City to the West End, remained so even after the coming of the railway. At the outset, of course, the south bank was still quite rural and the buses were for Deptford and Greenwich.

The horse tram was the first advance, using the greater hauling power possible with steel wheels on steel rails. Companies built lines along both East India Dock Road and the Mile End Road in the 1870s, but the Lower Road lines did not come until the next decade. On both banks the lines ended on the London side of the waterways, Bow and Deptford Creeks, owing to inadequate bridges. (The main tram route to Greenwich was via the Old Kent Road). The particularism often incipient in this type of development was shown also by the Greenwich to Woolwich line being of narrow (3′ 6″; 1.067 metre) gauge. The lines were, however, cheap and useful despite their limitations, the greatest, never overcome, being, as with some railways, failure to go into and through the City and West End. Only one cross-route was built, from the West India Docks to Hackney, and this had a chequered career.

Horse trams were slow, and the companies left gaps in the system. The radical early days of the LCC saw it take advantage of the proviso in the Companies' Act allowing the local authority to take over after 21 years, and all the Dockland lines thus came into the Council's ownership. It soon electrified most of them, and filled the gaps over the creeks, linking with the Essex towns and the systems round Woolwich. A very frequent service was provided, sometimes as often as every two or three minutes.

By this time, (1910-1914), the improvement of the internal combustion engine was bringing

3   London General two-horse bus operating a service to London Bridge railway station. (Museum of London)

3

148

4 Looking north along Manchester Road, Cubitt Town, 1925. The ship is the Milverton, built 1886. (London Transport)

5 Victoria Dock shelter, Connaught Road, 1939. Trolley bus route 699. (London Transport)

6 Woolwich bus and coach passenger terminal, 1937. Trolley bus route 698. (London Transport)

back the bus and the main routes saw them, as before, running to and from places beyond the trams, while a few local routes were begun, such as round the Isle of Dogs, and through the two road tunnels. The buses were owned by various companies, of which the London General Omnibus Company was much the largest. This dual and rival service of tram and bus remained throughout the inter-war years, although the formation of the London Passenger Transport Board brought all under one control. That body began by the conversion of the north bank trams to trolleybuses, completed in 1940, also adding new routes using the Silvertown Way opened in 1934. After the war, however, buses were favoured, the last trams of all running in our area in 1952, and the last trolleybuses following in 1960. Since then many services have been converted for one-man buses, with consequent slower running, while frequency has also deteriorated.

Crossing the River
Below London Bridge, the barrier created by the river, both physical and even psychological, has always been formidable, despite efforts to ameliorate it. The few people who needed to cross the river in the early nineteenth century were catered for, not too conveniently, by ancient ferries at Deptford, Greenwich and Woolwich, or simply by hiring a waterman and his skiff.

The spread of the City, the Port and industry downstream made the desirability of improved crossings evident by the 1820s, when the famous Thames Tunnel between Wapping and Rotherhithe was begun, but the best efforts even of the Brunels could not complete it until 1843, and even then it seems to have been as much an attraction as a route and its road approaches were never built. The development of passenger steamers enabled people to cross

the river by using suitable piers, such as Cherry Garden to Tunnel Piers. The short ferries also in time became steam-worked, both as a sequel to the arrival of the railways, Woolwich in 1850, Greenwich from 1872. A Blackwall-Greenwich service was also useful. In 1869, the Thames Tunnel was taken over for use by the East London Railway.

While people were thus, even if inadequately, catered for, a very considerable road cartage traffic had grown up, creating congestion and also subject to long detours if the journey was across the river, and particularly to the docks. Pressure thus arose for a vehicular crossing lower down.

The Thames Steam Ferry Company was the first to try. It opened a ferry between Wapping and Rotherhithe in 1877, with landings carefully designed to adjust ship and shore so as to avoid excessive gradients for horse-drawn vehicles. The undertaking had a chequered career, but closed in 1886, just about when a similar company was preparing another such crossing at Greenwich. This too was only a limited success. Meanwhile, serious investigations were being made into other possibilities. Sir Joseph Bazalgette of Thames Embankment fame proposed a tunnel at Blackwall, others urged a new bridge, eventually to bear fruit in 1894 as Tower Bridge. The Metropolitan Board of Works, as a recompense to the East End for the buying out

of bridge tolls which had taken place in the 1870s and 1880s on many of the up-river bridges, embarked on the Woolwich Free Ferry scheme to provide an equivalent toll-free crossing in the east. This well-known enterprise opened in 1889.

Ferries were, however, disrupted by the dense fogs which were not unusual, and the Thames Conservancy was opposed, on navigational grounds, to more of them. Bridges over the ship channels were also fraught with difficulties, and so, with improved tunnelling methods, tunnels became the preferred means for improving crossings. The LCC took over its predecessor's scheme and built the Blackwall Tunnel, opened in 1897, next came Greenwich (foot only) in 1901, Rotherhithe in 1908 and Woolwich (foot only) in 1912.

The only major road improvements in the area were the tunnel approach roads, until a further investigation between the wars into river crossings produced, as a by-product, an improved bridge over Bow Creek and a new road from Canning Town to Silvertown, the Silvertown Way, which radically improved road access to the Royal Docks and the Woolwich Ferry.

Transport
This review has, for simplicity's sake, been based on each mode of transport. But what of the whole? Since 1800, when those without

7   The Greenwich Steam Ferry. (Engineering 17th February 1888)

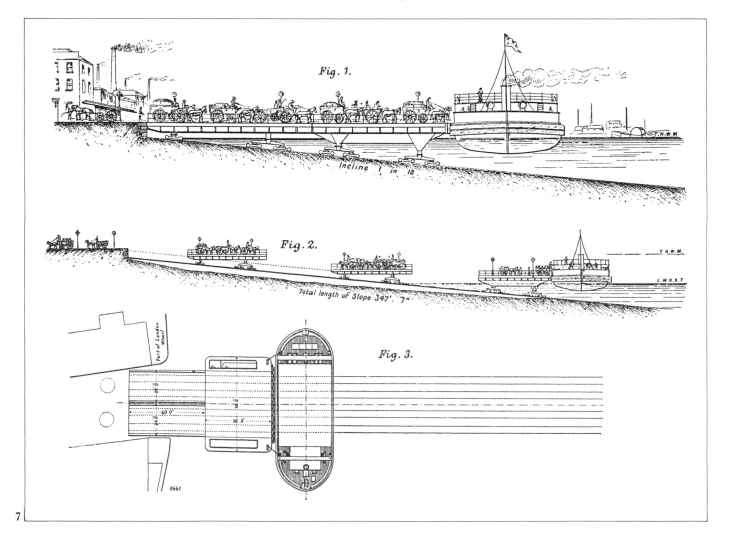

private carriages could only use their feet to move around, Dockland has seen a succession of one mode of transport after another, as technical development has produced vehicles giving more and differing qualities. But the replacement has not always been complete, and in fact, the actual routes havce often been similar or parallel eg the East India Dock Road and the Blackwall Railway, and furthermore, since the great expansion of the 1840s and 1850s, few new large works were undertaken until the building of Silvertown Way and then after the war the second Blackwall Tunnel and its approaches. We see the river, a single rather roundabout route, give way to trains on a more direct and perhaps more reliable route. Trams and then motor buses brought transport much nearer many homes, with a very frequent service, but at the expense of speed. Thus in an area like Dockland, where poverty was never far away and travel was only undertaken for necessity, the inner railway declined. Perhaps, too, the telephone has an influence, for how does one explain the disappearance of all through services between City and the Docks by 1940? Howcvcr, wc must also remember that many East Enders always found work in the West End, and the through service came into its own. The extension of the District Railway on to the London Tilbury and Southend line probably helped the decline of other lines as the greater convenience and frequency of a through electric service told. We might also reflect here that many East Enders provide these services, for Devons Road sheds at Bow worked all the North London Railway and the many bus garages still contribute, one suspects, a more than proportionate share of bus mileage in the West End. Trams and trolleybuses have gone,

8

given way to the bus, and the advantages of rail over distances in cities of the size of London are still evident. The slowness of one-man buses and modern traffic also points this same moral.

Looking into the future, transport is essential for the rehabilitation of the area. We may draw from the past some ideas — the desirability of through services, or at least of convenient interchange, as well as reasonable speed and frequency and certainly reliability. These, of which examples may be found above, are as necessary whatever the particular mode chosen, where a judicious combination of bus, tram and train — and possibly boat? — can still bring people to live in Dockland.

8 69 bus entering Blackwall Tunnel about 1912. (London Transport)

Short Bibliography

Barker, TC and Robbins, M
The History of London Transport 2 volumes.

Burtt, F
Steamerws of the Thames and Medway

Borley, H V
Chronology of London Railways

'Kennington'
London County Council Tramways Handbook

Day, John R
London's Trams & Trolley buses.

Day, John R
The Story of the London Bus

Pudney, John
Crossing London's River

Klapper, Charles F
Roads and Rails of London, 1900-33

Connor, J E
Stepney's Ownb Railway

Gibbon & Bell
History of London, County Council

Reminiscences of a stevedore

George Adams

On the 22 March 1955, I appeared with others before the Executive Council of the National Amalgamated Stevedores & Dockers Union (NAS & D) to be initiated as a stevedore member of the union. There was no medical examination nor test of any kind. We initiates just affirmed that we were capable of doing the work and promised to abide by the rules of the union. I was thirty years of age, and until then had worked as a Thames lighterman. Traditionally, admission as a stevedore passed from father to son, but as the number of sons coming forward was insufficient to fill the quota of registrations on offer the 'books' were thrown open to grandsons and sons-in-law; so my brother Terry and I changed over from lightering to stevedoring on our maternal grandfather's card.

By this time, the only difference between a docker and a stevedore in the enclosed docks was that the stevedore could only be a member of the stevedores' section of the NAS & D and seek work 'on a ship', discharging or loading. The docker could be a member either of the dockers' section of the NAS & D or the Transport & General Workers Union (T & G) and could seek work 'on the quay' in addition to discharging and loading ships.

All the stevedores in our family worked in the Millwall Dock except two who were 'over the water' working in the Surrey Docks, a fact which militated against us, and anybody else in similar circumstances, because our National Dock Labour Board (NDLB) registrations allocated us to work in the Royal Docks. Usually, before the inception of the NDLB or after when allocated to the same sector as his family, the 'newy' would be looked after by his relatives. Perhaps he would be found a place in a regular gang or the father or a brother would leave his 'corner' in a gang and 'float' with the newy, picking-up work with scratch (ad hoc) gangs until his charge had learnt his way around. However, the newy awarded his registration in a sector away from his family was out on his own, unless there were friends there who would be requested 'to put him right' ie instruct him how to conduct himself, what firms were the best to 'shape' for, what jobs to avoid, etc. Terry and I went out 'on the stones' for the 'call-on' the first morning innocent of all the nuances of 'the call'.

By 1955, there was only one place of call or 'stones' for stevedores in the Royals and this was by the 'White Gates', the railway level crossing on the Connaught Road where it turned sharply to pass by its famous eponymous pub. The stevedores' call at the Surreys was in Redriff Road adjacent to Lower Road. For the stevedores in the India and Millwall Docks there were three calling-on places: the main call was in th East Ferry Road adjacent to Glengall Road, Millwall; a smaller call was held by the "Blue Posts" pub (now tarted-up as "The Buccaneer") in West India Dock Road; and an occasional call in Robin Hood Lane alongside the old entrance to the Blackwall Tunnel, Poplar. The call at the Royals was held in a fenced enclosure opening off the road (fig 1),

1 The enclosure by the 'White Gates', Royal Docks, serving as 'the stones' for the stevedores. (August 1955, the 7.45am call.) On the left are 'hung-up' foremen looking towards the entrance for late comers from the Connaught Road. Of the two brick buildings in the back-ground, the one to the left is the 'Connaught Tavern', the other is the Board of Trade Office. (National Dock Labour Board)

whereas those at the Surreys and the India & Millwall were situated on the public road itself. Near to all the calls were coffee shops and 'six o'clock houses' ie pubs licensed to open for trade at 6 am. Some of the latter also sold tea and coffee.

There were two times of calling a day, the principal one took place between 7.45 am and 8 am attended every morning by those in work, 'in the collar', and by those without a job; the second call was held between 12.45 pm and 1 pm if labour was required, and was attended only by those still seeking work. Men would muster in or near the coffee shops and pubs from quite early in the morning. Some men, mainly gangers, dubbed the 'Dawn Patrol' would 'show out' well before 7 am 'to see what was about' ie ascertain the quantity and quality of work coming-up on the call. They would 'put themselves about' ie place themselves where they could be discretely approached, usually by an emissary, with an offer of work. Such covert dealings were against the rules, but were prevalent, nevertheless. Just before 7.45 am by which time 'the muster' was full-grown, the foremen shipworkers would lead the way on to the stones (fig 2), walking along one side of the

men would join the 'floaters'. The floaters were men who by chance or design did not belong in a regular gang and who sought for work congenial to them. The temporary floaters, however, scoured for jobs of a duration whose completion would free them ready for their own firm's next ship, because they had to look after their corner. If a man in a regular gang picked-up another job once too often knowing that it would render him unavailable when next his ganger required him, then when next he shaped-up for his regular ganger the man might 'get a drilling' ie be 'left roasting' on the stones while another was called-on in his place for the next ship or two. When work was plentiful regular gangs would shape-up wherever their gangers led: the floaters would gather where the best work would be on offer. When work was scarce 'ducking-and-diving' would take place: floaters would mob that part of the stones where fresh work was being called, perhaps — shades of Pearl Buck's "The Good Earth" — the breeze had gone around that a member of a regular gang was sick or injured; some would tarry and then plonk themselves in front of the crowd to 'get a fronter'; others who were pressed back by the crush in front would stand on tip-toe or

2 *Stevedores walking on to 'the stones' for the 7.45am call-on at Redriff Road, Surrey Commercial Docks. Early 1950s. (National Dock Labour Board)*

3 *Calling-on in progress on the stevedores' call, Redriff Road, Surrey Commercial Docks, early 1950s. Note the 'show-up' of TU cards. The men in the foreground are the outside men; those in the background are the inside men (see 'Cargo Handling'). (National Dock Labour Board)*

road or enclosure, with the main body of men coming on slightly behind to take up a position opposite and facing the foremen. Each local contractor would have his own stretch of the stones to stand at; outside contractors would go to the far end of the call.

On first acquaintance, the call had all the random bustle of a strange market place, in fact it was a labour market with its own pattern of conduct determined by feast or famine. Men who 'followed' a firm would shape-up opposite that firm's 'stand' if it had work or they were already working for it, but if there was no call for them there and their ganger had been 'given the breeze' that another firm wanted them the men would then shape-up at the other firm's stand. If there was no pre-arranged job for the gang the

scamper along the back to a thinner part of the crowd. Feast or famine, at a quarter to the hour the ensemble would freeze, there was a distinct pause, a silence with men facing foremen across a bare divide. Then the shipworkers walked forward in line as far as the mid-point each calling his gangers out if it was a fresh starter, otherwise the gangers woukld have gone to the middle without being called. The gangers would then call out their gangs by name, with the crane driver or winchmen being called first. At each engagement there was a reciprocal showing of TU cards (fig 3). If there was little work, as soon as the required gangs were called and any ancillaries were engaged the shipworkers and gangers walked off the stones. The call was then finished a minute or two after

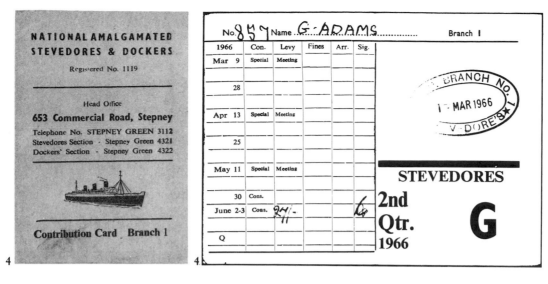

No. 857   Name G. ADAMS   Branch 1

1966	Con.	Levy	Fines	Arr.	Sig.
Mar 9	Special	Meeting			
28					
Apr 13	Special	Meeting			
25					
May 11	Special	Meeting			
30	Cons.				
June 2-3	Cons.	24/-		6	
Q					

BRANCH No. 1
1 - MAR 1966
STEVEDORES

STEVEDORES
2nd
Qtr.
1966

G

4   Left: *Front cover of the NAS & D Trade Union Contribution card.*

Right: *The inside of the NAS & D Contribution card giving the Member's union number, name, branch, section of the union, and the date. The branch stamp was applied when the Member paid his contribution as the new quarter's card was issued.*

it had started. On the other hand, if labour was in short supply the floaters would shape-up where they knew there was the best chance of being picked-up for well paid work. Then the situation was reversed with the men called on walking off the stones first leaving gangers 'hung-up'. These gangers would then move closer to the men's side trying to entice any of the remainder out or men could step out to them, ascertain what was on offer and accept or reject it. If the floater accepted he would then show his TU card (fig 4) thereby sealing the agreement (the stevedore did not tender his NDLB record book (fig 5) until he reached the ship's side). Hung-up gangers and shipworkers would have to stand on the stones until the hour, when dockers could offer themselves; they seldom came, but when they did they were usually NAS & D dockers, for the T & G discouraged their members from appearing on the stevedores' call.

There were but three written rules governing the call, one stating that a current TU card should be shown at the place of call before leaving for work, the second that no member should allow himself to be taken on before the call-on, and thirdly that no non-member should be taken on before the hour. The unwritten rules and the etiquette observed on the call required that no man seeking work stepped forward until called except if the person calling was hung-up; that every man was free to accept or reject the offer of work on the call; that the ganger had to call on his complement complete, if a regular member was missing then a replacement had to be called or accepted even if the ganger could see his man running down the road. In such instances, the replacement could give the 'blewer' the job back or not, as he wished — some replacements would even wait around until the hour to give the blewer his job if he showed out in time; finally, it was generally accepted that a gang having discharged a hold could expect to be picked up for the loading operation if it followed on.

As a floater you stood a better chance of being picked-up if you were known and better still if known as a good worker or if you were prominent in some way, either in appearance or

character. One character who was always cheerful and cracking jokes said to me, "My old dad taught me that if you make them laugh you're always going to be picked-up". A few men constantly 'subbed' off the employer, which ensured that they were re-engaged in order that the money subbed could be reclaimed. The free-call then was advantageous

N. D. L. B. No. 50/........02169

NATIONAL DOCK LABOUR BOARD
PORT OF LONDON

ISSUED TO.................................

CURRENT TO 30TH MARCH 1968

IF YOU CHANGE YOUR ADDRESS
NOTIFY SECTOR OFFICE AT ONCE

PORT OF LONDON   1967   40   50/   N.D.L.B. No. 02169

5   Top: *Front cover of the registered dock worker record book. '50/' indicates the Scheme port — London. 02169 indicates the RDW's number; '0' signifies that he is a lighterman; '2' that he is based in the City sector; '169' is his personal identification. (National Dock Labour Board)*

Bottom: *The inside of the RDW record book showing the first of twenty-six detachable record sheets, commencing at week 40. The employer and/or the NDLB would impress their stamp in the appropriate box to signify a 'turn' either at work, in attendance, failure to attend, sick absence or excused attendance. The employer or the NDLB would detach each sheet at the end week so that appropriate action might be taken by the NDLB. (National Dock Labour Board)*

when you were in a regular gang, were known, were fit, when there was a good run of work and you knew your way around, but when you were left roasting on the stones time after time you realised that as a casual you were a nonentity.

This was brought home to me vividly, about four months after going over as a stevedore, when the top joint of my right little finger was torn off by a rope sling while sending up a set of bagged asbestos. After I came out of hospital four days later, I went to the office of the firm I had been working for when the accident occurred and asked for an industrial injury accident form. It was passed over to me without any break in the conversation of the three persons sitting in the office. No one asked how I was nor who I was. I am not certain whether they even looked at me. I was a non-entity, of value only when in the collar.

At that time there was no sick pay, but if and when you commenced rehabilitation treatment, making you ready for work, the NDLB supplemented the state benefit so that the registered dock worker (RDW) received an amount equivalent to the guaranteed minimum applicable under the Scheme, the fall-back pay, which at that time amounted to £5.4.6d (£5.22½) a week. Other than that there was no other way for the casual to supplement his income when off sick or injured. Insurance companies would not touch dock workers, although one did in the late 1950s — it could not have known much about our working environment. The premium was quintupled after the first year of membership, and after the second year the shield of insurance was withdrawn from around us when we were all aimed out. One of the Friendly Societies did, however, accept dock workers some years later. Also, the T & G gave a limited amount of accident benefit to its members, and sick or accident benefit if a higher contribution was paid. In addition, there was a measure of help from your workmates, but this varied according to your popularity or notoriety. If you were off work for some weeks someone might 'send up a kite' ie send a sheet of paper aboard each ship asking for donations for the person named on the paper, or a bucket would be positioned at the dock gate accompanied by a notice asking people to 'kick-in' ie donate some money for the person designated. Some gangs helped their own sick or injured members. The gang I joined, when I transferred to the Millwall Dock, would kick-in 2/6 (12½p) a week from each of its thirteen members to help when a member was out: at one time we had three out simultaneously, which meant 7/6 (37½p) out of our earnings, not a trifling sum in those times. Because the above methods were inconsistent in their end results, men in various sectors of the port followed one another in setting-up organisations to collect contributions on a systematic basis and distribute distress funds on a more equitable scale (fig 6).

The rules of the various Distress Funds differed from sector to sector, some afforded a weekly sickness or accident benefit, butt all fulfilled their primary purpose of awarding a death benefit. Up to the late 1940s, when a man was killed at work the ship and adjacent quay would stop work for the remainder of the day as a mark of respect, but from then on the practice spread for work to continue and all the men's earnings on that berth for the day to be aggregated and given to the deceased's dependants. The Distress Fund helped

6 Top: *Interim report of Sector 5 Distress Fund, published at the end of the first six months of operation. Note that some Members are defaulting on their weekly contribution of 1s 0d (5p).*

Bottom: *First annual report of the Sector 5 Distress Fund. Sector 5 covered the area of the Port stretching from the west side of the river Lea to Limekiln Dock on the north bank including the East and West India Docks, Millwall Docks and all the registered wharves, but not Aberdeen Wharf.*

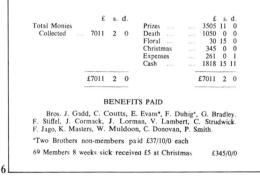

THE SECTOR FIVE DISTRESS FUND

This bulletin has been published so that you may assess the progress of the Fund. After operating for six months it has undoubtedly established itself, and been well received throughout, but its success and future depends entirely upon the agents who have an arduous and thankless task. Their efforts should be honoured by prompt payment, instead of the agent having to waste many hours of valuable time looking for the dodgers.

The primary object of the Fund is to give equality among all portworkers in the Sector, that in the unfortunate event of their demise, the dependant will receive the same amount of financial aid, instead of the previous custom which prevailed of "having to be known." It is not intended to be a Sick Club, as it would not be possible to function. One must realise that very large sums of money would be required each week, e.g., Christmas payout £345. to cater for the very high sickness and accident rate in the sector; also we cannot provide the administrative staff required to manage such a scheme. However the plight of men on long term sick deserves special consideration, and the Committee have decided that their position and any other form of distress grants will be reviewed in January 1962.

We deeply regret that we are unable to make any financial donation to our old men who are leaving us. The limits of the Fund would be surpassed, as so many of you are going. All that we can offer at present is to keep you in benefit if you wish to continue members of the Fund.

I bid you a respected and sincere farewell and wish you a peaceful and happy retirement.

	£ s. d.		£ s. d.
Total Monies		Prizes	3505 11 0
Collected ...	7011 2 0	Death	1050 0 0
		Floral	30 15 0
		Christmas ...	345 0 0
		Expenses ...	261 0 1
		Cash ...	1818 15 11
	£7011 2 0		£7011 2 0

BENEFITS PAID

Bros. J. Gadd, C. Coutts, E. Evans*, F. Duhig*, G. Bradley. F. Stiffel, J. Cormack, J. Lorman, V. Lambert, C. Strudwick. F. Jago, K. Masters, W. Muldoon, C. Donovan, P. Smith.

*Two Brothers non-members paid £37/10/0 each

69 Members 8 weeks sick received £5 at Christmas   £345/0/0

THE SECTOR FIVE DISTRESS FUND

The Officials elected for the second year of office are as follows:
Chairman: P. JAMES   Secretaries: F. MOORE, H. BROWN
Treasurer: E. WELFARE   Auditors: H. HOZIER, W. JONES
Chief Promoter: J. COUGHLAN

The first year report of the Fund has been one of steady progress, that has been maintained through very difficult periods. This is due in no small measure to the unselfish and devoted manner in which our agents have carried out their extremely trying tasks, and without whom this Fund could not possibly function. It is regrettable therefore, that this appeal has to be repeated. Please help your agent and pay promptly. By so doing much unpleasantness is avoided and valuable time is saved for all concerned.

The Committee has decided that financial grants be made to our long term sick members for Chrismas 1961. Unfortunately, there must be a time limit for this and eight weeks continuous up to Christmas is the rule, and anyone after this cannot be considered. The grant is graduated as follows. Any member who will have been away sick, for six continuous months from Christmas will receive £20; those members away sick under six months and over eight weeks will receive £10. For the old mmbers who have retired the sum of £750 has been granted for distribution among them.

This is all subject to the fund being in a position of financial stability to meet the commitments.

The question of continuity of payment for distress will be reviewed in January 1962.

The very deep sympathies of all members were extended to the families and relatives of our brothers who passed away in the recent months.
June: Brother S. Taylor
July: Brothers Farrall, Hookaway, Driscoll, Crane, Gore
August: Brothers J. Brooks, Stanton
September: Brother Bogg
October: Brothers Thake, Granger, Dupey, H. Brown, Durso, Harris

SECTOR 5 DISTRESS FUND, 63 West India Dock Road, E.14

Statement of Accounts week ending 7/10/61

Total Income of Lotteries	...	£15012/2/0
Paid in Prizes	...	£7506/1/0
To Society	...	£7506/1/0

Society Expenditure

Income from Loteries £7506/1/0		Death and Floral	
Donated by Newsagent £5/0/0		Tributes ...	£2314/15/0
Donated by Liaison		1960 X:mas Grants	£345/0/0
Committee ...	£19/0/0	Expenses	£736/14/9
		Cash in Hand ...	£4133/11/3
	£7530/1/0		£7530/1/0

Auditors: W. JONES, H. HOZIER
Treasurer: E. WELFARE

7 Example of a gang's note. The employer's registered number is impressed after his name. The 'No. of Turns 2' signifies 2 x half day's engagement. Station 'G' signifies the ganger, 'CR' the crane driver. 'Cons' is short for contingency payment, i.e., additional payment for responsibility or skill. The cement, general cargo and tiles are paid by the ton weight; the vehicles by the measurement ton, and the other cartons by the hundred. 'Plus 23.25%' is the percentage calculation of the increase in the piece-work rates since the publication of the rates schedule. 'D/W' denotes day-work, i.e., a period when piece-work could not be undertaken. 'P/W O/T 5/7' signifies piece-work over-time 5pm to 7pm.

whatever the cause of death.

The earnings due to the RDW varied according to the job. Each employer, and, theoretically, you could have had eleven different employers in a full week, were routed to the NDLB for consolidation into a weekly pay packet. A copy of the record of each day's earnings was made available on a pro-forma, 'the note' (fig 7) which could be collected from the employer's office on the following day. The old hands always had a shrewd idea of what the gang had earnt and scrutinised the note carefully. If the note was below expectations someone would take it back to the office and attempt to rectify the matter. I soon became lumbered with the task. From my days as a shop steward when lightering I had learned that in a dispute you should always give the other fellow a chance to save face, 'an outer'. So, when I went to the office I would respectfully suggest that, perhaps, they had inadvertently made a mistake. Had they mislaid one of the tally cards? This approach nearly always resulted in a beneficial result, whereas the lads who burst in bawling accusations of bare faced robbery aroused resentful opposition.

The large firms were genuine enough, but some of the small contractors had to be watched carefully particularly when there was a downturn in trade, such as in 1961/63. One of my acquaintances was picked-up as a replacement in a regular gang following a small firm. When the note was brought on board, the ganger just announced the figure and pocketed the note. The gang, except for the replacement, accepted the figure and tried to dissuade the replacement from querying the note, but he demanded the note and took it back to the

office. After some opposition it was admitted that the note was forty-five tons short. The gang were swallowing short notes in order to keep their corner. We, also, heard allegations at such times that some of the small contractors when billing their principals used the rates agreed by the Master Stevedores, but pinned a cheque to the invoice upon despatch.

Some of the smaller firms, also, did not possess the range of cargo handling gear carried by the large firms,[1] but made do or hired or 'borrowed' it. On one occasion we went on a loading job for a small firm and found that when we came to sling the Land Rovers going aboard there was no specialised vehicle slinging gear. So they 'borrowed' two PLA snotters (a snotter is a length of rope with a soft eye spliced in both ends) and the slingers had to pass the snotters fore and aft under each vehicle to sling it. When the load was hoisted, the two front side lights on every Land Rover were broken. On another occasion the superintendent of one large firm had to threaten to call the police before he could obtain the return of some of his gear being used by a small firm. The smallest contractors seemed to operate out of the Surrey Docks, some in fact were stevedores who contracted for a few ships and worked between times as a RDW. One of them hired a room and a telephone above a coffee shop when he functioned as a 'master', and claimed that he could live comfortably from the returns of but two ships a year. The smallest employer had one job a year, requiring six men, and, reputedly, operated from a caravan and a public telephone kiosk.[2]

To an outsider, or a participant looking back as I do now, the conditions then do appear harsh, haphazard and inefficient, but when you were in it, adept, acclimatised, wise to all its ways and had a corner it served its function and gave its satisfactions. Most men did take a pride in their work, most employers were efficient, and, on the whole, cargoes were handled fast and well. There were goodies and baddies on both sides, and the baddies have been blamed for the demise of the up-river docks and wharves. But even if everyone had been an angelic whizz-kid, the upper docks would still have atrophied and died, because of economic trends. For years, the tendency in north west European estuarial ports has been to move facilities towards the sea to accommodate the larger ships coming into use. As a consequence, the older and smaller docks up-river have been downgraded to short-sea and coastal traffic and then to barge traffic before closure: the Rochdale Report, 1962,[3] recommended the closure of the London and St Katharine Docks and the major development of the port at Tilbury. The Surrey Commercial Docks were at one time the largest timber handling docks in Europe: it has been estimated that the equivalent of 1½ packaged timber berths at Tilbury can handle what the Surreys handled. The container system of transport has ten times the throughput of the old conventional system: EHM Price of the Port of London Authority said in 1966 that, assuming a container berth could handle 1,000,000 tons per annum, the then 160 enclosed dock berths' and the 300 riverside wharves' general cargo trade could be catered for by 21 container berths.[4]

Unfortunately, the modernisation and re-orientation of the centre of gravity of the Port began to nite whent he Dock Workers (Regulation of Employment) (Amendment) Order, 1967, brought in the complete decasualisation of the RDWs. All were given permanent employment at a time when, as a consequence of the new development, the amount of employment began to shrink. Whereas under the casual system the employer could batten down in lean times, put all the casuals back on 'the pool' and keep his costs to the minimum, under the 1967 Scheme he had to carry all the men allocated to him permanently. In effect, he had a ball and chain clamped to his ankle and had to run the race under new and often fatal conditions.

Notes

1   S6 Devlin Report, 1965. Cmnd 2734.

2   Wilson, "Dockers" p 34.

3   Rochdale Report, 1962. Cmnd 1824 para 522.

4   Report of a lecture given at the University of London's Department of Extra Mural Studies by E H M Price. "Docks and Harbour Authority" magazine March, 1966.

Short Bibliography

Final Report of the Committee of Inquiry under the Rt Hon Lord Devlin into certain matters concerning the Port Transport Industry. August 1965. Cmnd 2734.

Wilson D F
Dockers, the impact of industrial change .

Report of the Committee of Inquiry into the Major Ports of Great Britain. September 1962. Cmnd 1824.

Hydraulic power

Tim Smith

The traditional method of handling cargoes, working cranes turning capstans, opening and closing lock-gates and sluices, moving swing bridges and loading and unloading railway trucks was by hard manual labour. During the second half of the nineteenth century the application of hydraulic power to these tasks reduced the number of men required to such an extent that it probably contributed indirectly to the labour disputes which bedevilled the Port in later years. Even so, by today's standards, even with hydraulic power the jobs remained highly labour intensive.

The following account covers the period from 1850-1900 when the use of hydraulic power grew so much that, by the turn-of-the-century, it was of major importance in Dockland. The dwindling remains of that era are also discussed. The various remains of hydraulic power from the twentieth century are dealt with in the gazetteer.

The use of water under pressure to distribute power was first proposed by Joseph Bramah in 1802 as a means of operating cranes at the London Dock.[1] Bramah had previously patented the hydraulic press (1795) which he used as a basis for his hydraulic crane. His ideas for hydraulic power networks were embodied in his later patent of 1812. The first practical realisation of Bramah's concept came about

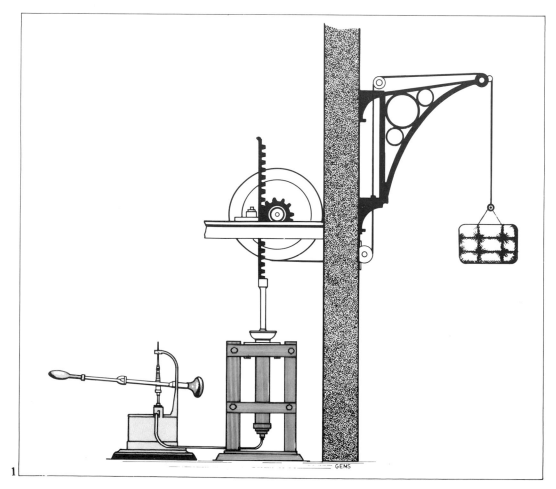

1 *Bramah's Hydraulic Crane (based on his hand-pump press). (Gloria E M Shayler)*

Hydraulic Network

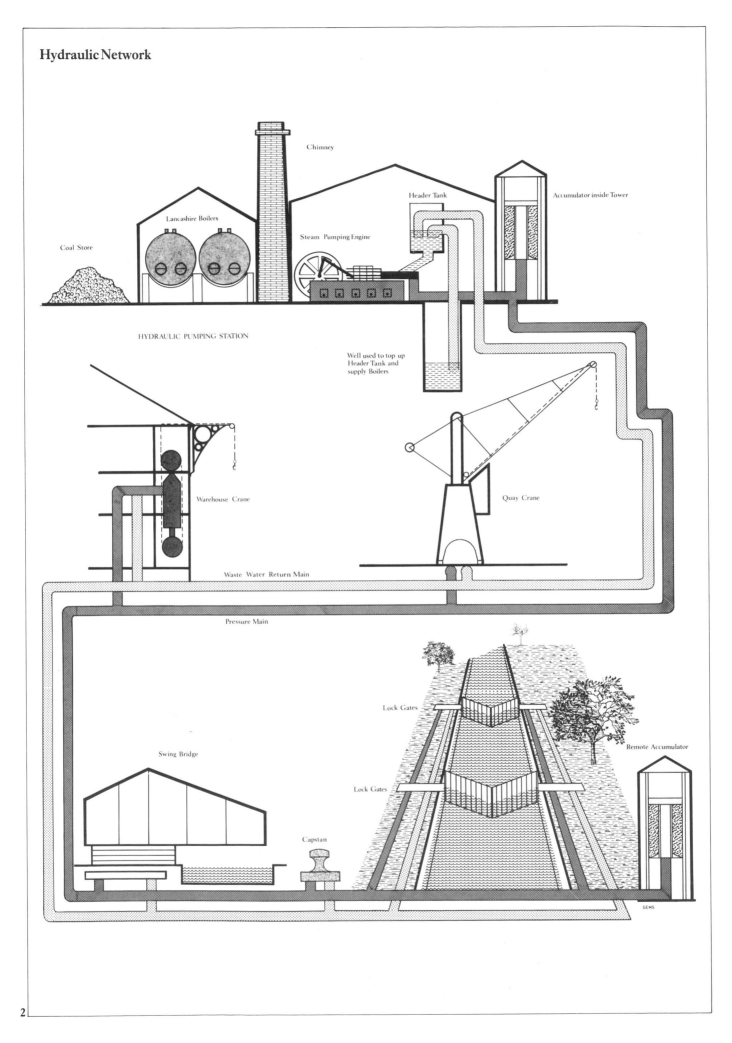

Chimney

Header Tank

Accumulator inside Tower

Lancashire Boilers

Steam Pumping Engine

Coal Store

HYDRAULIC PUMPING STATION

Well used to top up
Header Tank and
supply Boilers

Warehouse Crane

Quay Crane

Waste Water Return Main

Pressure Main

Lock Gates

Swing Bridge

Lock Gates

Remote Accumulator

Capstan

GEMS

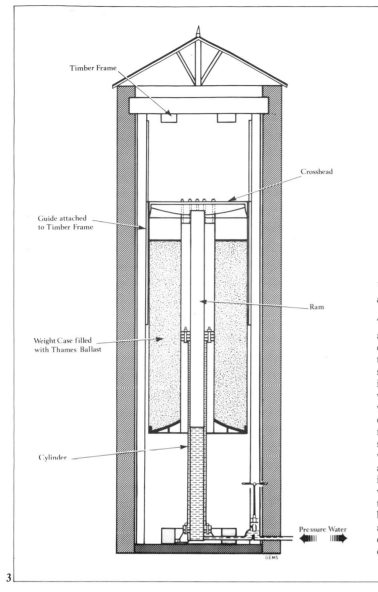

2   *Typical hydraulic network.*
(Gloria E M Shayler)

3   *Weight-loaded hydraulic*
accumulator. (Gloria E M Shayler)

Timber Frame

Crosshead

Guide attached
to Timber Frame

Ram

Weight Case filled
with Thames Ballast

Cylinder

Pressure Water

GEMS

3

Weight-loaded hydraulic accumulator

The weight-loaded hydraulic accumulator consists of a vertical cylinder and ram connected to the hydraulic main. The ram supports a crosshead from which is suspended a weight-case of wrought iron boiler plate filled with Thames ballast. The ram, crosshead and weight case can move up and down the tower, supported by guides. Pumping water into the network causes the accumulator to rise to the top of its stroke whilst using power to work a crane, for example, causes the weight to fall. At the top and bottom of its stroke the accumulator causes trips to close or open the throttle valve of the engine as appropriate.

through the entirely independent work of William Armstrong, a Newcastle solicitor, in the 1840s.[2] Armstrong first produced a robust crane which he demonstrated on the Newcastle Town Quay in 1846 using water from the local supply as his source of power. Although interest in his cranes, and other machinery which he devised, was widespread the inadequacy of many town water supplies often precluded its adoption and prompted Armstrong to develop the hydraulic power network with water pumped by steam engine. Central to this development was the weight-loaded hydraulic accumulator, a device which combined the functions of artificial head, pressure regulator and power reservoir. With it pressures well in excess of any town water supply (600-700 psi as opposed to 40-70 psi) could be achieved resulting in economies of water usage. In this form, with steam pumping engines, accumulators, a network of cast-iron mains and a variety of machines to operate, hydraulic power took on the roll of power distribution normally associated with electricity today.

The railway companies soon adopted hydraulic power, perhaps encouraged by the success of installations in the North-East,

perhaps by Brunel's ready acceptance of the new machinery for Paddington Goods Depot. Those docks, often railway owned, which handled coal were soon using hydraulic power to the full but where general cargoes were the norm only London, and, to a lesser extent, Liverpool introduced it before the 1870s. Even at Liverpool where the docks were administered by one body, the spread of hydraulic power was very much slower than on the north bank of the Thames where competition between dock companies fostered diverse schemes to cut costs.[3]

As can be seen in Table 1, all existing docks north of the Thames were using some hydraulic power by 1857; at new docks it was used extensively from the opening of the dock. The Surrey Commercial Docks were much later in adopting hydraulic power, in common with non-coal docks elsewhere. Perhaps the opening of the Millwall Dock, which catered for a similar trade in timber and grain, provided the necessary catalyst.

Both Poplar Docks and the Regent's Canal Dock were heavily involved in the seaborne coal trade which, in the early 1850s, was under threat of strong competition from the newly

F

161

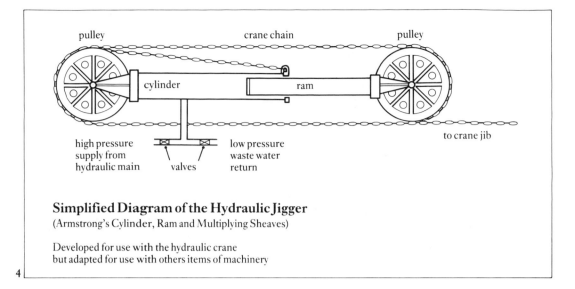

pulley   crane chain   pulley

cylinder   ram

to crane jib

high pressure
supply from
hydraulic main   valves
low pressure
waste water
return

Simplified Diagram of the Hydraulic Jigger
(Armstrong's Cylinder, Ram and Multiplying Sheaves)

Developed for use with the hydraulic crane
but adapted for use with others items of machinery

4

Table 1

Dock	Date of First use of hydraulic power	Nature of first hydraulic machinery
Poplar Dock (NLR)	1852	Coal Derricks, new dock
Regent's Canal Dock	1853	Coal Derricks, new jetty at existing dock
London Docks	1853	Cranes in a new warehouse at Eastern Dock
St Katharine Docks	1854	Cranes in existing warehouses
Victoria Dock	1855	Large scale applications at new dock
West India Dock	1855	Cranes at Import Dock
East India Dock	1857	Cranes
Millwall Dock	1868	Large scale applications at new dock
Surrey Commercial Docks	1872	Hoists, etc at new grain warehouse
Royal Albert Dock	1880	Large scale applications at new dock
Poplar Dock (Midland Railway)	1882	Various applications at new dock
Tilbury Docks	1886	Large scale applications at new dock
King George V Dock	1921	Entrance Lock machinery and a swing bridge only. Cranes and other machinery-electric

built Great Northern Railway and responded by mechanising discharging facilities and by introducing iron-hulled steam colliers like the screw-driven 'John Bowes' which first docked at Poplar in August 1852. Both docks purchased hydraulic coal derricks from Armstrong. The largest of the coal merchants, William Cory and Sons, installed their own hydraulic network in Victoria Dock in 1857 to operate eight hydraulic coal derricks at a cost of £15,000. A few years later the same firm began using the "Atlas", a 250 feet (76.2 metre) long floating platform with its own hydraulic network and six coal derricks each capable of handling 60 tons (60.96 tonnes) per hour. It was moored in Bugsby's Reach and could deal with two colliers simultaneously. Its success encouraged Cory's to purchase a second platform, 'Atlas II', from Elswick Works in the late 1860s.[4]

In early 1853 the London Dock Company

5

announced the completion of a new warehouse on the south side of the Eastern Dock. Its hydraulic cranes formed the basis of the first of three networks at these docks where three separate pumping stations were bult. The St Katharine Dock network followed a year later with a pumping station on the east side of the entrance lock, destined to be re-equipped in the 1890s to serve a combined London and St Katharine Dock system. This required alteration to much of the London Dock's networks which had previously worked at two different pressures. The enlarged system also took in the East Smithfield railway goods depôt which the Dock·Company leased from the Great Eastern Railway. Problems blamed on the ancient pipework around the Eastern Dock could only be solved by supplementing the supply from the London Hydraulic Power Company.

The East and West India Dock Company introduced hydraulic cranes to its docks in the mid-1850s, dealing first with the West India Import Dock. With a pumping station at the western end and five remote accumulators arranged around the dock this was the largest of the early networks. A smaller pumping station was built next to the Junction Dock, probably in connection with the introduction of hydraulic lock gate machinery. The two networks were combined so that each had a standby. Eventually a third pumping station, at the south west corner of the South Dock, enabled the small Junction Dock station to be closed. The opening of the Victoria Dock in 1855

showed how effective hydraulic power could be. G P Bidder claimed that the entrance lock machinery enabled a saving of forty men to be made.[5]. It was economic considerations like this which encouraged Dock Companies to commit heavy capital outlay on their hydraulic power networks. Thus the East and West India Dock Company reported to its shareholders ". . . . A considerable reduction . . . . has lately taken place in the branch of expenditure connected with labour, and the ordinary facilities in this respect will be further augmented by the employment of hydraulic machinery . . . .".[6]
—But it was not always possible to save money by installing hydraulic power. The same Company decided against its use at the Crutched Friars, Billiter Street and Fenchurch Street warehouses after receiving Armstrong's tender and comparing costs with the manual methods then employed.

With the success of hydraulic power in the docks it is not surprising that there were moves to extend its use to riverside wharves. When Beal's Wharf was rebuilt after a fire in 1856 hydraulic cranes were fitted, powered by two six-horse power horizontal steam engines in the basement acting through an accumulator. Several other wharfingers followed this example and those wharves known to have had their own hydraulic supply are listed in Table 2. Small networks such as these can rarely achieve the economies afforded by a large network and soon there were moves to provide a common supply, a public hydraulic power network. On 20 March 1860 the London Hydraulic Power

5 *Regent's Canal Dock, Accumulator Tower of 1852. The first pumping station at the Regent's Canal Dock was behind the London and Blackwall Railway viaduct, to the left of the tower which contained a single accumulator. The chimney remains are out of sight behind the tower. (Tim Smith)*

163

Table 2

Riverside wharves known to have had their own hydraulic pumping stations prior to the advent of LHP.

Wharf	Date of installation	Source	
Beal's Wharf	1856	GL MS 14949	
Cotton's Wharf	1862	GL MS 14949	*Note 1*
St Katharine's Steam Wharf	1868	GL MS 14943/2	
London & Continental Steam Wharf	1868	GL MS 15627/14	*Note 1*
Willson's Wharf	1870	GL MS 14943/2	*Note 3*
Irongate Steam Wharf	1870	GL MS 14943/2	
King and Queen Granary	1870	GL MS 14943/2	
Hermitage Steam Wharf	1871	GL MS 14943/3	*Note 4*
Free Trade Wharf (Upper)	1871	GL MS 14943/3	
Gun and Shot Wharf	1872	GL MS 14943/3	*Note 3*
Middleton & St Bride's Wharf	1873	GL MS 14943/4	
Hay's Wharf	1874	GL MS 15627/33	*Note 2*
Griffin's Wharf	1874	GL MS 14943/4	*Note 3*
Red Lion Wharf	1875	GL MS 14943/5	
Thames Tunnel Wharf	1877	GL MS 14943/6	
Ferry Wharf Wapping	1879	GL MS 14943/8	

Note 1   Date of earliest reference.

Note 2   On this plan the engine and boilers at Beal's Wharf are not shown, but the accumulator is shown, presumably indicating that it was, by 1874, served from Hay's Wharf.

Note 3   Possibly only Willson's Wharf had a pumping station. All three wharves were interconnected with hydraulic pipework.

Note 4   This could have been the second pumping station at this wharf. In 1873 an old engine house was converted into a waiting room for passengers but a hydraulic accumulator was retained in the corner of the room.

Sources: Guildhall Library (GL). Surveyors' Reports of Wharves and Warehouses Committee and various assorted plans.

Company Ltd was registered with a nominal capital of £100,000 and the objective of supplying water under pressure as a motive power to machinery.[7] For whatever reasons no more is heard of it and a second attempt was made ten years later with the setting up of the Wharves and Warehouses Steam Power and Hydraulic Pressure Company Ltd. Again little was achieved until E B Ellington revived its powers, obtained under an Act of 1871.[8] The first pumping station was built at Falcon Wharf, Bankside, in 1883 and St Mary Overy's Wharf became the first customer of the fledgling network. The following year the company's name was changed, by Act of Parliament, to the more familiar London Hydraulic Power Company (LHP).[9]

During the long period of gestation of a public network much had happened on the riverside wharves with many finding alternative means of powering cranes and other machinery. A popular choice was the gas fired boiler developed by Arthur Jackson and manufactured by Thomes Middleton & Co of Loman Street, Southwark. Fire regulations for the use of these boilers were less stringent than for coal or coke fired boilers. Unlike the latter which had to be placed in vaults, gas fired boilers were allowed to be kept in corrugated iron sheds attached to the outside of a building, often at a high level. They were, therefore, suitable for existing buildings as a minimum of building work was required. Networks of pipes leading from these boilers took steam to crane winches. At the newer wharves and warehouses, such as Oliver's Wharf on Wapping High Street, steam was generated in conventional boilers housed in basement vaults, often under a roadway. Occasionally larger central steam engines drove line shafting used to transmit power to cranes. By 1883 a few gas engines were also to be found. Wharfingers were encouraged to use the new public hydraulic supply by the lower insurance rates incurred if they gave up their own boilers. In 1900 about forty per cent of wharves were using hydraulic cranes, another forty per cent were using steam and the rest were divided between those using gas engines and those using electricity.

The London Hydraulic Power Company opened two large pumping stations in Dockland, one at Wapping in 1892, the other at Rotherhithe in 1902. Eventually LHP was supplying the London and St Katharine Docks, the Surrey Commercial Docks and the East India Docks, having taken over the pumping station there, and was providing a standby supply for the West India Docks and the Millwall Dock.

The many large railway goods depots in Dockland were all built after 1850 and all had independent hydraulic power networks from their inception. Some, like the docks, had specially built pumping stations, others utilised any available space under arches or in a warehouse to house pumping engines and accumulators. All used hydraulic cranes. Some had hydraulic wagon hoists to raise and lower trucks between street level and viaduct. The hazards of shunting in and around warehouses with locomotives had long been recognised and until the 1850s horse shunting was the norm in such locations. The hydraulic shunting capstan was used extensively in both railway goods depots and around Poplar Docks although at some places, like Mint Street (Midland Railway) Depot, horse shunting persisted for many years even though hydraulic power was available. On the quays of Poplar Docks (NLR) there were eight hydraulic tipplers which could tip up trucks to enable their contents to be loaded directly into vessels.

Both Bramah and Armstrong had recognised the need to power cranes and until the Second World War, cranes consumed well over half the total hydraulic 'pressure water' used in Dockland. Armstrong's original cranes had been pillar cranes and this type persisted throughout the nineteenth century for heavy lift duties on the quays.

6 Commercial Road Goods Depôt. (The drawings are not to scale. The building is about 60 ft long by 40 ft wide and the accumulator tower is about 50 ft high). (Gloria E M Shayler)

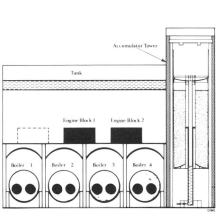

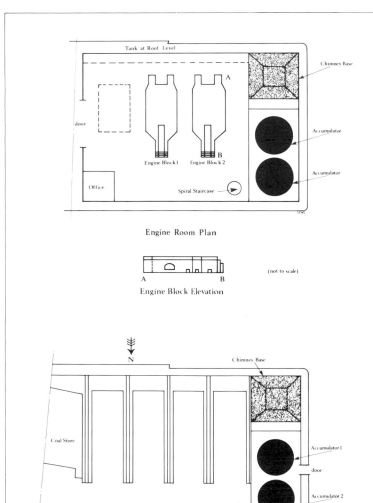

Engine Room Plan

Engine Block Elevation

(not to scale)

Section East-West

Boiler Room Plan

Commercial Road Goods Depôt — hydraulic pumping station

The Commercial Road Goods Depot was built by the London Tilbury and Southend Railway under an agreement with the East and West India Dock Company for handling traffic to and from Tilbury Docks. The goods depot, like the docks, was opened to traffic on 17 April 1886 but the huge warehouse was not completed until August 1887. The hydraulic pumping station was built on a corner site in Hooper Street and its machinery was supplied by Sir W G Armstrong Mitchell & Co, whose tender of £25,000 was lower than that of Messrs Tannett Walker & Co. Two steam pumping engines, probably of the type illustrated in Figure 7, were supplied together with two accumulators with rams of 18 ins (45.7 cms) diameter and 23′ 6″ (7.16 metres) stroke. The working pressure of the system was 700 psi (4.8 x 10⁶ Pa). There were four Lancashire boilers. The warehouse was demolished in 1975 but the pumping station building, minus engines and boilers but with the two accumulators in situ, survives. [See the article in London's Industrial Archaeology Number 2, 1980]

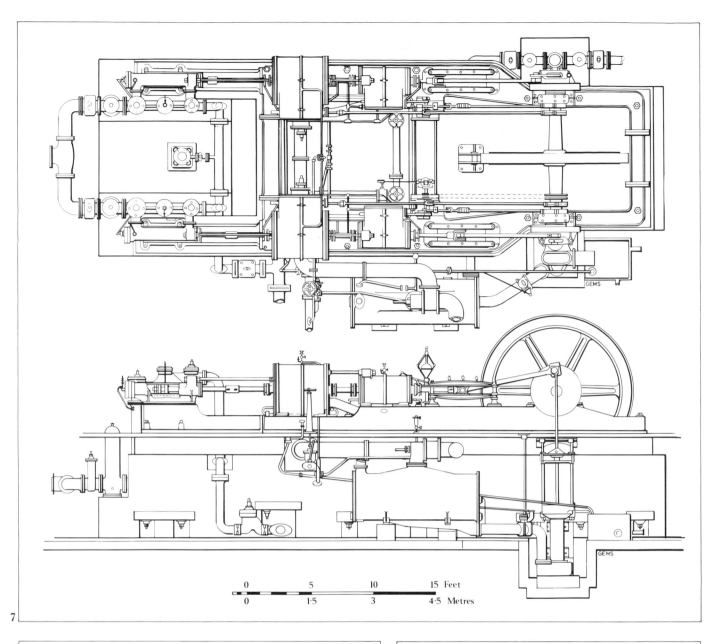

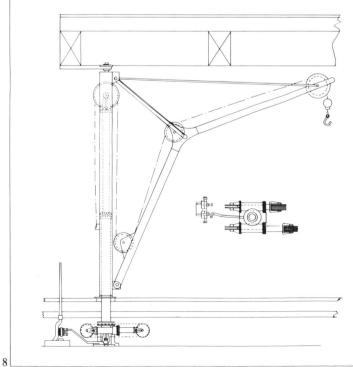

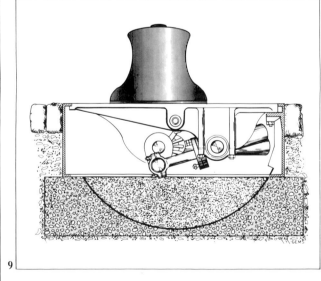

7 *Armstrong twin-tandem compound steam pumping engine of the mid 1880s. (Gloria E M Shayler)*

8 *Typical railway platform crane. (Gloria E M Shayler)*

9 *Armstrong turnover capstan used for shunting in railway goods depôts. (Gloria E M Shayler)*

10 *Development of the hydraulic quay crane. (Gloria E M Shayler)*

0   5   10   15 Feet
0   1·5   3   4·5 Metres

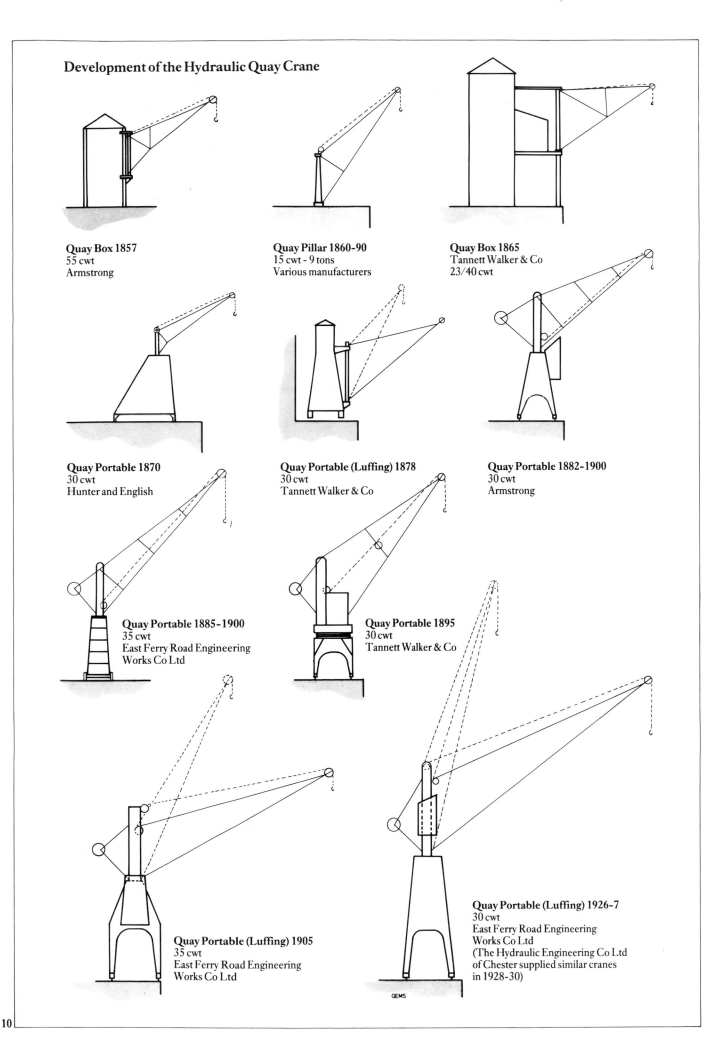

Development of the Hydraulic Quay Crane

Quay Box 1857
55 cwt
Armstrong

Quay Pillar 1860-90
15 cwt - 9 tons
Various manufacturers

Quay Box 1865
Tannett Walker & Co
23/40 cwt

Quay Portable 1870
30 cwt
Hunter and English

Quay Portable (Luffing) 1878
30 cwt
Tannett Walker & Co

Quay Portable 1882-1900
30 cwt
Armstrong

Quay Portable 1885-1900
35 cwt
East Ferry Road Engineering
Works Co Ltd

Quay Portable 1895
30 cwt
Tannett Walker & Co

Quay Portable (Luffing) 1905
35 cwt
East Ferry Road Engineering
Works Co Ltd

Quay Portable (Luffing) 1926-7
30 cwt
East Ferry Road Engineering
Works Co Ltd
(The Hydraulic Engineering Co Ltd
of Chester supplied similar cranes
in 1928-30)

GEMS

10

Until the 1870s the standard quay crane was the 'quay box'. Its timber box housing the hydraulic machinery afforded some protection against frost. The crane jib was mounted on the wooden wall or on the corner after the fashion of a wallcrane on a warehouse. The coal derrick was similar but the timber jib was pivotted to allow vertical movement (luffing) instead of horizontal (slewing). The fixed quay box was not an ideal type of crane to use at a time when ships were increasing in size and when the relative positions of holds were changing. What was needed was a crane that could be moved along the berth to wherever the hold was located.

In the 1860s it became the practice in the West India Docks for small portable steam donkey engines to be used for unloading ships in conjunction with pulley blocks attached to the masts and spars of ships. Because of the risk of fire a set of rigid rules for their use was enforced by the fire insurers. An alternative hydraulic device with no such disadvantages, the portable hydraulic jigger or hydraulic devil as it was known, was introduced by the London and St Katharine Docks Company. These required hydrants to be fixed at points around the dock so that the devils could be connected to the hydraulic main.

Experiments with moveable, or portable, quay cranes in the 1870s led to their widespread adoption during the following decade, the majority were of the non-luffing type, that is the jibs could not be moved vertically. Portable luffing cranes came into use on riverside wharves before the turn of the century but were not widely used in the docks until after the Royal Commission Report of 1902 was published.

At the St Katharine Docks, where the warehouses were built right up to the quays, precluding the use of the usual quay cranes, wallcranes, some of enormous size, were substituted. Many of the other dock warehouses were also equipped with wallcranes of a variety of types and sizes. Initially both hoisting and slewing jiggers were bolted horizontally to the floor beams of the warehouse. During the 1880s it became more usual to mount the hoisting jigger vertically against the inside wall, as E B Ellington did at St Mary Overy's Wharf in 1883. The final arrangement was to have all the jiggers mounted vertically. With this arrangement there was thought to be a risk that fire breaking out on one floor could spread more quickly to other floors so the jiggers were encased in a timber enclosure with access doors to allow maintenance. Sometimes brick enclosures were used and occasionally, as with very large cranes at Hays Wharf and at Free Trade Wharf, specially constructed brick or concrete shafts were employed.

The first hydraulic capstans were powered by standard Armstrong hydraulic engines with two or three oscillating cylinders acting on a crankshaft. In the second half of the nineteenth century Elswick Works produced nearly 4,000

*11 Early Armstrong moveable jigger as used on the quays. Later jiggers were adapted for use with wall cranes (see inset).
(Gloria E M Shayler)*

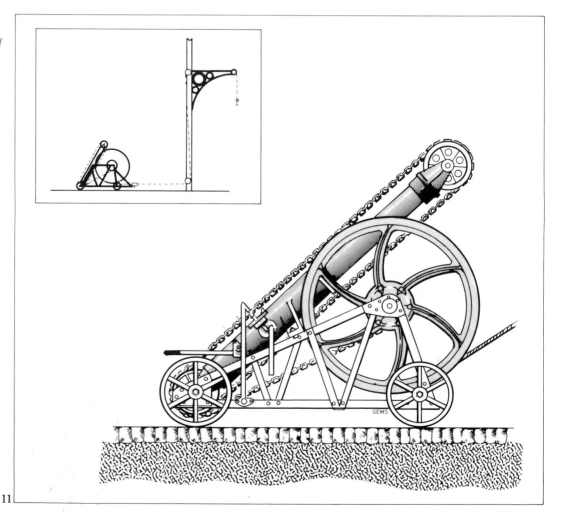

11

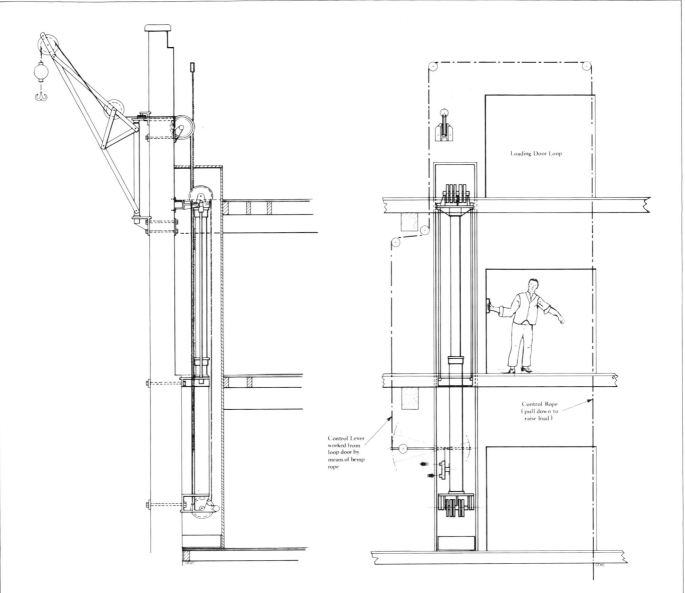

Loading Door Loop

Control Rope
(pull down to
raise load)

Control Lever
worked from
loop door by
means of hemp
rope

12

13

14

12 *Hydraulic wall crane for a warehouse. (Gloria E M Shayler)*

13 *A pair of wall-crane jiggers built by the Hydraulic Engineering Co of Chester. Note the guides to prevent the ram from turning about its axis. (Malcolm Tucker)*

14 *Ellington jiggers at St Mary Overy's Wharf. Note the two small slewing cylinders placed horizontally above the main jiggers and also the timber frame of the fire-prevention enclosure. (Tim Smith)*

15

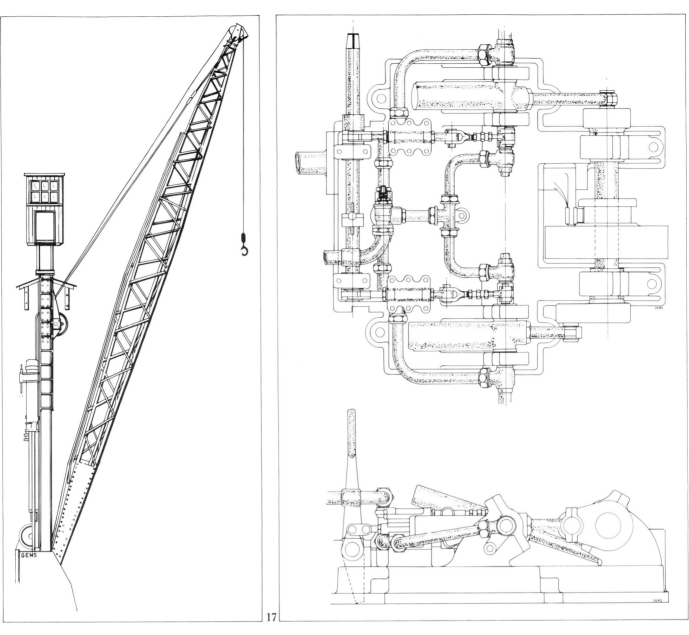

16

17

of these engines which were used for many purposes. Even after more compact units had been designed, such as those used with the Armstrong capstan which had three cylinders mounted underneath and operating directly on the capstan spindle, capstans continued to be produced to the earlier design. Other manufacturers supplied alternative designs and several examples could be found in Dockland.

There was a surprising variety of other types of hydraulic machinery, ranging from warehouse equipment such as grain elevators and conveyors, drainage pumps, presses, tea-bulking machines and even a tin sampling machine to sluice gates, lock-gate machines and moveable bridges. At the Victoria Dock there was a special hydraulic ship lift used to place vessels onto pontoons for repair. Manufacturers of hydraulic machinery included, besides Armstrong's, the local East Ferry Road Engineering Works Company Ltd, Tannet Walker and Henry Berry of Leeds, Glenfield and Kennedy of Kilmarnock, Carrick and Wardale of Gateshead and Cowans and Sheldon of Carlisle. The Hydraulic

Engineering Company of Chester supplied much equipment to LHP and its customers. The LHP engineer, E B Ellington, was also General Manager of the Hydraulic Engineering Co.

The swing bridges carrying Dockland roads over entrance locks and passages probably affected the lives of the populace at large more than any other piece of dock machinery, creating traffic jams and bottlenecks at inconvenient times while they were swung to allow a ship to pass. Three nineteenth century swing bridges survive, carrying Prestons Road over the Blackwall Entrance to the West India Docks (1894), Connaught Road over the passage between the Royal Victoria and Royal Albert Docks (1880) and Woolwich Manor Way across the passage connecting the Royal Albert with the basin at Gallions (1880). In addition, the hydraulic machinery used to swing the bridge which carried Redriffe Road over the cut between Greenland and Russia Docks has been preserved in situ. All four bridges used machinery supplied by Armstrong's Elswick Works at Newcastle. The Connaught Road

15 A variety of quay cranes on a jetty at Wapping. The second from the right is a hydraulic crane probably dating from the 1880s. Three others appear to be rebuilt from hydraulic cranes, whilst the fifth was built as an electric crane. (Malcolm Tucker)

16 Riverside crane at Rotherhithe built by the East Ferry Road Engineering Works Co Ltd (1930). (Gloria E M Shayler)

17 Two cylinder hydraulic engine for the Regent's Canal Dock. (Gloria E M Shayler)

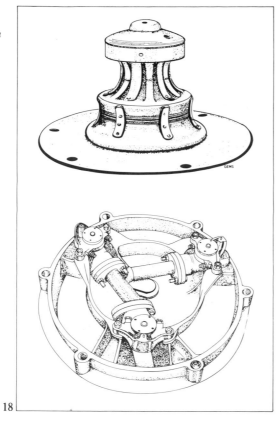

18

bridge has its own hydraulic system and its own pumping station, possibly to give security of supply as it used to carry the GE railway line to North Woolwich before the tunnel was built and main line goods trains after that.

There are remarkably few other pieces of nineteenth century hydraulic machinery surviving considering the large numbers that were produced. A hydraulic devil has been preserved by the Science Museum and a few wall-crane jiggers are in the Museum of London store. The machinery, including sluice gates, lock-gate mechanisms and several capstans, dating from the 1890s at the Blackwall Entrance and the Greenland Entrance locks is worthy of preservation. A few accumulators survive and, at Tower Bridge, the magnificent Armstrong steam pumping engines have been preserved and are open to view.

Survival of nineteenth century buildings associated with hydraulic power has been better and together they provide a rich heritage, a three dimensional archive of great value to future historians and industrial archaeologists. Fortunately many are listed buildings and it is to be hoped that this will ensure their continued survival. Of special interest is the accumulator tower at Regent's Canal Dock, once part of the

19

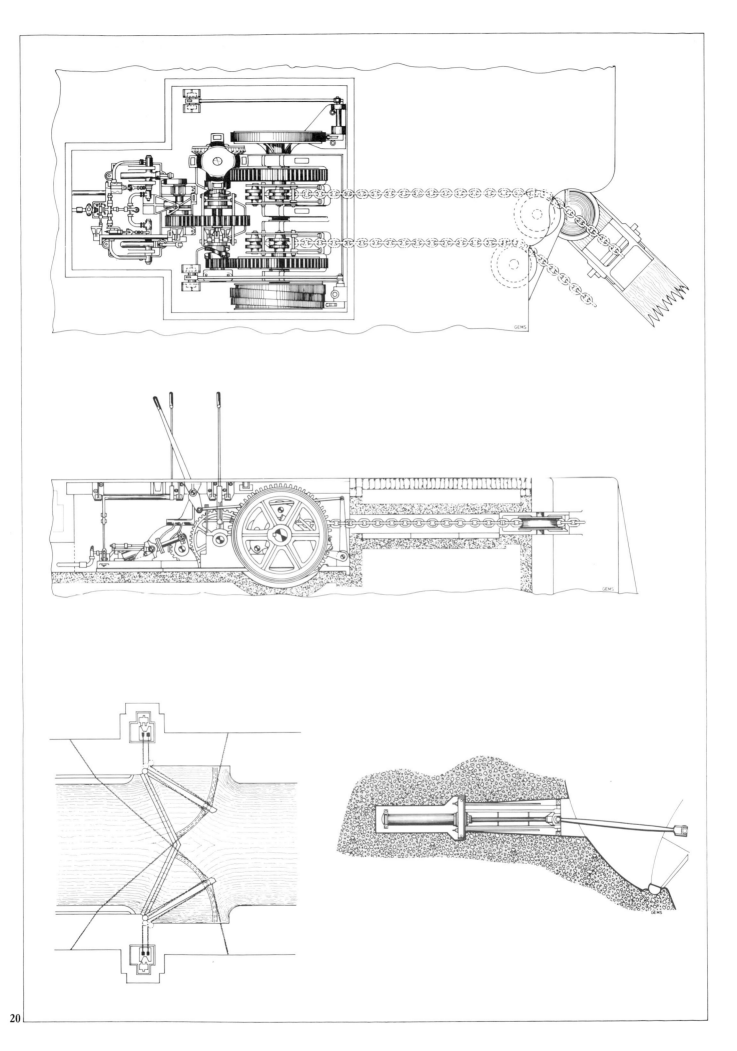

21 Preserved machinery of the hydraulic swingbridge in Redriff Road, Surrey Commercial Docks. (Malcolm Tucker)

21

22 Greenland Dock entrance lock showing direct coupling of the gate to the hydraulic cylinder and piston, an arrangement developed in the 1890s and first used at Barry Docks in South Wales. (Tim Smith)

23 East India Docks Hydraulic Pumping Station. Compare the architectural style with that of the later pumping station in the next photograph. (Tim Smith)

22

23

original pumping station there and thought to be the oldest surviving accumulator tower in the world, the pumping station of the now demolished Commercial Road Goods Depôt in Hooper Square, which, in its present state offers a great deal to the industrial archaeologist, and the superb Wapping pumping station of the London Hydraulic Power Company. The architectural treatment of the early buildings on East India Dock Wall Road and beside the Hermitage entrance lock contrast with the plainer, but no less attractive, Midland Railway Poplar Dock Pumping Station in Duthie Street. The museum at Tower Bridge provides an insight into the workings of hydraulic power but is quite rightly devoted more to the operation of the bridge. With the considerable importance that hydraulic power had in Dockland there ought to be an interpretive centre where future generations could learn how water once took on the role of power distribution.

24

24 *Poplar Dock (Midland Railway) Hydraulic Pumping Station, built 1882. Like most pumping stations it has lost its chimney. The accumulator tower housed two accumulators of 18 ins diameter by 20 ft stroke supplied by Sir W G Armstrong & Co. (Tim Smith)*

25 *Poplar Docks (North London Railway) Accumulator Tower. One of two remote accumulators on this system, the accumulators were 17 ins diameter by 17 ft stroke and were loaded to about 80 tons. (Tim Smith)*

25

Notes

1   Bramah's letter of 10 November 1802 to Robert Mallet is quoted by Mallet in discussion of Armstrong's paper "On the transmission of power by water pressure . . ." in Min Proc I Mech E, 1868, p 40.

2   Sir William George Armstrong, Baron Armstrong of Cragside, born 26 November 1810, died 27 December 1900.

3   Ritchie-Noakes, *Liverpool's Historic Waterfront*, HMSO, 1984, pp 121-128.

4   International Exhibition 1862, *Illustrated Catalogue of the Industrial Department*, vol II, pp 10-11.
Smith, Raymond, *Sea Coal for London*, 1961. The original Atlas was built as a floating platform for raising wrecks by the Thames Iron Shipbuilding Company in 1859.

5   Kingsbury, W J, *Victoria Docks*, Min Proc ICE Vol XVIII, 1858-9, (in discussion).

6   *The Times*, 13 January 1855, p 5.

7   Parliamentary Papers 1862, Vol 55. Returns relating to joint stock companies, etc 1 August 1861.

8   34 and 35 Vict Cap 121 (RA 13 July 1871).

9   47 and 48 Vict Cap 72 (RA 23 July 1884).

Short Bibliography

Capper, Charles
The Port and Trade of London, 1862 (Capper was manager of Victoria Dock)

Brace, Harold W
"History of Seed Crushing in Great Britain"

Jordan's Particulars of Docks, Warehouses, etc on the Thames, 1904

Brandwood, James
Reports on Docks 1858 (Reports relating to fire precautions)

London and India Docks Joint Committee
Guide for the use of visitors to the docks and warehouses 1897

Guide for the use of visitors to the docks and warehouses 1905

Guide for the use of visitors, *(East and West India Dock Co)*, to the docks and warehouses 1883

International Exhibition 1862
Illustrated Catalogue of the Industrial Department Volume 2, page 9. (Ship lift at Victoria Dock and Atlas Floating Crane Derrick platform).

Smith, Raymond
Sea coal for London.
Parliamentary Papers, 1857 Session 2 Volume XII.
Report from the Select Committee of the House of Lords on the Coal Shippers Acts.

Fraser-Stephen, Elspet
Two Centuries in the London Coal Trade: The Story of Charringtons

Sources and Acknowledgements

A fuller account of the history of hydraulic power in the Port of London is being prepared and a large number of sources have been consulted including material in the PLA Archives, the Wharves and Warehouses Committee Minutes and Surveyors Reports at the Guildhall Library, and the Vickers-Armstrong Records at the Tyne & Wear County Archives in Newcastle. Many GLIAS members and others have helped but Bet Parker must be singled our for her sterling work at the Guildhall Library.

Some personal reflections on London's lighterage industry

John Jupp

This is an article based on a thirty-thousand word interview of John Jupp by Chris Ellmers, as part of the Museum of London's Docklands Oral History Recording Project.

I was born in Ilford, Essex, in 1934, the son of a master plumber. I had always had a keen interest in the river which, I suppose, had commenced with my father taking me on trips across the Thames on the Woolwich Ferry. My father also took me to the King George V Dock, in August 1939, to see the new Mauretania docking after her first round Atlantic crossing. When I was young, I also had a strong desire to go to sea as an engineer, but, for certain reasons, I was not able to do this. I knew people that worked afloat, however, and, through a friend of my father, it became possible for me to enter the London lighterage industry at a period when labour was in short supply.

To meet the requirements of the Port of London Authority, for the movement of goods and passengers within the Port, a person was required to become a Licenced Waterman and Lighterman. In order to do this, one needed to be apprenticed to a Freeman of the Company of Watermen and Lightermen. Due to the raising of the school leaving age to fifteen years, the apprenticeship period had been reduced from seven years to six years, which still meant that you came out of your time at twenty-one. The person that I was apprenticed to happened to be employed by the Thames Steam Tug and Lighterage Company, who gave me a 'start' in August 1949.

The first job that I had was in the Company's City Office at 8, Lloyds Avenue. I was employed on general duties — on occasions I made the tea, but the main requirement of a boy was that he would run papers to shipping companies, to the PLA Headquarters and the Custom House. In other words, he would familiarize himself with practices which would become current during his career in the lighterage industry. I would also go down to the Surrey Docks each morning, at about eleven o'clock, taking papers to the Company's foreman. There was another requirement to go down to the Company's principal depôt at Millwall, on the Isle of Dogs, where it had its tug moorings, carrying the tug captains' orders for their following day's work.

Soon after that, I went to work at Millwall as a boat-boy, working around the moorings in a skiff and then I was assigned to become a deck-boy on one of the big river tugs. The tugs in those days worked a sixteen hour shift, from six am until ten pm, the crews having the following watch off. Tug crews worked six days a week, Monday to Saturday. In order to be at Millwall at six am I had to be up at half-past-four and travel there as best I could. You finished at ten pm and, hopefully, you came ashore in time to get the last bus off the Isle of Dogs. The time of starting could vary, though, to meet the tidal requirement and the longest shift operation was one of twenty-four hours, where the crew started at six o'clock one morning and came off shift at six o'clock the following morning. There were also twelve hour boats, some of which had three crews so that they could work continuously and there were, indeed, eight hour, or day, boats as well.

The first tug I served in was the 'Wortha', built by J I Thornycroft at Woolston Yard, Southampton, in 1929. She was quite large for her time and one of the first large cold start diesel tugs to see service in the London lighterage industry. The crew consisted of five persons — the skipper, mate, an engineer, a greaser and a deckhand. Mates, then, very often didn't become skippers until well into their fifties because the age of retirement had not been fixed. Many skippers that I knew didn't retire until they were well into their early seventies.

As a deckboy you were a general 'factotum'. The vessel that I was on was lit by paraffin lamps, so the first thing you had to do was get your lamps lit and if it was a winter morning, and the navigation lamps were used, they had to be lit straightaway so there was no delay in the tug getting underway. The next job was to get the galley fire lit and a kettle boiling for tea. Once the tug was underway you were required on deck to give ropes to lightermen. One of the

1 One of John Jupp's earliest memories of the Port is of the new Cunard-White Star Liner 'SS Mauretania' entering the King George V Dock, in August 1939, after her maiden round crossing of the Atlantic. (Museum of London)

2 John Jupp, (left), and fellow crew members on board Thames Steam Tug's motor tug 'Wortha' in 1950. (John Jupp)

other essential things you had to do, as you came alongside, was to make sure you were first in with the fender. You had to keep your eyes about you all the time, especially in darkness.

Skippers carried an awful lot of responsibility, as did the mates. They certainly didn't have the facilities and comforts that they have today — tugs at that time had open wheelhouses, no radio-telephones, or radar, and you didn't have the Thames Navigation Service to assist you. There was a great dependence upon the telephone — tugs would come alongside pierheads, or any convenient place where it was known there was a public telephone, and the mate, or skipper, would go ashore to report back to the Tug Superintendent at the City Office, to receive any fresh orders.

When I started at Millwall we often worked down to Tilbury 'calling at all stations' — which meant that you would have a tow which might vary — you might pick up some craft going short distances and then, perhaps, half-a-dozen barges for Tilbury or Northfleet. Thames Steam Tug's work was restricted to the movement of their own craft. Being one of the largest companies, they carried virtually every type of traffic — whether it was fine goods, in the form of foodstuffs, sugar or flour, etc, or certain liquefied commodities like oil and bitumen — and they operated over a wide area — from the oil refineries at Coryton and Shellhaven, right up as far as Brentford and Isleworth.

One of the things that tended to happen, to somebody like myself from outside the industry, was that you had some rather romantic ideas

about life on the river. The romanticism, however, was soon lost with the harsh realities of a winter's night, on a deck with freezing ropes, freezing water and the fact that you were there to do a job as quickly and as efficiently as possible and, hopefully, at the end of the shift, get home as soon as you could. These were the driving forces, and the mate was always there to push the job along, but he certainly did go out of his way to show me what he thought necessary for me to absorb as an apprentice.

I came out of tugs around 1950, during my initial two years as an unlicensed apprentice. My first experience of actually working craft was in the Upper and Lower Pool, mainly along the shores from London Bridge to Tower Bridge and down as far as Greenwich. This was working with Freemen, known as 'bosuns', who were resident to a group of wharves or a stretch of the riverside. Like most men, they were not permanent employees of the Company — the only permanent employees were tug captains and mates, what they called 'weekly men'. The bulk of the men were, if you like, on hire from the National Dock Labour Board, although the practice was that they would follow one company for lengthy periods.

So I worked with individuals who had the local knowledge. The requirements for an apprentice were many and various and you could find yourself doing all sorts of jobs — assisting Freemen in the movement of craft over short distances, working alongside ships, preparing craft for loading and discharging, mooring and all the duties that were part and parcel of an apprentice learning his job. Certain industrial agreements imposed limits on apprentices — such as restrictions on the number of hours and night-time work — and ensured that they were not used as cheap labour.

Work over short distances could be undertaken manually, without a tow, by resorting to the use of oars. These were twenty-six feet long and this method, which went back hundreds of years, was known in the trade as 'driving'. Certain lighterage companies, like E W Taylor of Limehouse, did not own their own tugs, and we had an arrangement with them whereby our apprentices could gain experience in 'driving' with their Freeman, from say Mark Brown's Wharf to Dunbar Wharf. I also had the opportunity to drive under oars in craft of my own Company and I can think of at least three or four occasions when they were fairly lengthy drives, from the Pool up to Brentford Dock.

The principle reason that I was under oars with craft was to ensure that I could acquire sufficient experience of that operation to answer questions on applying for my Apprentice's Licence, at the end of my first two years of apprenticeship. This was an oral examination conducted by the Examining Committee of the Court of the Company of Watermen and Lightermen, who examined on behalf of the Port of London Authority. During these initial years, I also benefited greatly from a newly introduced day-release scheme — in the hands of Ted Hunt, the present Queen's Bargemaster — which taught apprentices the fundamentals of lighterage. At the end of the six year period of apprenticeship, you again appeared before the Examining Committee and if, after asking exhaustive questions, they felt you were competent you would be granted your full Watermen's and Lightermen's Licence. That was again on behalf of the Port of London Authority, but at the same time they admitted you to the Company of Watermen and Lightermen.

In the early 1950s there were somewhere in the region of 6,000 craft on the river, backed up by a fleet of 330-350 tugs. Thames Steam Tug had around 600 craft, five very large river tugs and a number of smaller tugs — quite a comprehensive fleet. As new tonnage became

3 Thames lightermen driving barges, under oars, in 1954. This photograph was taken in Limehouse Reach, looking towards Millwall. (Museum of London)

available, in the 1950s, some companies went for some very large units, but Thames Steam Tug went for a smaller optimum, of around the 220 ton carrying mark, with their big hatch craft. Some of the largest craft in the industry, up to 400 tons carrying capacity, had been introduced prior to the war, for the carriage of sugar, and they were subsequently exceeded in size and by the 1970s craft of six or eight hundred and even a thousand tons were not unknown. As a result the lighterage industry became less manpower intensive and more capital intensive. With larger craft coming in you could use fewer craft, but still carry large tonnages. At the other extreme of craft size, most companies retained 'punts' that could only carry 25-35 tons.

Besides tank craft, in which some companies like Union Lighterage specialised, the London lighterage industry was divided into the 'Legal Quay Trade' — which meant dry goods, fine goods, foodstuffs, and general cargoes — and the 'Rough Goods Trade' — which included the carriage of coal, ballast and household refuse. Legal Quay craft were often 'Customs Approved' craft, with hatches capable of being locked securely in position by the use of hatch bars. Lightermen had to be familiar with a large variety of paperwork — you had to know about Customs' Entries, about Cargo Manifests and about Bills of Lading. You had to know how to process the various documents, who to lodge them with, and how to liaise with Customs so as to avoid delay to the lighterage operator and his customer, the merchant.

London had always been regarded as a lighterage port and in the 1950s its lighterage facility was a form of secondary transit system. Road haulage wasn't as extensive in the 1950s, or even the 1960s, as it was to become and, although most of the docks were served by railways, there were still certain parts of the docks not accessible by rail. Working in conjunction with other transport modes, lighterage provided flexibility for port operations.

That is not to say that there were not some difficult working areas. I, for one, found that the Hay's Wharf Group of wharves, on the south shore between London Bridge and Tower Bridge, could be difficult. One of the real problems was that, prior to decasualisation, all loading and discharging by registered portworkers — stevedores, dockers and tally clerks — was carried out under the piecework system. Any delay reduced the earning capacity of labour and the men were anxious to earn as much for a particular job as they possibly could, and they couldn't be blamed for this. Their real concern was to get the cargo out of a ship into craft, or onto the shore, as quickly as possible. The lighterman, on the other hand, unlike the stevedore and docker, would be concerned with getting the best possible 'stow' he could into his craft so that he could accommodate the allocated cargo and meet the requirement of correct freeboard.

In the 1950s major changes began to take place with the introduction of unit loads on board ships, and purpose built Roll-on/Roll-off ferries which could accommodate wheeled traffic. These were to have a profound effect on the short-sea trade and a lot of traffic, between Continental, Mediterranean and Scandinavian ports was ultimately displaced. Previously, that short-sea traffic, when carried by conventional vessels, was often discharged and loaded overside in London and carried to forward destinations by lighterage. The development of Roll-on/Roll-off facilities at ports like Felixstowe, Sheerness and Dover, lessened the demand for the conventional short-sea type vessel and, in so doing, also reduced the demand for lighterage facilities. Container ships and containerisation had a similar effect and even though containers could be carried in barges, they created stability problems and didn't fill the cargo carrying space of a barge to the full. Both these developments also reduced the efficiency of the up-river docks and warehouses generally, causing a decline in the number of places where lighters could actually trade.

In the late 1960s, as an individual, and also as a member of the Executive Council of the Watermen, Lightermen, Tugmen and Bargemen's Union, I became very interested in the concept of the Barge Carrying System, which utilized craft, with ready loaded cargoes, that could be carried in a mother ship across the oceans of the world. It was hoped that the introduction of Barge Carrying Systems would go some way towards countering the effects of Roll-on/Roll-off, containerisation and unit load vessels on the lighterage industry. The first operation to be introduced, in December 1969, was of the LASH (Lighter Aboard Ship) type. This was operated by Central Gulf Lines to a terminal at Sheerness. LASH craft were moved by tugs from the Medway to paper mills on Thameside, in the Northfleet area for instance, and ultimately they were going as far west as Brentford with pulp and other cargoes. The craft in the LASH system were 500 tons dead weight and subsequent systems, such as SEABEE (Sea Barge Express) were of 800 tons carrying capacity, a thousand tons dead weight. The SEABEE system was introduced by Lykes Line in December 1971, with a terminal at Gravesend and from there the units went right up to London.

The men engaged in the London lighterage industry were very versatile and adapted very quickly to these new developments. Unfortunately, however, it would appear that the Barge Carrying System was developed a little bit too late — being 'sandwiched' between the large bulk carrying vessels that were being introduced, and the pure container vessel. Although neither system now operates to London, they did employ quite a number of men and seemed to me to be very versatile.

Taking the impact of the various technologies that we have looked at — whether it be Roll-on/Roll-off, containerization, or even the Barge Carrying Systems themselves — the net

4 *A bustling scene in Royal Albert Dock, 1958, at the height of the prosperity of the London lighterage industry. Fleets of tugs towed steel lighters, loaded with cargoes, to and from the up-river docks and wharves. (Museum of London)*

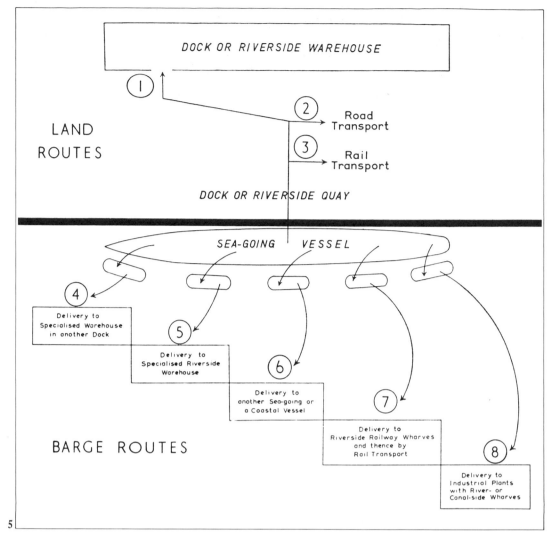

5 Schematic diagram showing the role played by lighterage in the Port of London. (James Bird)

DOCK OR RIVERSIDE WAREHOUSE

① ② Road Transport

③ Rail Transport

LAND ROUTES

DOCK OR RIVERSIDE QUAY

SEA-GOING VESSEL

④ Delivery to Specialised Warehouse in another Dock

⑤ Delivery to Specialised Riverside Warehouse

⑥ Delivery to another Sea-going or a Coastal Vessel

⑦ Delivery to Riverside Railway Wharves and thence by Rail Transport

⑧ Delivery to Industrial Plants with River- or Canal-side Wharves

BARGE ROUTES

5

6 In December, 1969, the world's first LASH ship, the 'Acadia Forest', began operating to Sheerness. One of the ship's 73 barges — each carrying up to 370 tons — can be seen in the water prior to being towed by the 'Knocker White' to buoys for removal to final destinations on the Thames. (Peter Coppock)

6

7

effect has been to see a considerable reduction in the demand for tonnage handled by the lighterage industry. The subsequent closure of all the up-river dock systems and most of the riverside wharves, for re-development, coupled with competition from road transport, and the pattern of distribution, has had profound consequences. Indeed, the industry has now been reduced to a shadow of its former self, in particular the Legal Quay side. The one major development to have happened within the last few years, has been the introduction of new types of craft for the handling of household refuse from up-river transfer stations to disposal points downstream, at Rainham and Pitsea.

In human terms, the results of these changes are clear — the Watermen, Lightermen, Tugmen and Bargemen's Union, in the late 1950s, had around 5,200-5,500 members. By 1971, when the Union merged with the Waterways Section of the Transport and General Workers' Union, the number had

fallen to around 1,800. Today, I would think that the actual number of registered lightermen in the Port of London is probably less than 225.

In my own case, I had continued to work with Thames Steam Tug and Lighterage Co until it was merged to form the Thames and General Lighterage Co in 1963. I then worked for the Thames and General until it ceased to trade, in December 1979, on takeover by the Ocean Transport and Trading Group. Not wishing to transfer to that group, I was returned to the National Dock Labour Board and re-allocated to train as a docker. I was subsequently employed at Tilbury Dock, at the West African Terminal, mainly in timber, logs and plywood. In February 1980, for purely personal reasons, I decided to leave the industry on severance.

The one thing that I shall always remember about my career in the lighterage industry is that it was a way of life and full of interesting and enterprising characters, and some would say that lightermen, at times, had 'more front than Woolworth's', but that's a different story!

7 One of the few areas where lighterage operations have expanded in recent years is in the field of waste disposal. In 1985 Cleanaway introduced these new fully-enclosed container barges to carry London's waste to Rainham for disposal. (Museum of London)

Postscript

R J M Carr

Introduction

This second edition of the Dockland History Survey has the addition of seventeen specific chapters by a wide variety of authors, covering aspects of Architecture, Civil Engineering, Social and Labour history, museum possibilities, cargo handling and lighterage, ships, industrial archaeology and transport. Nevertheless many subjects remain to be dealt with or have received at most only a passing mention. Many of the contributing authors could have written a whole book and it is appreciated that the work of the Docklands History Survey is by no means over. However the size and scope of this volume should make obvious the scale of the subject and what has been achieved so far.

Among the more obvious omissions that come to mind is river management and conservation. The Port consists of far more than the wet docks themselves. Between 1908 and 1925 the PLA carried out a massive dredging programme to create deep channels for large ships aligned to take the best advantage of tidal scour. These stretch from the Estuary to the entrance of the Royal Docks, and on a lesser scale the dredged channel continues to the Upper Pool. Scant mention has been made of this large-scale operation, the results of which lie unseen at all states of the tide. Again, the conservancy work of the PLA up-river is a major subject. Indeed, this mention of the higher reaches points up our almost total omission of that part of the Port above London Bridge. Brentford Dock and the up-river wharves have not been included, nor has the City with its numerous close connections with the Port. Lloyds Register of Shipping, the Baltic Exchange and the many shipping offices, receive no mention here.

Many other subjects have received little attention including cranes, cold storage, the wine and spirits trade, the former extensive coal trade, the bunkering of ships, port services such as victualling and ships' water supply and the disposal of rubbish. A chapter on pilotage would have been appropriate. Trinity House receives little attention, and the training of future deck officers has not been discussed. A history of the Schools of Navigation and Seamanship associated with the Thames would have been an interesting addition.

Industrial History

The industrial archaeology of Dockland is a gigantic subject and in the main is dealt with here by means of the gazetteer. Many a short entry could be expanded into a chapter or even a book without exhausting a fascinating topic. The Isle of Dogs had a dramatic industrial past which is worth detailed technical study. Among the major industries here most were connected with ironworking in some form and ship repairing or maritime related activities.

On the closure of the Thames shipbuilding yards from the mid 1860s[1] many of the facilities were made over to ship repair, which with the increasing tonnage of shipping operating from London became a most important Dockland industry. Many of London's dry docks were built in the late 1870s and continued in use till about 1980. The author was able to carry out a fair amount of field work at the very end of this period when the yards were grouped together and operated by River Thames Shiprepairs Ltd. A notable feature of the yards was the splendid survival of heavy machine tools such as plate bending rolls, shearer/punches, air-compressors and steam hammers, much Clydeside built and some dating from the nineteenth or early twentieth centuries.[2, 3] Few of these great machines now exist anywhere, even on the Clyde, but at least some recording was done which it is hoped will bear fruit in publications.

A history of marine steam engine building would make much mention of the Thames and chapters on Maudslay Sons and Field, The Rennies', John Penns and the Thames Ironworks could well have been included. Many important firms associated with the Dockland

1   *River Thames Shiprepairs, Royal Albert Dock, Blacksmiths' Shop, looking NW, May 1979. (R J M Carr)*

area deserve study including Stone Manganese, Merryweather & Sons and Brown Lennox and the pioneer engineering work carried out at Millwall by Fairbairn and Napier etc. is a rich field for the engineering historian. The whole history of British heavy engineering in the nineteenth century has a strong Thames-side flavour.

When we come to consider manufacturing industries the scope is enormous; with the import of numerous overseas products ranging from the basic to the exotic, Dockland was an obvious location for much of London's processing industries, even before the nineteenth century. Food processing and the Chemical industry loom large.

The Chemical Industry

Dockland has had a long experience of the chemical industry, often one associated with noxious fumes and pollution. At Deptford, the copperas beds were of importance before the eighteenth century. An account of them was written by Daniel Colwell and contributed to the Philosophical Transactions of the Royal Society in 1678.[4] Copperas (green vitriol $FeSO_4.7H_2O$) was made by the atmospheric oxidation and hydrolysis of iron pyrites and was important in London in the manufacture of ink and dyes.

Dockland can claim many industrial firsts. John Bennett Lawes set up a works at Deptford in 1841 which was to be the prototype for all future superphosphate plants,[5] later making use of coprolites from Cambridgeshire and Suffolk. Synthetic dyestuff manufacture in our area also had a respectable ancestry. Burt, Boulton and Haywood Ltd founded their Silvertown Works in 1848 and acquired Brook, Simpson and Spiller who were successors to W H Perkin, the originator of the industry. Perkin always wished it to be known that he considered the Silvertown Works the lineal descendant of the first synthetic dyestuffs factory.[6] In 1866 J B Lawes bought the Atlas Chemical Works, Millwall and commenced making citric and tartaric acids.[7]

The working of guano was a characteristic Thameside industry and soap works, tar and by-product plants, often associated with gas works, the manufacture of glue from bones, pigment manufacture for paints and the production of cattle feed are other typical examples of Dockland chemical industries, some of which still flourish. The manufacture of tailored fats for foodstuffs brings us to food processing.

Food Processing
Sugar refining was carried out in the early nineteenth century on a small scale at a number of sites but by the following century this was becoming concentrated in large industrial plants. The repacking of items such as sugar and dried fruit, tea bulking and blending, and spice grinding were often carried out in riverside warehouses and were very characteristic. Spice grinding is still carried on around St Saviour's Dock.

Other industries, after a pilot plant stage in London's Dockland, often moved to new sites in the provinces once the feasibility of the new industry had been established. This was very true of the chemical industry.

Gas and Electricity
With waterborne coal from North East England and the East Coast of Scotland and a plentiful supply of water from the river, Thameside is an obvious location for gas works and electric power stations. The manufacture of gas in London started in small centrally-located plants, but, as the gas companies grew, larger, more efficient works began to be established, many near the river. This process of aggrandizement culminated in the construction, from 1868, of the giant Beckton Gasworks on the north bank for the Gaslight and Coke Company. This was followed by the South Metropolitan Gas Company's East Greenwich Gasworks, whose construction started in 1881. The making of town gas ceased with the coming of natural North Sea gas in the 1960s, but the large number of gas works sites, many still used as holder stations, testifies to the importance of Dockland in the nineteenth and first half of the twentieth century. The re-use of these sites, often fraught with problems of contamination from carcinogenic by-products remains difficult.

A significant Dockland event was the setting up of the world's first central power station at Deptford by Sebastian de Ferranti in 1889.[8] He chose his site well. Not only is there still an active power station at Deptford but a large proportion of London's power-generating capacity was, until quite recently, in the Dockland area. Today, super-size power stations achieve great efficiency through economies of scale and London's relatively small up-river power stations have become redundant. However, even now, many of the large coal-fired power stations of South East England are situated on Lower Thames-side.

Civil Engineering
Civil Engineering has not been extensively dealt with and a chapter on the development of dock construction and the design and building of lock and dock walls is missing. The maintenance of dock water levels by pumping, (or impounding), is another topic where a history would be appropriate. The construction and maintenance of Thames crossings, bridges and tunnels, is another important story and an account of reinforced and pre-stressed concrete work in Dockland would have been a valuable contribution. Even a recent event like the contruction of the Thames Barrier and associated works might have been included. A serious modern study of the building of Victoria Dock has not appeared and would be well worth attempting. The engineering of this dock differed significantly from the work of Jessop, Rennie and Telford.

The River Police
Founded in 1798, thirty one years before the Metropolitan Police, the then Marine Police force had the task of patrolling the river in boats, originally rowing galleys, in an effort to reduce thefts from ships at anchor and cargoes awaiting dispatch at riverside wharves. Among those responsible for setting up the force were John Harriott, an Essex JP, and Patrick Colquhoun,[9] who managed to persuade the West India Merchants' Committee into providing initial funding. A Lumping Department was set up to register port workers regarded as honest. After a two year probationary period the Marine Police were deemed to be a success and were securely established.

In 1829 the Metropolitan Police was formed and ten years later the Marine Police became the Thames Division of the Metropolitan Police. Work continued much as before. From 1901-3 the first paraffin-engined patrol boats were introduced and by 1910 most patrols were in powered craft. In the Second World War, during heavy air raids, Thames Division crews gave sterling service ferrying trapped people to safety. After re-organization in 1978 the Division was operated in three sections — middle, upper and lower, with stations at Waterloo Pier, Shepperton and Wapping. The service continues with patrols over fifty-four miles of the Thames from Staines Bridge to Dartford Creek.

Notes

1   Pollard, S *The Decline of Shipbuilding on the Thames.*

2   For an account of machines of this type see Hume, J R, *Shipbuilding Machine Tools*, in Scottish Themes, Scottish Academic Press 1976.

3   A paper was published on the American air compressors, see Carr, R J M, *Ingersoll-Rand Imperial type 10 Air Compressors in London's Docklands.*

4   Campbell, W A *The Chemical Industry*, page 8.

5   Campbell, W A page 75.

6   Campbell, W A page 141.

7   Campbell, W A page 75.

8   Hennessey, R A S *The Electric Revolution*, page 74.

9   Colquhoun published a book in 1800, *A Treatise on the Commerce and Police of the River Thames.*

Biographical notes

George Adams

George Adams was a Thames lighterman from 1939 until 1955, apart from war service with the Royal Engineers in port working related companies, and seven months as national secretary to a youth movement. He was a stevedore from 1955 until becoming an instructor with the National Dock Labour Board in 1965. In 1975 he was appointed chief instructor responsible for administering the training of registered dockworkers in Scheme ports from Whitstable to Lowestoft. A member of the Chartered Institute of Transport and the Institute of Materials Handling, he has lectured part-time on port subjects at the Polytechnic of North London and other colleges. Author of *The Organisation of the Port Transport Industry*, he is now working as a docker at Tilbury.

Professor T C Barker MA (Oxon) PhD (Manchester) FRHS

Theo Barker is Professor Emeritus of Economic History in the University of London. Among his books is *A History of London Transport* (2 volumes) which he wrote jointly with Michael Robbins.

Vice Admiral Sir Patrick Bayly KBE CB DSC

Sir Patrick Bayly, after a full career in the Seaman branch of the Royal Navy, became Director of the Maritime Trust in 1970 when the Trust was only one year old. He has therefore been responsible for building up the Trust's fleet of historic ships and craft, now numbering 21 vessels.

Sir Patrick served in many parts of the world including a year in a China River gunboat and two years as Admiral President of the Royal Naval College, Greenwich. Here he first came into contact with the *Cutty Sark* of which he is now Chairman of the Ship Management Committee.

R J M Carr

Dr Robert Carr lectured at Bedford College, University of London from 1967 to 1978. From January 1980 he was appointed Survey Officer for the Dockland History Survey. He has had an interest in industrial archaeology and transport history for many years and compiled the gazetteer in the present volume. A Member of Council of the Association for Industrial Archaeology and a member of the General Purposes and Finance Committee and Council Member of the Newcomen Society, he also serves on the Council for British Archaeology and is a committee member of the Greater London Industrial Archaeology Society. He is Research Fellow in the Department of Civil Engineering, North East London Polytechnic and lectures in industrial archaeology at City University.

Paul Calvocoressi

Paul Calvocoressi studied history at Keele University and Architecture at Newcastle upon Tyne. He has been an officer of the Greater London Council's Historic Buildings Division since 1970. During these years he has dealt with conservation issues in the Dockland boroughs on both sides of the river.

Chris Ellmers

Chris Ellmers studied geography at Woolwich Polytechnic in the late 1960s, where the Riverside House Annexe offered uninterrupted views of shipping in the Thames and in the Royal Docks. He subsequently lectured in geography at both Thames and North East London Polytechnics. Since 1973 he has been employed at the Museum of London, where he now heads the Museum in Docklands Project. He lectures extensively on the Port and the industrial history of London and his work has featured in the press and on television.

Ivan S Greeves

Ivan Greeves joined John Mowlem in 1937 and worked as an Assistant Engineer in the Tunnelling Department on the extension of the Central London underground railway line from Bow Road to Leyton. The next years were spent on wartime construction including the breakwaters for the Mulberry Harbour.

In 1948 he took charge of the maintenance contract for the Port of London, employing 1,500 men in 1950. His association with the docks lasted for thirty years, during which time he had first hand experience of the many difficulties confronting engineers in the postwar rebuilding and expansion of the docks.

He was appointed a Director of Mowlem (Civil Engineering Limited) in 1962 and for sixteen years was in control of construction carried out in the Docks, River Thames and South East England. A chartered Civil Engineer for forty-four years, he has specialised in Dock and Maritime Engineering, and has been a Fellow of the Institution of Civil Engineers for the past thirty years.

Eve Hostettler

Eve Hostettler is a historian and teacher. Since 1980 she has worked for the Island History Project as part of a team engaged in research, recording and preserving the history of the Isle of Dogs.

Lord Howie of Troon

Currently general manager of Thomas Telford Ltd, the publishing arm of the Institution of Civil Engineers, he originally trained and practised as a civil engineer. From 1963 to 1970 he was Member of Parliament for Luton and held a number of posts in the Government Whips' Office before becoming vice-chairman of the Parliamentary Labour Party. Shortly after leaving Parliament, he became public affairs correspondent on the magazine *New Civil Engineer*, and continues to combine that post with his present position as general manager. In addition, Howie is trade union adviser to the Institution, and has published two short books on trade unionism with special reference to professional engineers and to the construction industry. He is a former president of the Association of Supervisory and Executive Engineers and is President of the Association for Educational and Training Technology, and is an adviser to the Council of Managerial and Professional Staffs. Lord Howie is now Pro-Chancellor of the City University.

Lord Howie was educated at Marr College, Troon and the Royal Technical College, Glasgow (now Strathclyde University). He holds a BSc and DipRTC in civil engineering and is a Fellow of the Institution of Civil Engineers and of the Royal Society of Arts. He is also a Member of the Societe des Ingenieurs et Scientifiques de France. Lord Howie was a member of the Finniston Committee of Inquiry into the engineering profession. He is also a member of the Worshipful Company of Engineers and a Freeman of the City of London.

John Jupp

John Jupp has first hand experience of the Port of London, having worked in the London lighterage industry from 1949-1980. As a member of the executive of the Watermen, Lightermen, Tugmen and Bargemen's Union he has been much involved with numerous official committees set up to examine the workings of the Port. He has also had a long interest in the Museum of London, where he is Honorary Waterman, and the Docklands History Group.

Philip MacDougall BA (Hons) M Phil

A resident of the Medway Towns, but born in London, Philip MacDougall has spent much of the last eight years in research on Royal Dockyards. His publications include *The Story of Chatham Dockyard* (1981) and *Royal Dockyards* (1982). Philip MacDougall is an historical advisor to *Bygone Kent* magazine and a number of his articles on Kentish dockyards, including Woolwich and Deptford, have appeared in this magazine. A thesis, submitted to the Open University in 1983, dealt with Chatham dockyards for the period 1770 to 1801.

Alan Pearsall

Always interested in maritime history, he has been a historian for the National Maritime Museum for the last ten years.

Tim Smith

Tim Smith has been an amateur industrial archaeologist since the early 1970s and is now Secretary of the Greater London Industrial Archaeology Society. He is employed at a British Telecom computer centre.

Malcolm Tucker

Malcolm Tucker is a chartered civil engineer, working for a well-known consulting engineering firm. He came to London in the late 1960s, at the time the upper docks were closing, and has been active since then in recording the industrial archaeology of the capital. He has a particular interest in buildings in all their aspects.

GAZETTEER

This industrial archaeological survey includes some architectural material but is not intended to compete with Professor Pevsner's *The Buildings of England*.

Broadly speaking entries are arranged geographically under Boroughs following the river from west to east.

Tower Hamlets

This borough stretches from the eastern fringes of the City to Bow Creek and includes the St Katharine, London, Regent's Canal, West India & Millwall and East India Docks. To the south a large bend of the Thames encloses the so called Isle of Dogs, a distinctive feature. Redevelopment of the London Docks is nearing completion but the West India & Millwall system is even now still capable of receiving ships. From an industrial archaeological point of view Tower Hamlets contains the most important surviving buildings in London's Docklands: the 'Skin Floor' at the London Docks and the group of buildings at the main entrance of the West India Docks which includes an original dock warehouse of 1802 by George Gwilt.

Former PLA Headquarters building
TQ 334 808
10 Trinity Square, EC3

Listed grade II*

The architect, Sir Edwin Cooper, was commissioned to make designs in 1913. The foundation stone was laid by the Chairman of the PLA (Lord Devonport) in 1915 and the building was opened by the Prime Minister (Lloyd George) in 1922, the main contractor being J Mowlem & Co Ltd. The PLA ceased to use the building in 1972.

Up to ground floor level the exterior is faced with grey granite, the rest is in Portland Stone. The height of the tower is 174', each side of the building having a length of about 260'. The style of the principal entrance is Roman in the Corinthian Order. The frieze is supported by four reeded and fluted Corinthian columns with side pilasters also reeded and fluted. There are external sculptures of 'Father Thames', 'Exportation' and 'Produce'. 'Commerce' and 'Navigation' are on the ground floor. The central rotunda (110' diameter by 67' in height) was damaged by bombing in 1940 but restored.

1 PLA Headquarters Building, aerial view before the Second World War. (Museum of London)

2 PLA Headquarters Building, book-keeping machine room about 1930, showing Mercedes & Burrough's book-keeping machines. (Museum of London)

Hydraulic accumulator tower   *TQ 338 808*
Mansell Street, E1

Remains of hydraulic accumulator tower for former railway goods station alongside line to Fenchurch Street.

3 St Katharine Docks, C Warehouse 1980. (GLC)

4 St Katharine's as it was. (Museum of London)

5 Hydraulic devil c1860, St Katharine Docks 1967. (GLIAS)

6 London and St Katharine Docks, fire fighting September 1940. (Museum of London)

St Katharine Docks   TQ 339 804

Date 1828-9. Western Dock, Eastern Dock and entrance basin of original scheme survive. 'I' Warehouse by George Aitchison Senior built on site of King's Warehouse 1858-60 also extant. 'C' Warehouse by Hardwick 1828 demolished 1981. Now given over to tourism. Historic ships collection in Eastern Dock.

Hydraulic capstans at entrance lock. Thomas Telford was Engineer to the Dock Company.

Co-operative Society building   TQ 340 811
Leman Street, E1

Co-operative Society building in red brick with decorations. The foundation stone of eastern part was laid in 1874 by Thomas Hughes. The western part was built in 1887. Imposing clock tower at SW corner.

Commercial Road Goods Depot
TQ 341 813
Hooper Street, E1

Part of building remains with approach viaduct on Pinchin Street. Two-storey red-brick hydraulic pumping station in Hooper Street, with two accumulators in situ.
   Ref: Tim Smith, Commercial Road Goods Depôt, GLIAS Journal No 2.

Oil Refinery   TQ 344 809
Pinchin Street, E1

Built by Pinchin & Johnson 1859. Linked through railway arches to large complex on Cable Street. Oil was produced by crushing seeds.

Sugar Refinery   TQ 344 809
Pinchin Street, E1

Untypically small refinery, last remnant of a once important industry established around Back Church Lane.

London Docks   TQ 345 805

Skin floor listed grade 1

Date from c1805. Redevelopment almost complete. The major item still surviving is the 'skin floor' (New Tobacco Warehouse) 1811-13. This is an important example of the structural use of cast iron at a period of rapid evolution. Also remaining are the lifting bridges which carried Wapping Lane, Garnet Street and Glamis Road over dock passage (see below). To the south west of the site the Hermitage Pumping Station may be converted into an artist's studio retaining the electric pumps. The site is surrounded by the original dock wall which is still largely intact. To the

north of the site in Pennington Street "lean-to" sheds survive. These were built c1811-13 and have interesting queen-post roofs. At the main entrance is **London Dock House** dating from the 1840s. Note engine house of former hydraulic pumping station (1856 by Cubitts) on west side of Hermitage entrance.

Wapping Pier Head   *TQ 345 801*
Wapping High Street, E1

Original entrance for London Docks 1805. Two attractive three storey terraces for dock officials by Daniel Alexander 1811-13. The entrance is filled in.

7   *Main entrance to the London Docks looking west 1945. (Museum of London)*

8   *Wine Gauging Ground, London Docks May 1920. (Museum of London)*

9   *Discharging bulk wine, MV Vargas, London Docks 1960. (Museum of London)*

10   *Skin Floor, roof 1970. (GLC)*

11   *Skin Floor, vaults 1981. (GLC)*

12   *St John's Wharf 1981. (GLC)*

St John's Wharf   *TQ 348 801*
80 Wapping High Street

Typical red brick Victorian riverside wharf both sides of the road, built 1870-73. Two bridges still cross the street. Previously there was an 1830s warehouse by the river. Traces of Elizabethan brickwork may be seen at ground level.
 Formerly used by Alexander Tugs, now Oddbins the wine merchants. Beautifully refurbished. Electric cranes installed in the 1930s removed c1982. Human bones discovered here in the 1980s were sent to St Thomas's Hospital for examination and are believed to be the relics of a murder victim.

Wapping River Police Station   *TQ 349 800*
98 Wapping High Street, E1

The present Police Station, the Headquarters of Thames Division, is on the site of the first River Police Station of 1798. There is a small museum (open to visitors by appointment) and immediately to the west a depôt for the maintenance of police launches, opened in 1973. Clad in moulded glass-reinforced plastic panels this is a prominent riverside feature. A Syncrolift raises boats quickly into the workshop at all states of the tide.

Wapping Underground Station
TQ 351 802
Wapping High Street, E1

Sir Marc Brunel's Thames Tunnel of 1824-43

from Rotherhithe ended here. The original shaft of 1843 is still in use. See also the entry 'Brunel Thames Tunnel' (under Southwark), especially for the extension of the railway northwards beneath the Eastern Dock of the London dock system.

Warehouses *TQ 342 802 — TQ 353 805*
Wapping High Street & Wapping Wall, E1

Some grade II listing

Typical Thames riverside warehouses, 5-7 storeys high, lining both sides of the street. **Metropolitan Wharf** and **Gun Wharves** are of particular note. Late 19th century/early 20th century. Note also **King Henry's Wharves** with very large wall cranes. **Oliver's Wharf** (1870 Victorian Gothic, now converted to flats. Considerable demolition has taken place recently.

London Hydraulic Power Company, Hydraulic Pumping Station *TQ 354 806*
Wapping Wall, E1

Listed grade II

London Hydraulic Power Company acquired land for building a pumping station here in 1889 and the completed station commenced its active life in 1892. Coal was delivered to the adjacent Shadwell Basin and water was obtained from this same dock. Six boilers provided steam for six inverted vertical triple-expansion pumping engines, hydraulic energy being stored in two accumulators of the usual kind. Two electric turbo pumps were added in 1923 and the plant was radically modernized in the 1950s, at least in part due to the introduction of a smokeless zone. The steam plant was altogether removed and replaced by electric pumps which continued until the closure of the station in the summer of 1977 when it was the world's last working hydraulic pumping station on a public supply system. Much of the plant has since been removed but there are plans for a hydraulic power musueum. The pumping station building with its ivy clad tower is quite a landmark.

Underground Water Storage Reservoir
TQ 354 805

Immediately to the South of the pumping station building is an underground storage reservoir which formerly held 420,000 gallons. The roof is supported on cast iron columns with a beam and jack-arch spanning system. There are plans to use this underground space as a club or car park.

Engineer's House *TQ 354 806*
37 Wapping Wall, E1

Immediately to the East of the hydraulic power station is this attractive house for the accommodation of the station's engineer built of the same red brick as the pumping station. Mr D Donnachie, the last station engineer of the London Hydraulic Power Company, still resides here and operates independently a maintenance and repair business for hydraulic equipment.

Rolling bascule bridge *TQ 354 806*
Glamis Road, E1

Scherzer-type bridge installed in the 1930s to allow ships access to the London Dock system, now in a somewhat decayed state. Water tank counterbalance. Despite the apparent low headroom clearance is adequate for a double-deck bus. Remains of a similar bridge may be seen in Garnet Street at *TQ 351 805.*

Ventilation and access shaft *TQ 355 806*

Listed grade II

Spiral stairs lead down to the Rotherhithe Road Tunnel although walking through to the south bank or to the northern vehicular entrance to the east of Butcher Row is somewhat unpleasant due to traffic noise and fumes. The shaft is surmounted by an attractive drum similar to one on the south bank at *TQ 355 802.* A concrete path approaches the north bank access shaft from Glamis Road and to the north east is King Edward VII Memorial Park.

13 The Prospect of Whitby, Wapping Wall 1981. (GLC)

14 Shadwell Entrance lock, looking east 1981. (GLC)

13

14

15

date roughly from the 1930s. On the South West corner of the site are some quite interesting 1916 buildings. Before the decline of shipping in the early 1970s the riverside berths were frequented by Dutch coasters. A steam engine/compressor is believed to have been present until c1980.

Plans to redevelop the site for the City Polytechnic have not been implemented and this important complex is now the subject of a planning enquiry.

Recording work was carried out by GLIAS c1978 and photographs etc deposited in the London Borough of Tower Hamlets Local History Library, Bancroft Road, E1.

16

Free Trade Wharf   *TQ 358 808*
The Highway, E1

Some grade II listing

Riverside wharf where a large group of principally late 19th century derelict warehouses entirely surrounds the historic saltpetre store of the East India Company which dates from 1795. This store consists of a pair of warehouses which retain their original roofs but the floors have been relaid with concrete in the 1930s. The c1870 warehouses which flank the store are of note. The offices of the former Free Trade Wharf Company are situated alongside The Highway to the North of the site. These

Thames House, former factory building
TQ 359 810
Butcher Row, E14

Building on the corner of Cable Street and Butcher Row, dating from late 1920s and subsequently used as a sweet factory (Batgers). Fairly ornate architectural treatment with clock.

Regent's Canal Dock   *TQ 363 810*
The Regent's Canal was built around the North of London to connect the Grand Junction Canal at Paddington with the docks. A dock was constructed where this canal joined the river for the opening in 1820. Enlargements took place in 1836, 1852 and 1865. Also known as **'Limehouse Basin'**.

17

Hydraulic Accumulator Tower
TQ 364 811
North of Regent's Canal Dock

Listed grade II

This octagonal tower dates from the first installation of hydraulic power at Regent's Canal Dock by Sir William Armstrong in 1852. Rusting remains of accumulator in situ. A fine architectural feature. There is also a truncated chimney. This may be the earliest hydraulic power station site in London.

18

Princes Lodge, ex Sailors' Home
TQ 367 812
747 Commercial Road, E14

Imposing building on the corner of Commercial Road and Salmon Lane. Former hostel for merchant seamen. Dated 1914-18. War memorial?

Passmore Edwards Sailors' Palace
TQ 369 810
West India Dock Road, E14

Listed grade II

Edwardian building with striking decoration over the door. Opened 1903. Now flats. Rodinglea Housing Association.

Former ship chandler's building
TQ 372 808
11 West India Dock Road, E14

Listed grade II

Imposing 3½ storey façade. Probably c1870. Until recently used as a furniture workshop. In the basement a small hydraulic chain testing machine dating from the 1920s was in use until c1982. This machine has been removed for storage by the Museum of London. The Museum made a photographic record of the basement before removal.
    Ref: East London Papers **15**.

15   Free Trade Wharf 1981. (GLC)

16   Free Trade Wharf August 1983. (Philip Dubuque)

17   Aerial view, Limehouse. (Museum of London)

18   Hydraulic accumulator tower, Regent's Canal Dock 1980. (GLC)

19   Disused entrance to Limehouse Cut, Narrow Street, August 1979. (R J M Carr)

19

The Isle of Dogs

The Isle of Dogs was the centre for much heavy engineering and shipbuilding in London during the 19th century, when the capital had a major share in these fields. Apart from the building of small craft London's shipbuilding industry essentially came to an end with the closure of Thames Ironworks in 1912. These works were situated near the mouth of Bow Creek, mostly on the East bank. Few remains survive — see Newham. The Isle of Dogs is still characterised by its iron working past and might be compared with the *Black Country* of the West Midlands.

The area around the West India Dock entrance in the North West corner of the Isle of Dogs is the most significant surviving feature in London's dockland.

West India Docks

The West India Docks (Act 1799, opened 1802-6) were the largest as well as being the first of the high security 'enclosed' docks which revolutionised the Port of London in the period 1800-1810 and set precedents for ports elsewhere. They contain the last surviving extensive group of early dock buildings, including the last multi-storey warehouses from the first period of dock construction and also buildings concerned with the administrative, maintenance and security facilities necessary for these docks.

Ref: Charles Hadfield and A W Skempton, William Jessop Engineer, David & Charles 1979, Chapter 10.

No 2 Warehouse   *TQ 373 806*

Listed grade I

1802, earliest multi-storeydock warehouse remaining in London. Cast iron stanchions (1814) are the earliest surviving in a London multi-storey warehouse. First warehouse of the enclosed docks. George Gwilt architect. Probably the most important surviving historic industrial building in Dockland. This is likely to be the location of the Museum of London's Dockland Museum.

No 1 Warehouse   *TQ 372 806*

Listed grade I

1803, extended to present height 1827.

20 Sugar sacks drying, North Quay West India Docks. (Museum of London)

20

Office *TQ 372 806*

Listed grade I

With portico (1803). Built against the buttressed boundary wall of the Import Dock. Architect George Gwilt. Portico added later by Sir John Rennie.

Former excise office outside the gate *TQ 372 806*

1807. At one time the Jamaica Tavern. Bow ended.

Cottages Garford Street, E14 *TQ 371 807*

Listed grade II

For West India Dock Company's constables (1819) by John Rennie. Now desirable residences. The larger one was for sergeant.

Gate piers of main entrance *TQ 372 806*

Listed grade II

Railings *TQ 372 806*

West of main entrance and also *depression* which marks the perimeter moat, the original outer security barrier of the West India Docks.

Salvation Army Hostel *TQ 371 807*

Listed grade II

Eastern range of 1902 in early neo-William and Mary style by Niven and Wigglesworth, surmounted by a cupola. Originally the Scandinavian Sailors Temperance Home. It was transferred to the Salvation Army in the 1930s.

21 P L A dredger No 10, West India Docks 1950s. (Museum of London)

21

Guard House *TQ 371 806*

Listed grade II

Small circular building (c1803), formerly one of a pair built as a lock-up and armoury. Architect George Gwilt. There was a drawbridge here over the perimeter moat, removed c1820.

Quadrangle Building (now called *Cannon Workshops*) *TQ 370 806*

Listed grade II

1824. Offices, engineers' workshops, stores and cooperage. Imposing entrance arch with Portland Stone dressing and granite door surrounds. Architect John Rennie the younger. Sheds on the North side are on cast iron stanchions and give some idea of how the early transit sheds must have looked, none of these early sheds having survived. Outside the engineers' office is a cast iron bench mark, reading 'THW 1800', indicating Trinity High Water level, the datum level of the Port of London.

The new name **Cannon Workshops** derives from a small cannon which formerly stood by the entrance. the Quandrangle Buildings are mistakenly also known as **The Barracks**. At no time were they used as living accommodation.

Forge *TQ 371 805*

1825/6. Close to the Quadrangle Buildings. Latterly used for chain and equipment repairs. Hearths were probably late 19th century. Floor of hardened earth.

Ref: Site report by GLIAS Recording Group — Supplement to GLIAS Newsletter No 78 February 1982.

Western boundary wall *TQ 371 803*
West Ferry Road, E14

Gateway listed grade II

350 yard intact length of early 19th century wall following the curve of West Ferry Road. Bricked-up gateway with two cast iron obelisk-pattern bollards with initials WIDC (West India Dock Company).

Remainder of West India Docks

Import Dock (1800-02) 30 acres *TQ 375 804*

Export Dock (1803-06) 24 acres *TQ 375 802*

Both docks listed grade I

William Jessop and Ralph Walker engineers. 2600′ (½ mile) long, original impounded depth 23′. Largest of all the early docks. The quay walls by Jessop set the pattern for later docks but are mostly obscured above water level by jetties and modern copings. The Import Dock was one of the wonders of the age when opened in 1802.

The City Canal   *TQ 371 801 — TQ 384 802*

Opened in 1805; saved two miles of sailing but the time and cost of double locking and hand haulage resulted in financial losses from the start. After use for the floating of timber it was converted into the present South Dock in 1866-70. The dock was connected in 1926 to the two Northern Docks and to the Millwall Docks. At the site of its Eastern entrance (*TQ 383 799*) is the present-day entrance lock to the whole West India and Millwall dock system. Some original work remains at the Western entrance (see below). An electric pumping station c1914 (for impounding) straddles the canal to the East of West Ferry Road (*TQ 372 802*).

Western entrance lock of City Canal (later South dock)   TQ 371 801

Listed grade II

(1803-05) By William Jessop to same design as original locks of the West India Docks. Now the only lock chamber of the first generation to remain, although blocked by an impounding station at inner end. Ashlar masonry of high quality.

22

Features of Millwall

The riverside windmills have long since disappeared and the remains of the once flourishing ship-building industry are few. The Great Eastern was launched from Napier's Yard (see below) in 1858, but 10 years later the trade was being transferred to the Clyde with metal and chemical industries taking its place. Sites include Associated Lead Manufacturers, Burrell's Colours, Millwall Iron Works (of William Fairbairn fame), Millwall Lead Works, Samuda's Yard etc.

22   Western entrance to the City Canal blocked by pumphouse August 1979. (R J M Carr)

23

24

Millwall Dock   *TQ 375 792*

Opened in 1868. Engineer John Fowler. Crossed by a moveable road bridge at *TQ 377 794*. These docks were largely used for the discharge of grain. A graving dock was built on the south side (*TQ 378 788*). The original Millwall Dock Company purchased the surrounding 200 acres in the vain hope that it would become an industrial estate. Timber ships were the last users.

Former St Paul's Presbyterian Church
TQ 372 789
West Ferry Road, E14

Listed grade II

By T E Knightley, 1859. Foundation stone laid by John Scott Russell; his name may still be clearly read. Oral tradition has it that the

23   Discharging grain, Millwall Dock. (Museum of London)

24   McDougall's flour mill Millwall Dock, looking south-east July 1979. (R J M Carr)

25   Plant attendant, hydraulic engine house Millwall Dock 1953. (Museum of London)

25

building was erected for Scottish shipyard workers. Laminated timber arches internally (bolted, not glued). Used as workshop and store. For more details see illustrated article in *Industrial Archaeology Review*, Vol **5**, Part 3, Autumn 1981, pp 264-7.

Former **Millwall Ironworks**   *TQ 375 784*
West Ferry Road, E14

Three substantial buildings c1860 remain. Site acquired by shipbuilder C J Mare about this time.

On NE side of road *(TQ 376 785)*, a **two-bay engineering erecting shop** with decorative cast iron plaque on gable wall '1860 CJM & Co'. (This shop is now occupied by Stratford Metals). Unlisted.

Launching site of **SS Great Eastern**
(18,915 tons gross)   *TQ 374 783*

Napier Yard next to Millwall Ironworks. No contemporary features remain on land but on the foreshore the remains of the timber slipway constructed for the infamous sideways launch in 1857-8 were uncovered in 1984.

Refs: I K Brunel by L T C Rolt, Longmans, 1957 and John Scott Russell by George S Emmerson, John Murray, 1977.

Burrell's Colour Works   *TQ 375 783*
West Ferry Road, E14

Some grade II listing

On South West side of road, prominent from the river, two substantial three-storey ranges with hipped roofs which are shown on the 1860 OS, and a truncated chimney of considerable size. This group of buildings is now Burrell's Colour Works which is still manufacturing pigments for paint. Some of the interior scenes are rather dramatic. A considerable oral tradition exists regarding the working conditions. Owing to high costs only expensive pigments now made here. A remnant of Napier Yard extant when the Great Eastern was built. The top floor was a mould loft.

Fire Station   *TQ 380 784*
West Ferry Road, E14

Fire Station in "Queen Anne" style, 1904. Design by LCC architects' department.

Public Convenience   *TQ 382 784*
Manchester Road, E14

Pre-war concrete Ladies and Gents convenience with rotary ventilators on top.

Former **M shed**   *TQ 377 799*

Three-storey, late 1960s, prestressed concreted coffered slab floors and steel barrel vault roof; an unusual, sophisticated design by the engineers Harris and Sutherland.

Hydraulic Swing Bridge
over Millwall Cut   *TQ 378 798*
(the connection put in after the formation of the PLA between South Dock and Millwall Dock)

By Horseley Bridge and Thomas Piggot Ltd (1928), a very late example. Nice set of control levers. Removed c1984.

Ref: Ian McNeil Hydraulic Power, Longmans 1972, p 154.

Fred Olsen Building   *TQ 379 796*

East side of Millwall Dock, by Foster Associates c1968.

Site of Globe Ropeworks   *TQ 381 787*
East Ferry Road, E14

The buildings have been cleared but the rails on which the rope making machines ran may still be traced. The site is shortly to be landscaped as a public amenity area.

The firm of Hawkins and Tipson started their first works here in 1881. In 1971 the business was transferred to Thamesmead and elsewhere. A number of excellent photographs of the works survive. Hawkins and Tipson still have connections with the Isle of Dogs through former employees.

Ref: The Story of Hawkins & Tipson, Charles Hawkins, 1952.

Cubitt Town

Begun about 1843 by the building firm of that name. Timber wharves, brick fields, a pottery and a cement factory were established here together with an extensive housing estate largely for Irish labourers, now mostly demolished. The Island Gardens *(TQ 382 782)* were laid out by the Naval College to improve their view (the view from the Island could hardly be improved on); the Northern entrance to the Greenwich Foot Tunnel (1897) is here *(TQ 382 782)*. The housing estates throughout the Island demonstrate interesting variations in municipal style. A branch of the Blackwall Railway passed through the West India and Millwall Docks and terminated in a passenger station near Ferry Street *(TQ 379 783)* at the West of Island Gardens where part of the viaduct remains. It was initially horse drawn for fear of fire in the docks. The passenger service was withdrawn in 1926.

Former **Cumberland Mills** *TQ 386 784*
Saunders Ness Road, E14
(by Newcastle Draw Dock)

Late 19th century oil seed mill. Now a
scrapyard. Shell of two-storey building and
handsome chimney. Important feature in the
riverside scene. Some demolition here 1982.

Storm Water Pumping Station *TQ 384 797*
Stewart Street, E14

Listed locally

The roof of the beam engine house, to the East,
was removed c1982. Storm water handled by
electric pumps in the small building to the West.
(See Goad Insurance Plans for a note of former
machinery.)

Lifting Bridge *TQ 382 799*
Manchester Road, E14

Built 1969 with small hydraulic pumping station
(electric pumps, oil hydraulics) to operate
bridge motors.

Isle House *TQ 383 801*

Listed grade II

(1824) For Blackwall Dockmaster. By John
Rennie (the younger). Fronts the river.

Blackwall Basin *TQ 382 802*

Listed grade I

(1800-02). First non-tidal entrance basin for
the West India docks by W Jessop. Earthen
sides when built. Original locks rebuilt to larger
dimensions c1895.

26

27

29

30

26 *Cumberland Mills August
1979. (R J M Carr)*

27 *High-speed torpedo steam
launch for the Argentine Republic by
Messrs. Yarrow and Hedley,
Blackwall. (Illustrated London
News 6 February 1875)*

28 *Blackwall Reach from the
south entrance to the West India
Docks, July 1925. (National
Maritime Museum)*

29 *London Graving Dock
Preston's Road, looking north
February 1980. This dry dock
opened in 1878. (R J M Carr)*

30 *London Graving Dock,
Blacksmith's shop looking north
February 1980. (R J M Carr)*

Bridge House   *TQ 383 802*

Listed grade II

(1819) For Dock Superintendent by John Rennie (Senior). A flat roof replaces the original.

Swing Bridge   *TQ 383 802*

Across Blackwall Entrance Lock, Preston's Road (1897) by Sir Alexander Binnie, Hydraulic Swing Bridge with deep plate girders. A good example of the period, but a major traffic bottleneck. Similar bridges remain in the Royal Docks (see Newham). Hydraulic machinery by Armstrong Mitchell.

Blackwall Entrance Lock   *TQ 383 802*

William Jessop's original 1802 entrance lock for the West India Docks was rebuilt to larger dimensions in 1894. The entrance has been out of use since c1950? A dam and a hydraulic main cross the lock.

    Ref: GLIAS Newsletter 81 page 2. A series of articles appeared in Engineering in 1894.

Poplar Docks (ex North London Railway)
TQ 383 803 and TQ 381 804
Preston's Road, E14

Eastern Dock and accumulator tower listed grade II

Established 1852, second basin (to the West) 1875. Of principal surviving interest are two hydraulic accumulator towers of c1875 with attractive pyramidal slate roofs topped by finials. Gutted. The shell of the hydraulic pumping station of c1875, with a third accumulator tower, was demolished c1981. Electric cranes of the 1920s now broken up.

    (See account in GLIAS Newsletter 62, pp14-18.)

Blackwall/Mouth of Bow Creek Area

This is a compact heavily industrialised area coincident with the River Lea delta and characterised by heavy industry — gas works, electric power stations, railways, docks and shipyards. Some of this industry survives and small sea-going ships still sail up Bow Creek to the North of the East India Dock Road bridge.

Early dry dock, Blackwall Yard
TQ 387 806
(Blackwall Engineering formerly R & H Green and Silley Weir)
off Blackwall Way, E14

The early dry dock listed grade II

The Eastern of the two dry docks at Blackwall Yard coincides with the site of a dock which existed in 1803. It had been enlarged to approximately its present length by 1850. Granite blocks set in the walls at the entrance have bearing faces for struts at 45° in plan, probably to help support an early caisson gate. This dock is out of use and silting up but the other dry dock at Blackwall Yard, dating from 1890s, is still in use for ship repairing and a forge with a pneumatic hammer is at work.

31

31   *Blackwall Yard 1981. (GLC)*

32   *Blackwall Yard, engineers' shop. (Museum of London)*

32

Former shipbuilder's house now offices for
Blackwall Engineering   *TQ 385 806*
Blackwall Way, E14

Three-storey brick and stucco, with imposing
central stairwell. Mid 19th century house of the
Green family who owned Blackwall Yard.

Former Hydraulic Pumping Station
(ex Midland Railway)   *TQ 384 806*
Duthie Street/Blackwall Way, E14

On local list

Built in 1882 to serve the Midland Railway's
railway yard and dock, now filled in. A fine
example of the Company's characteristic
architectural style, in red brick with lozenge-
pattern cast iron window frames. The dock was
built on part of Blackwall shipbuilding yard
belonging to Wigram's.

34

33

Former Hydraulic Pumping Station
(ex East India Dock Co)   *TQ 386 808*
East India Dock Wall Road, E14

Listed grade II

Built 1857. Striking architecture. One of the
earliest of the surviving hydraulic pumping
station buildings of the dock companies in
London. Now used for furniture storage.
Latterly the East India Dock purchased power
from LP.

East India Docks   *TQ 388 810*

Some grade II listing

The East India Company obtained its Act for
these docks in 1803, four years after West India
Docks Act. Prior to this 'East Indiamen' had

*33   Accumulator Tower, Midland
Railway hydraulic pumping station
Duthie Street 1972. (GLC)*

*34   Hydraulic Pumping Station,
East India Dock Wall Road 1977.
(GLC)*

35   The Arno-Mendi *coaling in
the East India Docks during the
1926 coal strike. (Museum of
London)*

35

been unloaded in the River at Blackwall as owing to their size they were unable to come further up-river. The goods imported by the East India Company were of high value and little bulk and were taken to the City by (horse-drawn) road van for warehousing. Large warehouses in the City at Cutler Street were built in stages from 1769 (the major part from 1792) to accommodate the trade and so little warehousing was built around the docks themselves. The engineers for the East India Docks were John Rennie and Ralph Walker. The Docks opened in 1806 and were closed by the PLA in 1967. There were two docks, an Import Dock to the North with a smaller Export Dock to the South and an entrance basin. The Export Dock was heavily bombed during the 1939-45 war and the post-war Brunswick Wharf Power Station was constructed on the site. The Import Dock has been partially filled and the Western end is used as a container stacking yard. There is still water at the East end of the Import Dock. Granite setts and railway lines survive on the north quay. Portions of the original dock wall, and some sheds, especially along Leamouth Road are noteworthy survivors. On the east side of Leamouth Road some of the **Pepper Warehouse** dating from c1811 also survives. Brunswick Dock, constructed in the 1780s, was on the site of the East India Export Dock.

36

Brunswick Wharf Power Station
TQ 388 808

Built 1952-56 on the site of the East India Export Dock which was heavily damaged by bombing. Contains two 63 MW turbine sets and four of 55 MW by Metropolitan Vickers installed after the repeal of the 'Control of Turbo-Alternators' legislation in 1953. The station is noteworthy in having an impressive set of 11 boilers in line, working at 62.0 bar pressure and a temperature of 482°C. These were built for coal firing but have subsequently been converted to burn oil by the addition of internal brickwork etc. The conversion back to coal burning is not worthwhile and the station is expensive to run on oil but it occupies an

important position on the Grid. There has been discussion for some time of the closure of Brunswick Wharf but the station still appears to be on standby. The riverside at Brunswick Wharf was the terminus of the London & Blackwall Railway which ran from Fenchurch Street station and was opened in 1840 with engineers George Parker Bidder and Robert Stephenson. Before the power station was built a hotel stood here for the accommodation of travellers who transferred from railway to steamer (cf Gallions Hotel at Beckton). The construction of the wharf itself is of some interest in that cast iron piling was used (see the paper *Engineering in the Port of London, 1803-33* by Professor A W Skempton, Transactions of the Newcomen Society **53,** pp 763-96).

East India Docks Impounding Station Building   *TQ 390 808*

Now on CEGB property as part of Brunswick Wharf Power Station grounds, this Edwardian neo-Georgian pumping station building dating from c1911 was thoughtfully designed to harmonise with the classical buildings of the East India Docks already in existence. Pilasters embellish the dark-red brick exterior. The building is in poor condition and the interior is essentially empty.

Site of Rennie iron bridge and other bridges across Bow Creek   *TQ 392 814*

An early 19th century iron bridge to the designs of John Rennie (the elder) formerly spanned the River Lea (Bow Creek) at this point but was demolished in 1931-5. The name 'Ironbridge' is applied to items in the vicinity; 'Ironbridge Wharf' (a scrapyard) on the West bank by East India Dock Road, *TQ 391 813*, and the 'Ironbridge Brewpub', *TQ 389 813* on the North side of East India Dock Road, an inn which in 1981 brewed its own real ale in the basement. The real ale venture, however, seems to have been a failure as the pub has been turned into a 'disco' called 'Plums'.

Apart from the modern **road bridge** which carries East India Dock Road across Bow Creek there are two other bridges to the South. At *TQ 391 813* there is a **pipe bridge** of inverted bowstring construction thought to date from the last quarter of the 19th century which from its alignment probably carries a gas main. South of this again at *TQ 391 812* are the remains of a **railway bridge**. Between these two bridges the stone abutments of the Rennie bridge may still be seen. The red brick abutments are embellished with attractively delicate decorations towards the top. The Eastern Counties and Thames Junction Railway built a branch off their line (from Stratford to the mouth of the River Lea) to the Pepper Warehouse of the East India Docks. The Act for this (single track?) branch across Bow Creek was obtained in 1846. Although venerable in appearance the present (bow string) bridge is unlikely to predate 1860. It is supported on massive cast iron columns filled with concrete. The terminus of the Eastern Counties and Thames Junction Railway's main line was on the East side of the mouth of Bow Creek at what became known as **Thames Wharf** *(TQ 396 805)* where there was a pier and coke ovens to convert seaborne coal into fuel for railway locomotives. The Eastern Counties Railway purchased the Eastern Counties and Thames Junction Railway and the line from Stratford was extended from a junction about 500 yards North of Thames Wharf the 2½ miles to North Woolwich (the so called North Woolwich extention).

J J Prior (Transport) Ltd, depôt
TQ 390 810
Leamouth Road, E14

Wharf etc. for the fleet of sand carrying ships belonging to the firm of J J Prior Ltd. Some of these small motor vessels date from 1915 and may be seen on the Thames up-river. Most of the fleet have names ending in 'P' such as *Sidney P*. There is a maintenance slip here.

Bow Creek embankment works
TQ 395 810 and environs

The meanders of the River Lea by its mouth are contained by fairly elaborate embankment works constructed 1931-5 as part of a scheme to provide employment during the economic 'slump'. The banks consist partially of loose stonework held in place by wire netting. The Rennie iron bridge was presumably removed as part of these works. A large floodgate has been erected at *TQ 393 813* as part of the Thames Barrier scheme.

Site of Orchard House Yard   *TQ 393 808*

Among the ships built here were the steam coasters *Robin* and *Rook* (sister ships), in 1889/90. *Robin* was sold to Spanish owners on 13th May 1900 and as the *Maria* continued to operate around the North West coast of Spain with cargoes of coal and scrap iron until 1974. She was bought by the Maritime Trust, restored and can at present be seen in the Historic Ships Collection in the East Basin, St Katharine Docks, *TQ 341 803*, Lloyds agreed to a specification for steel ships in November 1889 and the *Robin* was built under survey, Lloyds' surveyors visiting the ship at Orchard House Yard 83 times during construction. After she was launched in September 1890, fitting out took place in the East India Docks. *Robin* was then towed to Dundee for the engines to be fitted. This took place during 23 October-11 November, again under survey, and the vessel, together with engines, received the classification '100 A1 Lloyds (steel)'. The *Robin*

retains her original engines and boiler. The *Rook* was wrecked off Holyhead one Christmas in the 1920s.

Orchard Dry Dock remains   *TQ 394 807*
Some grade II listing

This dry dock has been filled in but the caisson remains and is a noticeable feature from the river with a painted advertisement for the Orchard Dry Dock Company and pre all-figure telephone number. The dry dock is thought to date from the last quarter of the 19th century.
   Ref: Contributions to the Maritime History of Great Britain, Kent Services, 1948.

Trinity Buoy Wharf   *TQ 395 807*
Orchard Place, E14

Some grade II listing

This is the maintenance headquarters of Trinity House and buoys, lightships and so on for England and Wales are serviced from here. There is also a **training school** for the instruction of new staff. The works include a **blacksmith's shop, machine shops** and an **electrical department**. Some fine late 19th century machine tools etc. were still in existence in early 1981 and reputedly some may have been obtained second-hand from the nearby Thames Ironworks which closed in 1912. Notably, in the large machine shop, were a pyramidal three-rolls by Craig & Donald of Johnstone near Glasgow (said to be c1905) and a shearer/punch by S Appleyard of Halifax; typical shipyard machines. Fog horns are tested by a small department near the river. A **travelling rail crane** by J Booth and Bros Ltd, Engineers, Rodley, Leeds, of 1924, stands out of use at the Thameside wharf — all traffic to and from Trinity Buoy Wharf is now by road. The **stone lighthouse** which marks the entrance to Bow Creek (the only substantial lighthouse in Greater London) has not been used for navigational purposes for some time, perhaps not this century, but has been in use for the training of lighthouse keepers. Attempts to investigate its history have been unsuccessful; the records and drawings formerly at Trinity House, EC3, were destroyed by fire c1941 but the lighthouse is thought to date from c1880. For a more detailed report see *GLIAS Newsletter 72, pp3/4*. Trinity Buoy Wharf is quite a large establishment but appears modest from outside. From the river a collection of brightly painted navigation buoys may be seen near the point but from the landward side only a small decorative light reminiscent of a buoy lantern on the North side of the main entrance gate at the end of Orchard Place indicates anything of note. The maintenance works at Trinity Buoy Wharf are being run down and work is to be transferred to depôts out of London, the most likely candidate being Harwich.

Queen Victoria Seamen's Rest *TQ 375 811*
121-131 East India Dock Road, E14

Still functioning as a Merchant Seamen's Hostel. Modern annexe to the South built 1965-80. Methodist foundation dating from before 1890.

Statue of Richard Green, Shipbuilder
TQ 379 810
East India Dock Road, E14

Listed grade II

Outside swimming baths. Illustrations of 19th century shipbuilding on the West side of the base. Richard Green depicted seated with dog and book on lap. 'Richard Green 1866, Edward W Wyon, Sculptor 1865. He was a major benefactor of many East London Charities.

Tunnel Furnishers *TQ 382 811*
208 East India Dock Road, E14

Small department store in strong 1930s style, clad with green tiles. There is a tower to the east.

Site of former Poplar Hospital *TQ 384 811*
East India Dock Road, E14

Demolished 1982. A chimney at *TQ 384 812* still remains and there is also a plaque along East India Road inscribed 'AD 1900'.

Rutland Terrace *TQ 388 814*
Oban Street, E14

Dated 1881. Attractive row of terraced houses (presumably for gas workers?). A number of streets in the area have systematic Scottish names.

Former gasworks *TQ 388 816*
Now Poplar Holder Station (North Thames Gas)
Leven Road, E14

Three gas holders of varying date. Attractive c1860 office with arched windows to the East of the gate *(TQ 387 814)*. There is another building of similar date set back from the road. The original gas works belonged to the Commercial Gas Company which was formed in 1837. Production ceased here in 1967. At one time there was a wharf on Bow Creek for sea-going colliers.

Devon Wharf *TQ 384 816*
Leven Road, E14

Joseph Ash & Son, foundry building towards Bow Creek. New galvanising plant being installed, 1983.

LT Poplar Bus Garage *TQ 384 817*
Leven Road, E14

Large stock brick garage with five entrances facing south. Alongside Bow Creek. Former tram depôt built c1905. An imposing building.

Newham

Dockland occupies only the southern part of the Borough and is dominated by the Royal Docks while to the east are Beckton Gas Works and Sewage Treatment Centre. The Lower Lea Valley was an important area for the development of the chemical industry and includes the historic site of Thames Ironworks. Newham is the longest section of the Gazetteer in terms of entries.

'Three Mills' — Tide Mills   *TQ 383 828*
Three Mills Lane, E3

House Mill and Customs & Excise Building: Listed Grade I
Clock Mill: Listed Grade II

Two mills remain; the older is the **House** Mill rebuilt 1776. The other is the **Clock Mill** rebuilt 1817. The clock on the Clock Mill is dated 1753 and has a bell cast in 1750. The mills are semi-tidal impounding to 12.5′ OD. All the levels have risen due to embankment of the rivers. The original depth of navigation at the locks was 4½′. It is now 12½′. These tide mills are the only surviving examples in the Greater London area and are the largest in the Country. They form a group of buildings on a site which has been used for distilling since 1727.

The wheels, all undershot, are as follows:

1

1   *Three Mills looking east 1969, the House Mill to the left, the Clock Mill to the right. (GLC)*

House Mill

Wheel no	Diameter	Width	Floats	HP
1	20′	3′ 1″	2′ 11″ x 2′ 8″ Poncelet[*]	20-25
2	19′	3′ 0″	2′ 10½″ x 1′ 7″ Straight	20-25
3	20′	3′ 5½″	3′ 3½″ x 2′ 10″ Straight	20-25
4	20′	8′ 1″	4′ 8″ x 2′ 10″ Lapped Poncelet	40-45

Stones: 4 pairs 4′ 4″ diameter; 8 pairs 4′ 2″ diameter

[*]curved blade

Clock Mill

Wheel no	Diameter	Width	Floats	HP
1	20'	3' 10"	3' 8" x 1' 9½"	20-25
2	19' 6"	2' 7"	2' 5" x 1' 8"	20-25
3	20'	4' 0"	3' 9" x 2' 10"	20-25

Stones: engine 8 pairs 4' 2" diameter, water 4 pairs 4' 4" diameter; water 1 pair 4' 2" diameter; water 1 pair 3' 8" diameter. Rev/min of stones 130; HP required 12.

The most easterly of the three wheels is marked in raised lettering on the annular ring 'Fawcett & Co Phoenix Foundry Liverpool'. The wheels were last used in 1952 when the buildings were occupied by Messrs Nicholsons.

The House Mill dates from 1776 and is listed grade I. It has a brick south façade (to the road) and a timber framed and clad elevation to the north. The four-storey building straddles the Three Mills Wall River. Despite many years of disuse it is still in remarkably complete condition with some of its machinery intact. It is being acquired by the Passmore Edwards Museum to be restored and converted to a museum of social history.

The Clock Mill has been converted to offices. It has external walls 18" thick of London stock brick. The main building has a timber trussed roof with slate covering. Timber floors are supported on large section timber beams which rest on circular cast iron columns; timber blocks at the head of each column distribute the loads more evenly.

On the north and south elevations, brick arched openings have vertical sliding timber sash windows. Projecting over the river, from the south side, is a weather boarded loading hoist, or 'lucam'.

2 Three Mills, interior of the Clock Mill 1975. (GLC)

2

At the west end of the main structure are two kilns, also in stock brick. The circular slate covered roofs to the kilns were added in the 19th century.

The Clock Tower, alongside the kilns, is of a rather more ornate construction. The brick walls are reduced in thickness as their height increases. All the openings in the walls are of pointed brick arches. The bell turret is timber framed with timber cladding. A similar tower is shown on drawings of the site before the present buildings were erected; a brass plate on the clock mechanism — 'Charles Penton Moorfields MDCCLIII — repaired by Bruton 1813': and the clock itself was cast in 1750.

Ref: Tide Mills in England and Wales by Rex Wailes, Newcomen Society Transactions, volume **19**, *12th October 1938.*

Abbey Mills Pumping Station   *TQ 388 833*

*Listed grade II**

Constructed 1865-8 as part of the Metropolitan Board of Works scheme for the drainage of London. The central building, in Venetian Gothic style, was designed by Sir Joseph Bazalgette as engineer, and Vulliamy as architect to the M.B.W. It is characteristic of the palatial manner in which the Victorians carried out their public works. A recent party of foreign industrial archaeologists visiting Abbey Mills, when asked what they thought this building was, suggested it might be 'a palace for a princess'. Its purpose is to house sewage pumping machinery.

The plan is cruciform with an octagonal lantern over the crossing and subsidiary domed square towers in the re-entrant angles. Each arm of the cross terminates in a massive porch based on North Italian models and use is made of polychromatic decoration in various materials.

The two Northern Low Level Sewers (10' 3" and 10' 6" diameter), the Isle of Dogs Branch Sewer (9' 0" diameter) and the West Ham diversion Sewer (11' 6" diameter) meet at the station and the sewage and part of the storm water from the Low Level system is lifted about 40' to the Outfall sewers, which lie in the embankment on the north-east side of the station, in which the flow gravitates to Beckton

3 *Abbey Mills, the A station 1968. (GLC)*

4 *Interior of A station 1955. (GLC)*

5 *Interior of A station 1968. (GLC)*

6 *Abbey Mills, interior of (C station) the gas engine house 1968. (GLC)*

Works, about four miles distant. Storm flows above a prescribed limit are diverted and pumped direct to Abbey Creek.

The low level area of North London from which all dry weather flow is pumped to the Northern Outfall Sewers at Abbey Mills covers in all 52 square miles and comprises all or part of the London Boroughs of Camden, Ealing, Islington, Hackney, Hammersmith, Kensington & Chelsea, Newham, Tower Hamlets, Waltham Forest, Westminster, Haringey and the City of London.

Station A (main engine house), 1865-8, originally housed 8 beam engines, two in each arm of the building, with a gross capacity of about 112,000 gallons per minute. The engines and the associated sixteen Cornish boilers were built by Rothwell & Co, Bolton. These engines were on a scale to match the building, cylinders 4′ 6″ in diameter, stroke 9′, beams 40′ in length, and flywheels 28′ in diameter. These sets were removed in stages between 1931 and 1933 and replaced by 8 electrically driven centrifugal pumps (visually reminiscent of 'Daleks') with a gross capacity of 224,000 gallons per minute. Practically all the dry weather flow pumping is done by these pumps. The two massive brick chimneys, made redundant when the boilers were removed, were monumental East London landmarks. They were demolished in 1940, it was said, because they were thought to be a navigational aid to German bombers.

Station B (diesel engine house), built 1891-6, re-engined 1934 and modified again in 1972. Plant now includes two electrically-driven and two diesel-driven pumps which are used for dealing with flows from the Isle of Dogs Branch Sewer and the diverted flows from the West Ham pumping station. The gross capacity is about 50,000 gallons per minute. The gas engines have now been replaced by 1,500 rpm diesel engines. The pumps are primarily used for storm water pumping to the Outfall sewer or to Abbey Creek but are at times used for dry-weather pumping.

Station C (gas engine house), built 1910-14, until recently contained gas-engined centrifugal pumps with a gross capacity of 156,000 gallons per minute. The gas engines have now been replaced by 1,500 rpm diesel engines. The pumps are primarily used for storm water pumping to the Outfall sewer or to Abbey Creek but are at times used for dry-weather pumping.

Station D, built 1970-1, as part of the scheme for diverting the West Ham flows into Abbey Mills, is used for pumping storm water only to Abbey Creek. The electrically driven pumps, with a gross capacity of 90,000 gallons per minute, are operated by remote control from Station A.

West Ham Beam Engines   *TQ 389 832*
Abbey Road, E15

On local list

West Ham pumping station was built to raise West Ham sewage to the level of Sir Joseph Bazalgette's Northern Outfall sewer (1864) along which it could then flow under gravity to Beckton works for treatment. Work started in 1897 and by c1900 the station was completed, originally as a combined pumping and electric power station. Subsequent growth in the demand for electricity meant a separate power station had to be built elsewhere. Now only two Lilleshall beam engines remain — a tight fit in their modest engine house.

The pair of Woolf compound rotative beam pumping engines at West Ham are double acting and developed 240 hp at 120 lb psi steam pressure. Their maximum speed was 12 rpm but usual running speed was 8-10 rpm. The high pressure cylinders have a bore of 30″ with a stroke of $4' 9 \frac{11}{16}''$ while the low pressure cylinders are of 48″ bore with a 7′ 6″ stroke. The engines are interesting in that they are fitted with Meyer slide valves. These have a travel of 8″ and are fitted to both high and low pressure cylinders. (For details of the valve gear see the *DALISY bulletin* **4**, *no 1, pp 4-9.*)

The double web cast iron beams of the two engines are each of about 17 tons in weight and are 28′ long. They were cast in 1895. The engines, built by the Lilleshall Co Ltd of Oakengates, Shropshire, have a plate on the cylinders giving a date of 1900. The nine-

spoked flywheels are somewhat unusual in being cast in three segments and are 22′ in diameter, weighing about 20 tons. Barring was by hand or steam, the barring engine being of the inverted vertical duplex type. The engines drove bucket pumps with a bore of 5′ 3″, the stroke being the same as that for the high pressure cylinder ($4' 9 \frac{11}{16}''$); one pump is connected to the high pressure piston tailrod while the other is directly coupled to the beam. Each stroke lifted 600 gallons, ie. 1,200 gallons per revolution of the engine, to a head of about 43′.

The condensers are of the surface type and are situated in the sewage discharge main. They contain 143 four inch diameter tubes through which the cooling medium, sewage, flowed. The arrangement gave operational difficulties due to blockages with resultant flooding so that frequent cleaning of thee tubes was necessary. The nine Lancashire boilers, 30′ long by 7′ 6″ diameter, have been removed and the house is now used as a store. They were coal fired, mechanical stoking being employed latterly. A small Bellis & Morcom steam engine which used to drive a coal conveyor was dismantled soon after closure of the steam plant in 1972 and together with plans is in the keeping of the Passmore Edwards Museum, London E15.

The last beam engine to run was number 2 which ceased operation at 12 noon on 10 January 1972. There were plans on closure to remove the engines for preservation but local objections that Newham was losing its heritage prevented this. With the present economic recession in mind it now seems unlikely that the West Ham beam engines will be the subject of a preservation scheme, especially as beam engines are preserved elsewhere in London, notably at Kew Bridge, but there is still hope. When the West Ham pumping station closed it contained in addition to the beam engines three inverted-vertical compound steam engines with open cranks driving centrifugal pumps for discharging storm water to the river. Two of these had cylinders of 20″ and 33″ bore and a stroke of 24″ and were built by John Cochrane and Co, Barrhead, in 1900. The third was (German?) and apparently smaller. They were all removed in 1973-4, two were scrapped but the third went to the London Graving Dock Co at Tilbury for preservation and was installed on the jetty, where it was restored by apprentices. The jetty has been demolished recently (c1982) but before this a party of apprentices from British Shipbuilders, Newcastle, dismantled the engine and re-erected it at their training school on Tyneside. It is said that a boiler is available there and the engine may be steamed.

Gas Holders   *TQ 387 834*
Stratford Gas Works, Union Street, E15

On site of West Ham Gas Company's Stratford works of 1845. Coal was brought in by the Great Eastern Railway and the works also had access to the Channelsea River. The company passed

217

to the Gaslight & Coke Company in 1910 and production ceased here in 1967.

Chemical Works   *TQ 388 828*
Berk Spencer Acids, Crows Road, E15

Between the London, Tilbury and Southend Railway and the Channelsea River is this large chemical plant which manufacturers sulphuric acid. Much pipework visible with escaping vapour (steam?). The works made use of water transport. A small motor barge regularly berthed at *TQ 386 827* in Channelsea River until c1984.

Footbridge   *TQ 383 825*

Modern metal and reinforced concrete footbridge across Bow Creek to carry very high voltage electric power cables which link generating stations down-river on the Thames with former power station sites along the Regent's Canal now used solely for distribution. In traditional style, resembles those of the Birmingham Canal Navigation. About 100 yards south of the LT District Line railway bridge. Concrete abutment on the west with a metal span. A sympathetic addition.

Gasholders   *TQ 385 825*
Former Bromley-by-Bow Gasworks

Listed grade II

Very fine set of 7 late 19th century gasholders. At one time there were 8 and the vacant space is still obvious. Can be compared with the set just to the North of St Pancras Station. Bromley-by-Bow gasworks was owned by the Imperial Gaslight & Coke Co. Production ceased here in 1972. Use was made of a dock on Bow Creek *(TQ 385 819)* and there were rail conections to the Great Eastern Railway and the London, Tilbury and Southend Railway. These holders are part of the same works described under the entry 'Entrance Lock to Gasworks Dock' (below).

Entrance Lock to Gasworks Dock
TQ 386 818
Former Bromley-by-Bow Gasworks

Remains of entrance to North Thames Gas Board dock for its adjacent gasworks. Lifting gates. Coal for gas making was imported via Bow Creek. There are no remains of the gasworks of note apart from the fine set of gas holders at *TQ 385 825*. The gasworks dock is said to be largely intact.

West Ham Power Station   *TQ 389 818*

Coal fired power station constructed 1949-52. Generation is by means of four English Electric 30 MW sets with steam supplied by eight chain-grate boilers working at 43.1 bar and 460°C. The station is still active. Fine views of the surrounding industry may be obtained from the top of the station, including the adjacent Cohen's scrap yard.

It transpires that at one time a public two-phase supply existed in parts of West Ham with Scott-connected transformers at this power station being used to convert the three phase grid. This helps to explain the survival of the Westinghouse synchronous motors in the dry dock pumphouse at Royal Albert Dock (see GLIAS Newsletter 82 p 6). The first power station, built on this site by West Ham Corporation, started generation in 1904. Extensions were made in 1912 with more plant being installed 1921-30. No remains of this earlier work have been noted.

Canning Town Railway Station
TQ 393 816

On the former Great Eastern Railway line to Thames Wharf and North Woolwich. Little of the former station now remains after rebuilding c1980. Originally called Barking Road the first station was opened c1846. Between the railway and Bow Creek a new town called **Canning Town** sprang up and 200 houses had already been erected c1848 when they were described as providing 'the maximum of comfort with the minimum of expense'. Barking Road station was renamed Canning Town in July 1873 and was moved to the present site to the north of Barking Road in 1888.

Site of Thames Ironworks   *TQ 395 810*
Bow Creek

The site was occupied by C J Mare and Co who opened shipbuilding and ironworks in 1846. The enterprise became the Thames Ironworks and Shipbuilding Co in 1857. *HMS Warrior* was launched from this yard in December 1860.

Thames Ironworks remained active in the late 19th century and early 20th century, specialising in liners and large warships. Quality work of this kind was at less disadvantage due to the Thames being distant from sources of coal and iron. The yard built a number of large warships for Japan etc in the early 20th century but closed in 1912 after the launch of *HMS Thunder*, 22,500 tons. In later days the firm diversified its work to include bridges, structural steelwork, steam engines and machinery etc and even commenced the manufacture of motor cars at a site in Greenwich. The Company also had premises to the west of Bow Creek *(TQ 395 808)* linked to the main yard by a ferry. The well-known post card on sale at the Museum of London showing men arriving for work purports to illustrate this ferry.

Little now remains on the site. In the late 1960s some concrete engine beds were to be found, see The Industrial Archaeology of the Lower Lea Valley, by Denis Smith, East London Papers **12**, pp 83-114.

Ref: 'Thames Ironworks Gazette', Water Lane Reference Library, Stratford and Guildhall Library and the excellently illustrated article in the 'Engineer' 13 December 1894, pp 567-577.

Royal Victoria Dock   *TQ 410 805*

The first of the large Victorian docks constructed 1850-55, one and a quarter miles long. The promoters were railway contractors; Samuel Morton Peto, Edward Ladd Betts and Thomas Brassey and the engineer was G P Bidder, well-known for railway construction. The dock was directly connected to the railway system and hydraulic power was installed from the start. Opened by Prince Albert in 1855 the prefix 'Royal' was bestowed in 1880 by the Duke of Conaught on behalf of Queen Victoria. Construction methods were radically different from those of the earlier docks (West India, London, St Katharine's, etc) which were durably built in stone for sailing ships. (By the 1850s the concept of 'progress' was dominant and a dock with a definite life span was envisaged.) Five finger-jetties were constructed on the North Quay to increase capacity and there was a Tidal Basin at the Western end. As originally constructed the sides of the dock were largely earthern banks. The dock was extensively rebuilt 1935-c1944.

Ref: Minutes of Proceedings of the Institution of Civil Engineers.

Original entrance lock   *TQ 399 804*
Royal Victoria Dock

This was the original entrance to the Victoria Dock, constructed 1850-55. Repair and strengthening work carried out and new lock gates fitted in 1928. The construction of Silvertown Way meant that ships could no longer make use of the entrance but unsoundness necessitated rebuilding anyway by the 1930s. The lock was reconstructed by Mowlems 1963-67. Latterly it was used for lighter traffic.

Tidal Basin Public House   *TQ 399 808*
29 Tidal Basin Road, E16

Large late Victorian/Edwardian public house named after the Tidal Basin formerly situated at the western end of Victoria Dock. Compare with the Connaught Tavern *(TQ 416 808)* at the other end of Victoria Dock and the Gallions Hotel *(TQ 439 807)* north of Royal Albert Dock basin. The Tidal Basin was dispensed with during the 1930s.

Bonded Tobacco Warehouses   *TQ 405 808*
North side of Royal Victoria Dock

Imposing 'shed-like' range of buildings; from west to east S, R, P. O, N and K sheds.

7   The Royal Docks looking east. (Museum of London)

8

8 *Tobacco Warehouse interior 1922. (Museum of London)*

Reminiscent of Vickers' Engineering shops, Barrow-in-Furness. Dating from 1880?

'W' Warehouse   *TQ 403 808*
Royal Victoria Dock

Listed Grade II

One of the original warehouses of Victoria Dock dating from c1855.

North Quay   *TQ 402 806 — TQ 416 806*
Royal Victoria Dock

Constructed 1937 replacing the five finger-jetties of the original Victoria Dock. The new quay was south of the original dock edge and on the space reclaimed new transit sheds were erected during the early 1940s.

'M' Shed   *TQ 408 808*
Royal Victoria Dock

South of the Custom House. This pre-World War II red brick tobacco warehouse has a reinforced concrete frame. In the 1960s the tobacco warehouses became redundant. Tobacco companies were then able to pay duty and have tobacco delivered direct to warehouses at their factories.

Custom House Station   *TQ 407 809*
(formerly Victoria Dock Station)
Victoria Dock Road, E16

The station was radically redeveloped c1980. An impressive footbridge leads south over the former PLA railway tracks to the Custom House *(TQ 408 808)* and Royal Victoria Dock. Custom House station is situated on the

'avoiding line' to North Woolwich which was made necessary by the building of Victoria Dock. This line and the original Custom House station were opened in November 1855.

Victoria Dock Superintendent's office
TQ 408 809
Royal Victoria Dock

After the closure of the PLA Trinity Square building the Chief Engineer (PLA) occupied the top floor.

Seamen's Institute   *TQ 408 810*
Victoria Dock Road, E16

Now a students' hostel, 'Angel Hostel', for the Merchant Navy College. Foundation stone dated 1933. Conveniently opposite Custom House station.

Silvertown Way, E16
TQ 398 807 — TQ 403 803

Constructed in reinforced concrete by Dorman Long and Co 1933-34 to solve the problems of access to the Royal Docks, this raised roadway across the original entrance to Royal Victoria Dock proved insufficient to cope with the post World War II growth in road transport. It is 1.09 mile long and 80' wide (roadway 56' with two 12' pavements). Leslie Hore-Belisha performed the opening ceremony on 13 September 1934. This was Britain's first flyover. The consulting engineers were Rendel, Palmer & Tritton.
   Ref: Engineering **138** *(1934), 302.*

Tate & Lyle, Plaistow Wharf   *TQ 402 801*
North Woolwich Road, E16

Imposing and impressive building, built 1947-50, to grand effect in Portland stone. Note the Lyle & Sons trademark 'Out of the strong came forth sweetness' in the stonework depicting a lion and bees. Tate & Co established themselves at Silvertown in 1871 and Lyle and Sons in 1881. Plaistow Wharf was originally used to store petrol. Latterly has been involved in the manufacture of Golden Syrup.

Lyle Park   *TQ 405 798*

Provided by the well-known sugar refiners for the use of their employees. A refreshing oasis in a heavily industrialised area, this small park, now in the care of the London Borough of Newham, is very well maintained and boasts some most attractive features. Bounded to the south by the river. There is a charming section with seats giving the effect of a walled garden. Not to be missed if one is exploring the district. However, this philanthropic venture is difficult to find which is perhaps why it is relatively free from vandalism. There is a keeper on duty.

Rank/Spillers Granaries   *TQ 405 804*

A huge complex of reinforced concrete granaries erected in the 1930s and replacing earlier granaries/mills.

From west to east these granaries are Rank's, Spillers (Millenium Mills) and Rank's. At least two pneumatic grain elevators, complete with hoses, survive to the north of this complex.
Ref: Concrete 34 (1939), 360-2.

Ref: E Clark, Minutes of the Proceedings of the Institution of Civil Engineers, 25, 292. International Exhibition 1882: Illustrated Catalogue of the Industrial Department Vol. 2 p 9 (illustration).

CWS Granary   *TQ 413 803*
Victoria Dock

Situated on the south side of Victoria Dock this large granary was well situated to receive imported grain. It was built in reinforced concrete in 1938-44 and replaced a steam powered mill which had machinery driven by rope, not unlike a Lancashire Cotton Mill. Architect L G Ekins.
Ref: Goad insurance plans, CWS Annuals c1900 and the periodical 'Concrete'.

9   Granaries, south side of Royal Victoria Dock 1977. (GLC)

9

11

10   Discharging grain, Royal Victoria Dock 1926. (Museum of London)

11   CWS Granary looking south west July 1979. (R J M Carr)

No 4 Shed   *TQ 415 804*
Royal Victoria Dock

For the berth used by the United States Line until c1965. This berth was constructed 1958 as part of the extensive remodelling works carried out on Royal Victoria Dock which started before World War II.

Scotch Derrick   *TQ 416 805*

One of a fast disappearing type (this example was introduced to lift containers). The standard dockside cranes in the 'Royals' had insufficient capacity to do this. Traditionally used in timber yards.

Victorian Office Building   *TQ 415 801*
Thames Road, E16

A fine late 19th century office building for Thomas W Ward Ltd. Fairly ornate decoration with the letters 'TWW' set in white bricks. Iron and Steel business. Silvertown Machinery Works. Demolished c1984. A sad loss in an area with few notable buildings.

Railway Yard   *TQ 417 800*
Thames Road, E16

The railway yard still sees a little activity and two privately owned diesel shunting locomotives were stabled here until recently. Prior to 1855

Pontoon Dock   *TQ 411 802*
Royal Victoria Dock

The site of the revolutionary hydraulic ship lift of c1855 was *TQ 413 804*. Ships were raised out of the water by a system of hydraulic jacks and placed on pontoons which could be shunted to the finger of the Pontoon Dock for repair work to be carried out. The number of ships which could be accommodated was essentially limited only by the number of pontoons available. Now the fingers of the Pontoon Dock have been concreted over.

10

this portion of railway formed the Eastern Counties Railway's extension to North Woolwich (opened June 1847) but on the building of Victoria Dock in 1850-55 the problems posed by the railway crossing the dock entrance *(TQ 398 804)* via a swing bridge prompted the building of an avoiding line to the North of the dock. This was opened in November 1855 and the section of track to the south of Victoria Dock known as 'The Woolwich Abandoned Line' became a siding worked from the East.

Brick Chimney and Boiler House
TQ 417 799

Part of the works of Crosse & Blackwell. Still in use to provide steam for process work in the manufacture of sauces and pickles. c1930s. A prominent feature of the riverside landscape.
See also the entry for Tay Wharf.

Silvertown By-pass E16
TQ 416 801 — TQ 420 801

Construction contemporary with Silvertown Way (above) and part of the same improvement scheme. Gives good views of the former ship repair works at the West end of Royal Albert dock. Bowstring bridge in reinforced concrete carries the road over the Canning Town to North Woolwich railway.

St Mark's Church, Silvertown   *TQ 419 802*

Listed grade II

Redundant Anglican Church by S S Teulon 1861-2; heavily fire damaged. This building is currently being restored and converted with funds provided by both the LDDC and the London Borough of Newham to house the Victorian Collections of the Passmore Edwards Museum.

Tay Wharf   *TQ 420 800*
Factory Road, E16

Remains of ornamental gateway, nicely restored. Inscribed 'Tay Wharf 1900'. This is the entry to the former Keiller's jam and marmalade factory which operated from 1880 to 1967. It now belongs to Crosse & Blackwell who make sauces and pickles here.

Seamen's Hospital   *TQ 415 811*
Felsted Road, E16

Still functioning, the present 'Albert Dock Hospital', consists of 1930s buildings laid out on an attractive campus. The first Albert Dock Hospital dates from 1887 and the present buildings were opened in 1937.

Board of Trade Building   *TQ 415 808*
Connaught Road, E16

Magisterial red brick building with imposing portico facing east, c1915? The legend 'Board of Trade' is inscribed in the stonework above the doorway. At the back are outbuildings with greenhouse-like clerestories.

Reinforced concrete shed on columns
TQ 418 808

Within the Royal Albert Dock estate, opposite the Board of Trade building in Connaught Road is this interesting reinforced concrete shed raised on reinforced-concrete columns to allow railway wagons to pass beneath. Could well be of structural interest, dates from c1930? Thought to be ex-GWR goods station.

Connaught Tavern   *TQ 416 808*

Listed grade II

Large public house architecturally noteworthy for the district; by Vigers and Wagstaffe 1881 in Queen Anne style.
   Ref: Building News **7** *October 1881* cf the better known Gallions Hotel *(TQ 439 807).*

12   *Connaught Tavern, rear view 1971. (GLC)*

12

Gentlemen's Cast Iron Urinal   *TQ 416 808*
Connaught Road, E16

Listed grade II

A piece of ornate late Victorian cast-iron street furniture. Painted grey. Now closed. Among the last few survivors in London.

Connaught Passage   *TQ 417 806*

Built 1880 to connect Victoria and Albert Docks. The Canning Town to North Woolwich railway line was diverted beneath the passage by a tunnel at the dock company's expense to avoid delay to trains when ships were passing. This tunnel has rather steep gradients (1 in 50) and some freight trains continued to cross at ground level using the Connaught Road swing bridge where there was a 15 mph speed restriction until the 1970s. The course of the tunnel, just to the East of the swing bridge, can be traced by a pair of ventilation shafts. In 1937, as part of the rebuilding works for Royal Victoria Dock, the Connaught Passage was deepened from 28 to 31 feet without the interruption of shipping. In 1958 the cutting was widened from 84 to 100 feet, again without interrupting traffic.

Ref: R R Liddell, Proceedings of the Institution of Civil Engineers, 10, (1939), 283. See the chapter by Ivan Greeves.

Connaught Road Swing Bridge
TQ 416 806

Built originally for both road and rail use, crosses the Connaught Passage. Hydraulically operated. Still usable (?) although machinery pit flooded. The maker's plate reads: Westwood Baillie & Co, Engineers, Shipbuilders and Contractors, Poplar, London 1879.

Ref: GLIAS Newsletter 82 p 5 and Proceedings of the Institution of Civil Engineers, 10 (1939), 283.

Hydraulic pumping station
TQ 418 807

A local dock hydraulic pumping station to provide hydraulic power for the Connaught Road swing bridge and vicinity. Still functionable, complete with c1925 electric pumps and small accumulator in an adjacent tower. A nice survival. Just to the east of the small hydraulic pumping station building is a shaft, used to pump out water which seeps into the Connaught Passage railway tunnel. This was lined with steel rings in 1937 when the Connaught Passage was deepened. It is believed that submersible electric pumps are installed at the bottom of the shaft. Surmounting the shaft is an attractive cupola (c1880?) reminiscent of those of the Woolwich foot tunnel. This was damaged c1982.

Former Ship Repair Works
TQ 419 804

Originally R & H Green & Silley Weir, became part of River Thames Shiprepairs Ltd, on nationalisation. Dating from c1880, closed 1980.

Buildings consist of main offices (c1930s), to the South West *(TQ 418 804)*, machine shops *(TQ 418 805)* and on the other side of the pair of associated dry docks (see separate entry for the docks below), a large boiler shop. The machinery was removed, much for scrap, after a sale in July 1980. This was until recently one of the most interesting industrial sites in Dockland.

Ref: Sale Catalogue, July 1980.

13 Top of pumping shaft for Connaught Passage railway tunnel July 1979. (R J M Carr)

14 Royal Albert dry dock with the SS Manhattan. The large travelling crane was still in situ 1985. (Museum of London)

15 River Thames Shiprepairs (RTS), machine shop August 1979. (R J M Carr)

16 RTS, pattern store January 1980. (R J M Carr)

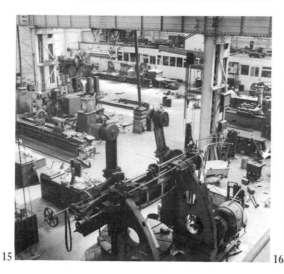

13

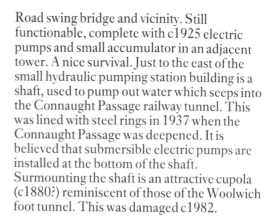

14

15

16

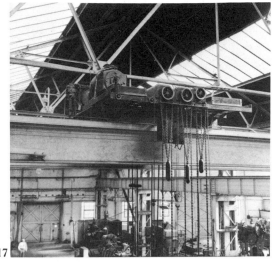

17

18

19

Dry Docks *TQ 419 805*
Royal Albert Dock

A pair thought to date from the 1880s, the larger
to the West 574′ 6″ long, 92′ wide and 24′ 11″
deep, the smaller to the East, 500′ long, 66′ 7″
wide and 24′ 6″ deep. The smaller is now
unusable and harbours a floating dock (said to
be ex Harland & Wolff's, from Newfoundland
Dock, Surrey Commercial Docks), constructed
1942.

The floating dock is 168′ long, 48′ wide and
has a lifting capacity of 950 tons. Maker
unknown.

By the dry docks to the west is a large Stothart
& Pitt travelling crane of 25 tons capacity, dated
1919.

Pumphouse for Draining Dry Docks
TQ 420 805

Situated at the north end of the peninsula
between the above two dry docks. Contains
machinery for draining the dry docks and
providing a local supply of compressed air
power. Pumping is by two large Tangye
centrifugal pumps driven by Westinghouse
two-phase synchronous electric motors and a
pair of deep-well reciprocating pumps driven by
Laurence Scott DC motors. The centrifugal
pumps are primed by two small Tangye
2-cylinder reciprocating pumps with
Westinghouse DC motors. The 2-phase supply
is provided by Scott Connected Transformers
which convert the local 3-phase mains. (At one
time parts of West Ham had a public 2-phase
power supply. See the entry on West Ham
Power Station.) The pumphouse is in quite
good order. After the closure of River Thames
Shiprepairs Ltd, the last firm to operate the
Royal Albert Dry Docks, it was placed in the
hands of the PLA.

The pumps are in the northern part of the
pumphouse. To the south is a fine bank of four
Alley & MacLellan Sentinel 2-cylinder
inverted-vertical air compressors driven by
Electric Construction Company DC motors
dated 1919. Outside, to the south, are air
receivers rated at 100(?) psi.
Ref: GLIAS Newsletter 82, page 6.

Former Ship-Repair Building *TQ 422 804*

This was used by Harland & Wolff who had
large machine shops here. Most of the
machinery had gone by 1980. The plan of the
building is interesting, the North side being
elliptical.

King George V Dry Dock *TQ 422 803*

The largest dry dock in Greater London,
opened 1921. On the River Thames only the
large dry dock at Tilbury is bigger. Can
accommodate ships of 20,000 tons. Now used
for yachts and boats.

The caisson was so designed that it could also
block off the passage to Royal Albert Dock.
Ref: Engineering **112** *(1921), 2-7, and plates.*

*17   Travelling crane, RTS
machine shop August 1979.
(R J M Carr)*

*18   Lathe head, 1912 Pearn
Richards lathe, RTS August 1979.
(R J M Carr)*

*19   Craig and Donald large plate
bending rolls, RTS plate shop August
1979. (R J M Carr)*

Pumphouse for King George V Dry Dock
TQ 423 804

Subterranean, to the North East of the dry dock. Contains two sets of electric motors driving centrifugal pumps. The pumping equipment, by Drysdale & Co, Bon Accord Works, Yoker, Glasgow, has been unusable since flooding c1979.
  *Ref: Engineering **112** (1921), 2-7 and plates.*

Board School   *TQ 423 803*
Saville Road, E16

Typical late 19th century board school just outside the dock estate.

Main Superintendent's Office
TQ 424 808
Saville Road, E16, Royal Albert Dock

Office for the Royal Docks.

Royal Albert Dock   *TQ 425 807*

Opened in 1880 by the Duke of Connaught on behalf of Queen Victoria, the prefix 'Royal' was included in the title from the outset. The Act was obtained in 1875, the Dock was designed by Sir Alexander Rendel and the contractors were Messrs Lucas and Aird. Single storey transit sheds were erected rather than warehouses, the emphasis being on fast turn round, and it was the first dock, in London to be lit by electricity.

20   Mending anchor cable pre-1939, King George V dry dock. (Museum of London)

21   Work on a ship's propeller King George V dry dock about 1930. (Museum of London)

22   Barclay's Bank, Royal Albert Dock 1977.

Vacant ground   *TQ 424 814*
North of Royal Albert Dock

Prior to World War I it was intended to construct a large dock on this site but a more modest scheme to construct a smaller dock to the South of Royal Albert Dock (the Royal Albert Dock extension) was finally decided upon. This dock, opened in 1921, was named King George V.
  The vacant ground to the North of Royal Albert Dock was occupied by allotments and sports fields but is now being built upon.

Central Buffet, North Quay, Royal Albert Dock   *(approx) TQ 424 808*

Listed grade II

1883 by Vigers and Wagstaffe. To afford facilities to ships' passengers at the Royal Docks.

23   Thames sailing barges in the Royal Docks, 1930s. (Museum of London)

23

Transit Sheds   *TQ 422 805 — TQ 436 804*
Peninsula Road

Construction makes use of roof trusses in reinforced concrete. Demolition taking place 1982/83. Stolport will be located here.

King George V Dock   *TQ 430 803*

The last dock but one to be built in the Port of London, opened 1921. Can accommodate ships of over 30,000 tons gross. Generally similar to the Royal Albert Dock to the North it was known as the Royal Albert Dock Extension during construction.
   Ref: Engineering 112 (1921), 2-7 and plates I-IV.

Dolphins   *TQ 424 802 — TQ 436 801*
On South Side of King George V Dock

A feature of this dock, unique in the Port of London. Allowed lighters to pass freely between ships and the quay, permitting simultaneous loading/unloading over both sides of the ship. The dolphins were connected to the South Quay by footbridges.

Thames Refinery, Tate & Lyle   *TQ 422 800*
Factory Road, E16

Large cane-sugar refinery. Tate & Co established refineries at Silvertown in 1871 and Lyle & Sons started in 1881. After recent modernisation little older plant remains. To the south *(TQ 422 797)* is a jetty at which sugar cane is imported (generally from the West Indies, South East Africa etc). Until July 1979 Tate & Lyle operated their own fleet of ships (Sugar Line Ltd) but from then has relied on chartering, mostly foreign ships. The unrefined brown sugar is removed from vessels at the jetty by cranes with grabs. Thames Refinery was built by H Tate & Sons in 1878 to manufacture cube sugar. The amalgamation of Tate and Lyle took place in 1921. The company's distinctive road vehicles are still a feature of operations.

Cairn Mills, Loders and Nucoline
TQ 425 799
Factory Road, E16

Manufacturer of tailored fats for the food industry. Commenced operations 1887, now part of Unilever. Raw material, ground nut oil, imported via Tilbury and brought up river to the Company's own wharf here by lighter. Plant almost all modern. Products used in chocolate, biscuits and cakes etc.
   10″ x 12″ glass negatives deposited with Passmore Edwards Museum 1979. These depict views of the works c1920.
   Ref: The Fascination of Fats, Unilever International 17, 8-13.

24

Standard Industrial Estate   *TQ 428 798*
Henley Road, E16

On the site of the former Standard Telephone and Cables's Woolwich works, demolished c1979, being redeveloped (1983) as an industrial estate for (relatively) small businesses. W T Henley started a factory for submarine cable and electrical gear on a 12 acre site here in 1853. Satellite communication dishes now present.

Cupola over shaft of foot tunnel
TQ 432 798

Listed grade II

A prominent feature of the open space at North Woolwich to the North of the Ferry approach there is little of comparable visual interest in the vicinity. The foot tunnel to Woolwich itself was constructed by means of a Greathead shield using compressed air and is lined with cast iron segments. The engineer was Sir Maurice Fitzmaurice, the tunnel being completed in 1912. Compare with the Greenwich foot tunnel.

North Woolwich Old Station Museum
TQ 432 799
Pier Road, E16

Listed grade II

Owned by the Passmore Edwards Museum Trust, North Woolwich Old Station was converted to a Museum with a capital grant from the London Docklands Development Corporation and is administered by the Governors of the Passmore Edwards Museum with revenue funding provided by the London Borough of Newham through its Leisure Services Committee. Concentrating on the history of the Great Eastern Railway, the Museum includes, amongst many objects illustrating the history of the Railway, a restored

24   The King George V dock at night about 1960. (Museum of London)

25

26

25 Turntable area looking east, North Woolwich station 1974. (GLC)

26 North Woolwich station looking west 1974. (GLC)

ticket office of the period 1914/1939. Track has been relaid and there is 'live steam' operation. The railway line now stops short of this station building and a new station to the North West with a small passenger shelter, was fashioned c1980 from part of the remains of the old railway terminus. The original dignified Italianate station building, standing at right angles to the line of railway, was completed for the opening of the Eastern Counties Railway extension to North Woolwich on 14 June 1847. During World War II it was damaged by bombing.

Floating Pier, North Woolwich
TQ 433 797

Woolwich Pier was used by the tugs of the Alexandra Towing Company and several could usually be seen alongside until recently. The Pier is thought to date from the last quarter of the 19th century. The floating landing stage is linked to the shore by a bowstring girder bridge.

Edwardian Police Station   *TQ 433 798*

On the corner of Pier Road and Albert Road is this typical police station of the period, dated 1904.

Royal Victoria Gardens   *TQ 435 798*

Welcome riverside green space in the care of the London Borough of Newham. A raised viewing shelter with provision for senior citizens allows easy viewing of the shipping in Woolwich Reach over the river wall now that the latter has been raised in conjunction with the Thames Barrier flood prevention scheme. The Park is thought to date from the last quarter of the 19th century.

Engine House, etc   *TQ 437 798*
Woolwich Manor Way, E16

Adjacent to the Park (Royal Victoria Gardens) is this small group of late 19th century engine house buildings. One of the buildings has a louvered 'clerestory' (probably at one time a boiler house). TWA main drainage pumping station.

Site of former ship-repair works
TQ 439 801
Woolwich Manor Way, E16

Harland & Wolff's works stood here until c1978. There are now few remains. Traces of a railway track down towards the River existed c1982.

Former Gallions Radio Station building
(approx) TQ 440 800

The function of this VHF ships radio station has been transferred to the Woolwich Barrier Radio, *TQ 416 793*. Building c1960?

King George V Entrance Lock   *TQ 439 802*

The present entrance lock for the Royal Docks, opened 1921.

Will admit ships of up to 30,000 tons gross. (The largest ship to use this lock was the RMS Mauretania in 1939.)
   Ref: Engineer.

Steamship pier   *TQ 441 800*
South of Gallions entrance

For ships using the Gallions entrance to the Royal Docks.

Pair of steamship piers   *TQ 422 802*
North of Gallions entrance

For the use of ships using the orignal (closed) entrance to the Royal Albert Dock basin and the

Gallions entrance for the King George V entrance lock.

Pair of Lifting Bascule Bridges over King George V entrance *TQ 437 802*
Woolwich Manor Way, E16

Originally built in 1921. Destroyed by V2 rocket c1944 and replaced. The original bridge was electrically powered so presumably is the present bridge. Still used.

Local hydraulic power system, King George V entrance *TQ 439 802*

This provides power for the lock gates, sluices, capstans (and bridges on Woolwich Manor Way?). Still in use.

Hydraulic Pumping Station *TQ 437 802*

Small automatic pumping station (installed c1970?) to provide power for the King George V entrance lock and environs. Electric pumps. A modern accumulator tower is situated just to the north west of the bascule bridges which carry Woolwich Manor Way across the King George V entrance.

Basin South Depôt *TQ 440 802*

This was the nerve centre for dock maintenance until 1980. Here all railway fittings (turn-outs, crossovers, etc.) for the 280 miles of railway network were fabricated.

A large carpenters' shop made items of high quality joinery for dock offices as well as heavy carpentry for compound timber piles. A precast concrete yard made concrete piles for the various docks. Heavy timbers were always kept in stock for emergencies.

Royal Albert Dock Entrance Lock (Gallions Entrance)
TQ 442 805

550′ long by 80′ wide, gives access to the Royal Albert Dock Basin (1880) from the River. There were formerly two, that to the south, the original entrance, used as a barge lock, 550′ long and 80′ wide *(TQ 441 804)*, has been filled in.
Ref: The Engineer, vol 1, pp 6-10.

Pair of entrance piers *TQ 443 804*
Royal Albert Dock entrance

To assist ships using the Royal Albert Dock entrance locks.

Royal Albert Dock Basin *TQ 439 805*

Entrance basin for Royal Albert Dock opened, 1880. It was in use as a pleasure-boat marina until c1979 but is now totally disused.

Royal Albert Dock Basin, Impounding Station *TQ 442 806*

Built from 1911. Replaced a steam pumping station. Contains centrifugal electric pumps to maintain the water level in the Royal Docks, until the 1950s (at least) the largest extent of impounded water in the world. The installation of this impounding station enabled the water level in the Royals to be raised to 2′ 6″ above THW. Also known as the Gallions impounding station.

PLA Housing *TQ 441 803*

The house facing the river was for the Chief Dockmaster. The others were occupied by the Chief Police Inspector and Assistant Dockmasters.

Hydraulic Swing Bridge over Royal Albert dock entrance *TQ 437 805*
Woolwich Manor Way, E16

Plate girder construction. The maker's plate reads: Westwood Baillie & Co, Engineers, Shipbuilders and Contractors, Poplar, London 1879.

Hydraulic Swing Bridge *TQ 436 804*

Connects the 'Peninsula Road' with gate No 15 and Woolwich Manor Way. Movable to allow ships to pass, it is currently kept open. Dates from 1921. Plate girder construction.
Ref: Binns A, The King George V Dock London, Min. Proc. Inst. Civ Eng **216** *(1923) p 372.*

27 Swing bridge connecting the 'Peninsula Road' with gate 15, Royal Docks July 1979. (R J M Carr)

27

Gallions Hotel *TQ 439 807*
Gallions Road, E16

*Listed grade II**

Former hotel by Vigers and Wagstaffe 1881-3.
For the use of liner passengers embarking at the
adjacent jetty. A subway used to connect with
the Royal Albert Dock basin. Latterly passenger
activity transferred to Tilbury. The PLA railway
has a station (Gallions) served by boat trains
from the main-line railways. The hotel was built
on piles and had stables beneath the ground
floor (still extant 1974). Compare with
Brunswick Wharf, Tilbury Hotel.
  *Ref: (literary) Rudyard Kipling, The Light that
Failed (1890); 'Is it Tilbury and a tender, or
Gallions and the Docks?'.*
  *See also Peacock, T B, PLA Railways,
Locomotive Publishing Co 1952.*

Steamer Pier *TQ 444 807*
Royal Albert Dock entrance

To assist ships entering/leaving the Royal
Albert Dock entrance lock and also for the
embarkation/disembarkation of passengers
from liners using the Royal Docks, in
connection with the adjacent Gallions Hotel
(see that entry above). Of the order of 500 yards
in length. Known as Cory's Jetty. Coal from the

North East came to a depôt here for disembarkation by the Company.

Modern Storm Water Pumping Station
TQ 437 808

Thames Water Authority Gallions pumping
station is housed in a polygonal building in
striking style. Electric pumps. The crane for
moving heavy materials about inside runs on a
circular track. Constructed 1976-7.

Prefabricated Houses *TQ 432 812*
Stannard Crescent, E6

Characteristic post World War II 'prefab
estate'. Beckton Gas works looms in the
distance. Demolition December-January
1982/83. Only one remaining 30 January 1983.

Coal Yard *TQ 439 812*

Coal merchants stockyard from which a fleet of
lorries operate. Thought to date from at least
before 1939. A student from Thames
Polytechnic on a project, visited this yard c1979,
took photographs (and wrote a report? — which
should be available in Thames Polytechnic
library). Apart from sociological interest the

*28 The Royal Docks looking north
west 1950. (Museum of London)*

yard is also of interest in that it affords good views of Beckton Gasworks.

Beckton Gas Works   *TQ 443 813*

Huge town gas works, out of use. Access difficult. At one time the largest gas works in Europe. Much plant in store, extensive demolition c1985. Named after the first governor of the Gaslight & Coke Company.

Construction started in November 1868 and the first gas was produced on 25 November 1870 with full production commencing soon afterwards. Sited on desolate marsh, workers' housing was built close by. Described as 'this busy if not altogether lovely colony' Beckton was often enveloped in its own private fog.

Ref: Everard, Stirling History of the Gaslight & Coke Company, Benn, 1949.

Terrace of Houses for Gas workers
TQ 435 816
Winsor Terrace, E6

Late 19th century provision of accommodation for workers at Beckton Gas Works. This fine terrace of houses is just outside the main gate of the works. Windsor Terrace is presumably named after the well-known promotor of gas lighting. There are palms in some of the (North facing) gardens (indicating a mild climate in winter?)

Ref: Everard, Stirling History of the Gaslight & Coke Company, Benn, 1949.

Waste Heap, 'Beckton Alps'   *TQ 431 821*
Corner of East Ham Manor Way and Newham by-pass

Large heap of waste from the adjacent Beckton Gas Works (from the by-products plant); some has been removed by road truck. Red coloured material becoming exposed. An important feature of the landscape (now officially recognised as such). The remaining part of the Alps has been landscaped to provide a dry ski slope. It was rumoured that (parts?) of a (an industrial?) railway locomotive (ex Beckton Gas Works?) were discovered buried here c1982 during removal of the heap. The new industrial estate to the South East boasts an 'Alpine Way'. One of the distinctive industrial railway locomotives which used to work at Beckton Gas Works may be seen at Bressingham steam museum, near Diss, Norfolk.

A bridge was built over Manor Way to enable further tipping of "Blue Billy" waste from the gas purifiers, on ground to the west. This was never used as World War II prevented the import of material from Germany and alternative purifying methods were used later.

Beckton Pier No 1   *TQ 448 813*

Monumental late 19th century jetty constructed on cast iron columns, for the unloading of coal from colliers for Beckton Gas works. Access difficult, good views may be obtained from a boat. No 1, that to the North, is the larger of the two Beckton jetties. (Said to rival Blyth Staithes in size). Length about 400 yards.

Beckton Pier No 2   *TQ 446 810*

Similar to Pier No 1 to the North. About 250 yards in length. Coal conveyors and elegant swan-necked (hand powered?) cranes, reminiscent of ships' davits, on jetty now removed. Originally there were eight hand powered cranes each of 2 tons capacity by the East Ferry Road Engineering Works Co Ltd, 1928. On the bank, to the North West, are large reinforced concrete storage hoppers (built in 1930s). This pier appears to be the more complete of the two.

Northern Outfall Sewer   *TQ 452 816 (the outfall) — TQ 371 830 (and beyond)*

Part of Sir Joseph Bazalgette's main drainage scheme for London.

A prominent feature of this part of London. A corresponding Southern Outfall Sewer runs North-Eastwards to meet the River at Crossness.

There are crossing places for pedestrians from Lonsdale Avenue at *TQ 426 822* and *TQ 412 824* as well as several imposing built-up plate girder bridges where the outfall is carried over roads and waterways, etc.

19th century Sewage Treatment Works
TQ 451 817
Thames Water Authority, Beckton

Victorian works to serve Sir Joseph Bazalgette's Northern Outfall Sewer (1864-8) which meets the River close by. An attractive group of buildings with a chimney characteristic of the period. (Some kind of preservation has been discussed.) The huge modern Beckton Sewage works surrounds this interesting survival to the North.

Digested Sludge Pump House   *TQ 452 817*

Attractive pump house building containing valve wheels etc. Believed to be used in the loading of the fleet of Thames Water Authority sludge ships which berth at the jetty, adjacent to the South.

Effluent Storage Tank   *TQ 451 815*
Thames Water Authority Beckton Sewage Treatment Works.

Prominent storage tank by the River constructed from small prefabricated panels, dating from the 1920s when treated sewage was stored to await high tide. Valve wheels on top. (Probably another reason for its installation was to increase capacity.)

Southwark

This borough is on the south bank of the river opposite the City and extends eastwards to the Surrey Commercial Docks. To the west it is very densely built up and small industries abounded. Only a selection of locations is included in this gazetteer. There were a very large number of interesting warehouses characteristic of the district.

1 *Oxo building 1984. (GLC)*

Site of the Rennie Brothers' engineering works *(approx) TQ 317 805*
Rennie Street, SE1

George and John, the two sons of the famous engineer John Rennie, had an engineering works here from 1821 to 1833. A steam engine constructed by this firm may be seen in the Brunel engine house, Rotherhithe, *TQ 352 798*. This is a centrifugal pumping engine from Chatham Naval Dockyard.

Ref: Boucher CTG, **John Rennie,** *Manchester University Press, 1963. Rennie G, History of J & G Rennie down to 1850, MS in Rennie Collection, National Library of Scotland, Edinburgh.*

Remains of former Blackfriars Station
TQ 317 805

This station closed in 1886 when the present Blackfriars Station on the North bank with its associated rail bridge, the easternmost of two, was opened in 1886. The superseded station was used for goods until c1965. The sign 'Dover Shed' may still be read on the side of the viaduct but redevelopment now in progress.

The railway bridge of 1864 by Joseph Cubitt, immediately to the west of the present rail bridge, was largely demolished 1984–85, leaving piers in the river.

2 *Joseph Cubitt's Blackfriars railway bridge in 1983. (now demolished) (GLC)*

Remains of Albion Mill   *TQ 317 805*

Just downstream of Blackfriars Bridge on the south side of the river, near the steps, are remains of the footings of Albion Mill, the first mill designed to grind corn on a large scale by steam power. Engines were by Boulton and Watt and the machinery by John Rennie the elder. The mill, very advanced for its time, started work in 1784 but burnt down in 1791, probably as a result of an over-heated bearing not being attended to. The remains are said to be visible at low tide.

Southwark Street
TQ 316 804 — TQ 326 801

A new street driven through old property by the Metropolitan Board of Works in 1864 at a cost of £500,000 (cf Holborn Viaduct).

Kirkaldy's Testing and Experimenting Works   *TQ 318 802*
99, Southwark Street, SE1

Listed grade II

David Kirkaldy, after working in the Clydeside shipbuilding industry, established his first materials testing works at The Grove, Southwark, in 1864. Such was the success of this pioneer venture that purpose-built premises to the design of T R Smith were erected in the then newly completed Southwark Street at No 99, the move being accomplished in 1873. The building in Southwark Street still houses Kirkaldy's unique patent hydraulic testing machine of 1864, which was constructed by Greenwood & Batley of Leeds. After the death of the first David Kirkaldy in 1897 work continued as a family business which did not cease until 1964. A materials testing museum is being set up at No 99 Southwark Street which should soon be open to the public on occasions. Note the inscription. 'Facts not Opinions' over the front door at the NW corner of the site.

See David Kirkaldy (1820-1897) and Engineering Materials Testing by Denis Smith, Transactions of the Newcomen Society **52**, *49-65 and GLIAS Newsletter* **79** *page 2.*

Bankside Power Station   *TQ 319 804*

Great care was taken in the design of this power station so that it would not present an 'eyesore' to those looking southwards from the City. The architect was Sir Giles Gilbert Scott. Perhaps we may now judge the success of this endeavour; will Bankside power station be listed? Built rather late, and of small size, the plant was not installed until 1963. Towards the end of its life power was provided by just one 100 MW English Electric turbo alternator using steam at 103.4 bar and 538°C from a single oil-fired boiler. The oil firing plus small size had given this station a very limited life and it was closed by 1981. At the adjacent CEGB

offices in Sumner Street an archive collection relating to power stations in Greater London is being set up. Bankside gas works, opened 1814, occupied part of the site. This works had a life of 124 years.

3

Site of Lead Works   *TQ 323 804*

Works dated 1880 demolished 1982. The firm, Grey & Marten was established in 1833. Lead working was once an important industry in Southwark.

See supplement to GLIAS Newsletter 79 (April 1982).

St Mary Overy's Wharf   *TQ 326 803*

Listed grade II

Large warehouse constructed 1882/83 to designs of the architect G A Dunnage. Walls were of brick with a fair amount of ornamentation. There were brick basement vaults. Floors were supported on cast iron columns with fireproof construction for the ground and first floors, the upper floors being of timber. The roof had a timber queen post construction. Plans to accommodate *HMS Discovery* in a dry dock constructed on the site of St Mary Overy's dock have been considered

4

3   City Lead Works, Grey & Martin Ltd, demolished 1982. (GLC)

4   Pickfords Wharf, Clink Street 1981. (GLC)

236

5 *St Mary Overy Wharf looking south west June 1979. (R J M Carr)*

6 *Fire damaged roof trusses St Mary Overy 1981. (GLC)*

7 *Hay's Dock from a boat August 1979. (R J M Carr)*

which would involve an extension jutting into the river. Demolition of St Mary Overy's Wharf was allowed on appeal by the Environment Secretary in late 1982, against his Inspector's recommendation. Recording work carried out by GLIAS.

In September 1883, St Mary Overy's Wharf was the first to make use of the newly established public hydraulic power supply which had been set up by the Wharves and Warehouse Steam Power and Hydraulic Pressure Company (renamed the London Hydraulic Power Company in 1884). Close by to the south, **Stave Wharf** and **Rosings' Wharf** are now demolished. To the east, **New Hibernia Wharf** went c1979 and redevelopment is almost complete. A new dry-dock was completed 1985.

Ref: 'St Mary Overy's, Rosings' and Stave Wharves', Supplement to GLIAS Newsletter 87, August 1983.

London Bridge Station *TQ 329 801*

Originally opened in 1836 as the London terminus of the London and Greenwich Railway, the station was progressively enlarged in the 19th century as other companies, the London & Croydon, South Eastern and London & Brighton Railways also terminated their routes here. Recent rebuilding has left little of the original buildings. On 11 January

1864 the Charing Cross Railway Company (alias the South Eastern Railway Company) opened the line westwards on a brick viaduct over Southwark with the extension to Cannon Street station being opened on 1st September 1866 and by the addition of two new London termini the traffic load on London Bridge was considerably lightened.

Ref: London's First Railway by R H G Thomas, Batsford, 1972; especially chapter 7.

Hay's Dock *TQ 331 802*
Tooley Street, SE1

Some grade II listing

Small dock, formerly with lock gates, surrounded by impressive warehouses by W Snooke & H Stock, originally built c1856. There was much damage in the great Tooley Street fire of 1861 which necessitated rebuilding. As a compromise towards the completely fireproof construction practised in the cotton mills of the North these warehouses had alternate fireproof floors of brick jack-arch construction, other floors being timber on cruciform cast iron columns.

In the 19th century quite large sailing ships were accommodated in the dock despite its small size but mostly goods arrived in lighters from ships down river. Trade was predominantly in foodstuffs; cheese, eggs, bacon, butter, meat, fresh vegetables, coffee, wines and spirits. As early as 1867 the first New Zealand butter and cheese was imported and gradually the firm expanded from its nucleus of Hay's Dock to own all the wharves on the south bank from Tower Bridge to London Bridge with one exception and a further four wharves upstream of London Bridge. Much refrigerated and cool storage accommodation was provided.

The warehouses around Hay's Dock are being drastically redeveloped, only 'A' block on the east side is to retain its original columns and floors. The Dock itself will become an underground car park surmounted by a glazed roof vaguely reminiscent of the Crystal Palace. The Dock structure will be retained should it be required to return to dock use next century.

8 *Hay's Dock Warehouse interior 1980. (GLC)*

9 *Hay's Dock Warehouse interior 1980. (GLC)*

8

9

Among the notable buildings associated with the Hay's Wharf group are: —

St Olaf House   *TQ 329 803*
Tooley Street, SE1

Listed grade II

Head office for the group. By H S Goodhart-Rendel in Continental modern style 1931. Design allows lorries to pass beneath.

Cotton's Wharf   *TQ 330 803*
Tooley Street, SE1

Some grade II listing

Warehouses rebuilt after the great fire of 1861 by William Snooke and Henry Stock, the contractor being Sir William Cubitt.
   Ref: Three Hundred Years on London's River: The Hay's Wharf Story, 1651-1951, A Ellis, Bodley Head 1952. The Geography of the Port of London, J Bird, Hutchinson 1957 pp 133-137.

Tower Bridge   *TQ 336 802*

Listed grade I

Built 1886-94 in Gothic style, to harmonise with the historic buildings of the Tower of London. The stonework conceals a steel semi-suspension bridge and has no structural function. The engineer for the work was Sir John Wolfe-Barry. The architect, Sir Horace Jones, died in 1887 and the architectural detailing was completed by a Mr Stevenson, one of the engineer's assistants. Until 1976-7 the bridge bascules were raised by hydraulic power; the hydraulic engines were situated in the bases of the piers whilst power was provided by the bridge's own hydraulic pumping station situated on the South Bank to the East of Tower Bridge Road *(TQ 337 801)*, (see below). Hydraulic lifts in the towers gave access to the overhead walkway which has been closed to the public from c1900 until recently through lack of use. Parts of the bridge interior and the walkway are now open to the public as a tourist attraction upon payment of an entrance fee. The impressive bascule chambers are not open.

10

Tower Bridge Workshops   *TQ 335 800*

The upper floor of this narrow two-storey building contained belt-driven machine tools for the maintenance of Tower Bridge. On the ground floor were blacksmiths' and carpenters' shops.
   See GLIAS report.

Tower Bridge Hydraulic Power Station
TQ 336 801

Listed Grade II

Situated to the East of Tower Bridge Road on the South side of the river are a distinctive chimney and accumulator tower. Two

10 *Hay's Dock, 1980. (GLC)*

11

12

13

14

11   Tower Bridge, chimney and accumulator tower of hydraulic pumping station looking south east, June 1975. (Paul Calvocoressi)

12   The Anchor Brewery, Shad Thames 1981. (GLC)

13   Shad Thames looking east September 1984. (Philip Dubuque)

14   Filming in Shad Thames "Dave Allan at Large", Thames Television March 1983. (Philip Dubuque)

accumulators are still in situ, whilst under the arches beneath the roadway are two steam pumping engines of 1894 by Sir W G Armstrong Mitchell & Co Ltd, Elswick, Newcastle.

Anchor Brewery   TQ 336 801
Shad Thames SE1

Listed grade II

Courage's brewery dating from 1789 but substantially rebuilt by Inskip and McKenzie after a fire in 1892. A museum of brewing close by on Tower Bridge Road flourished briefly c1981 but is now out of business. In the brewery itself a considerable amount of plant survived when closure came in 1982 but its quantity overwhelmed existing recording capacity and no work was done. Being converted to flats 1985.

Shad Thames   TQ 337 800
London, SE1

Some warehouses listed grade II

Dramatic canyon formed by warehouses either side of the street crossed at a variety of heights by lattice wrought-iron bridges built to carry barrows from warehouses immediately alongside the river to warehouses further inland. Small streets like this close to the river were once common but this is the best surviving example and one of the most remarkable features of London's Docklands. Now almost unique.

15

16

17

15 *Butler's Wharf.*
(Philip Dubuque)

16 *Butler's Wharf, first floor*
interior 1981. (GLC)

17 *Butler's Wharf interior 1981.*
(GLC)

Butler's Wharf   *TQ 338 800*
Shad Thames, SE1

Most listed grade II

Considerable group of warehouses either side
of Shad Thames extending 150 yards inland,
was the largest wharf on the Thames when
completed in 1871-3. The riverside was given
bold architectural treatment with prominent
end pavilions having rusticated quoins, massive
bracketed cornices and pedimented parapets.
The main entrance from Shad Thames had
massive Doric columns. Architects were Tolley
and Dale and the builder was John Aird & Son,
Belvedere Road. It is thought that the work of
1871-3 involved rebuilding rather than
complete renewal. In 1865 a new block of
buildings had collapsed into the river.

A Mr Butler was associated with the
Company from the late 18th century, at first
with partners, the firm becoming public in
1872. In 1892 the Company was registered as
Butler's Wharf Ltd. By 1945 it had three
subsidiary companies. The Wharf closed in
March 1972, East German ships being the last
to call. Like Hay's Dock much of the traffic was
in foodstuffs. The General Steam Navigation
Co Ltd ships "Hirondelle" and "Swift" worked
services from Butler's Wharf for many years.
The considerable lighterage traffic was handled
mainly by the Union Lighterage Co Ltd. With
lightermen the Wharf was unpopular owing to
its difficult working conditions and the varying
rates of pay for different commodities. Fruit
traffic was worked by Macandrews & Co Ltd
ships. Mud at low tide was a problem. This was
removed by men known as "luters" who worked
in the mud with large rakes.

The Architect/Planners and Developers
Conran Roche are implementing a revitalisation
scheme which will retain 90% of the buildings.
17 are listed. The riverside may be a stopping
point for the intended joint GLC/LDDC river
bus service to Greenwich. Butlers Wharf was
one of three sites considered by the Museum of
London for its Docklands industrial museum.
In October 1983 Louise Roche was
commissioned by Conran Roche to carry out a
study of the general and social history of the
Wharf and it is hoped to publish the results of
her work.

*Ref: Many minute books of the Company survive.
The National Monuments Record, Fortress House,
23 Savile Row, W1, has a number of photographs
taken 1909-20. See also The Builder, January
1865.*

Warehouse W11, Butler's Wharf
TQ 338 799
Maguire Street, SE1

Listed grade II

At the corner with Shad Thames is this large
19th century granary with timber framing, an
example of adaptive re-use. The eastern end
has been refaced with white Suffolk brick. As
part of the Butler's Wharf revitalisation scheme
it will be adapted internally to display the timber
frame. Small windows on the south can be seen
from Maguire Street.

Shad Thames Pumping Station
TQ 338 799

Thames Water Authority storm water pumping

19

18

20

18 *Loading coriander sacks, Shad Thames April 1982. (Philip Dubuque)*

19 *St Andrew's Wharf, Shad Thames 1981. (GLC)*

20 *View north out of St Saviour's Dock April 1983. (Philip Dubuque)*

St Saviour's Dock *TQ 339 798*

Several warehouses listed grade II, London Borough of Southwark Conservation Area

This is actually the mouth of one of London's "lost rivers", the Neckinger, which is now a tidal inlet densely surrounded by warehouses. A lease of 11 January 1554 describes the area as one of meadows and pastures with a water mill. The small grain mill at the mouth of St Saviour's Dock was built by the local ecclesiastical authorities, Bermondsey Abbey, and presumably used the tides as well as the flow of the river (cf Three Mills *TQ 383 828*). Recent demolition at the south end of the Dock has let a little more light into this fascinatingly gloomy waterspace so that the unusually named public house "Dockhead Stores" may now be seen from a boat in the Dock. The surviving

station constructed for the LCC 1906-8. Original gas engines now replaced.
   See supplement to GLIAS Newsletter 71 (December 1980). There is also a film.

mills and warehouses date mainly from 1850-1900.

St Saviour's Dock is now choked with mud which in latter days caused trouble for the lightermen bringing cargoes to the warehouses from ships down river. Being tidal, lighters sat on the mud at low water and could become stuck if loaded and be swamped when the water rose. In the 1920s the dock was said to be clear of mud.

The mills and granaries of this area dealt in grain, peas and spices and were characterised by small wooden mullioned windows. **St George's Wharf** has bands of blue brick and small cast iron window frames. **Lime Wharf** (1883) is of red brick with a gabled sack hoist. **St Andrew's Wharf** has a tower to provide water for fire fighting and a cast iron footbridge crosses the street. This is thought to date from c1850. In Mill Street is **New Concordia Wharf,** once part of St Saviour's flour mill of 1882 rebuilt 1894-8 after a fire. This mill has a very fine brick chimney reduced in height about six years ago. Now highly-desirable flats. **Unity Wharf, Crown Wharf, Shuter's Wharf** and **Reed's Wharf** are also of note. Spice grinding by means of edge runners is still carried on in the area, producing characteristic aromas.

Rotherhithe Street *TQ 350 798 —
TQ 352 799*
Between Elephant Lane and St Mary Church
Street.

Narrow riverside street lined with mid/late 19th
century warehouses, including **Thames
Tunnel Mill** recently converted into flats;
Grice's Granary now a picture library, which
has interesting timber framing with massive
hanging knees, and **Hope Sufferance Wharf**
alongside the churchyard. (St Mary's Church
[1714-15, tower 1747] has strong riverside
connections).

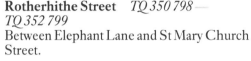

22 Powell's Wharf 1974. (GLC)

*23 First floor Archer's Wharf
1974. (GLC)*

24 Grice's Granary 1974. (GLC)

Brunel Thames Tunnel
TQ 350 801 — TQ 352 798

World's first underwater tunnel, started 1825, finished 1843, by Marc Brunel and son I K Brunel (the latter was almost drowned when the works flooded, and operations ceased for some time). Originally intended for carriage traffic the approaches for wheeled vehicles were never completed and until taken over by the East London Railway carried only pedestrian traffic, becoming a tourist attraction rather than a means of crossing the river. Acquired by the East London Railway 1865 and included in its line from New Cross to Shoreditch, opened to Wapping (only) in 1869. This line was used by BR (steam hauled?) freight trains until (the 1960s?) as well as the LT metropolitan line trains (electric from 1913). (The construction of the ELR Northwards under the Eastern Dock of the London Dock system required considerable works (the engineer was Sir John Hawkshaw) and the line was not completed to the GER until 1876.)

For an account of the construction of the Thames Tunnel *see* **I K Brunel** *by L T C Rolt, Book 1.*

Rotherhithe Road Tunnel   *TQ 352 797*
Brunel Road, SE16

Shaft listed grade II

Built by Greathead shield 1904-8, for LCC, by Maurice Fitzmaurice. A portion of the shield forms an arch at the Southern entrance where the tunnel joins Jamaica Road/Lower Road. A footpath enables pedestrians to make use of the tunnel but owing to traffic noise etc this is not a very pleasant way to cross the river. A shaft with a spiral staircase gave access to King Edward VII Memorial Gardens on the North bank.

Rotherhithe LT Railway Station
TQ 352 798
Brunel Road, SE16

Opened by East London Railway 1869. Modified by refurbishment works in early 1980s. The entrance to the Brunel Thames Tunnel may be seen from the North ends of the platforms. The retaining walls of the cuttings here are heavily braced. Water from this cutting runs into the tunnel from whence it is pumped to the surface. The current pumphouse is situated over the railway just to the North of the station platforms. Some earlier reciprocating pumps (c1900) are housed in a cavity in the West wall at the North end of the platform.

Gas Works Site   *TQ 356 800*
Rotherhithe Street, SE16

The only significant survival is a gas holder of recent date. The works belonged to the Surrey Consumers' Gas Co (founded 1849) until the amalgamation with the South Metropolitan Gas Co in 1879. There were horizontal retorts built 1851-60, and a producer gas plant. Gas production finished here in April 1959.

Coal was unloaded at a substantial jetty *(TQ 355 801)*, now used for the disembarkation of sea-dredged aggregate. Compare the jetty with those at Greenwich *(TQ 388 783)*. East Greenwich *(TQ 396 801)* and Beckton *(TQ 446 811* and *TQ 448 813).*

25 *Construction of the Rotherhithe Tunnel 21 August 1907. (GLC)*

25

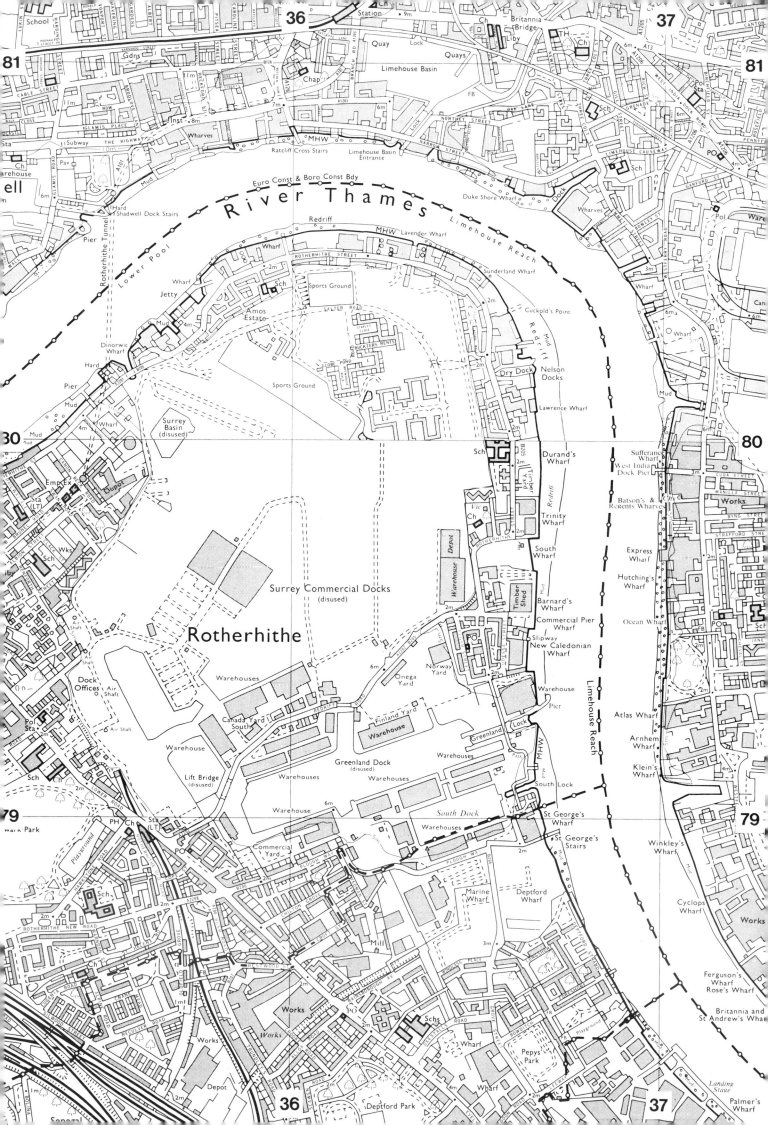

Globe Wharf   TQ 359 805
Rotherhithe Street, SE16

Large late 19th century rice warehouse. Six storeys, nineteen bays wide by thirteen bays deep. Timber floors on iron columns. Part of the SE corner has been sliced off and roofed over. Until its recent closure this wharf handled all the rice coming into London.

Canada and Columbia Wharves
TQ 365 802
Rotherhithe Street, SE16

Two large late 19th century/early 20th century warehouses with some polychrome brickwork.

Nelson Dock   TQ 366 802
Rotherhithe Street, SE16

Small ship-repair yard on an historic site. There is a dry dock with a curious caisson (made from the stern of a ship?) and to the north a slipway up which vessels were drawn by a hydraulic engine. This device consisted of a cylinder with a modest stroke and the ship was attached by a series of detachable metal bars. The ship would be drawn up a few feet at a time, a bar detached, and the process repeated. A tedious procedure. The engine is believed to be still in situ in its original engine house.

Between the 1750s and 1821 Nelson Dock was one of three yards owned by Messrs Randall and Brent who were pioneers of steamship building. Between about 1851 and 1866 it belonged to Messrs Bilbe and Perry who were pioneers of composite construction (timber cladding on iron frames) and built a number of clippers for the China tea trade.

Nelson Dock House   TQ 365 802
265 Rotherhithe Street, SE16

*Listed Grade II**

A fine three storey mid 18th century house. Now used as offices.

Surrey Commercial Docks

The first dock to be built in this system was the Howland Great Wet Dock which obtained its Act in 1696 and was opened in the early 1700s. Later it was associated with the whaling trade and became known as Greenland Dock from 1763. The present Greenland Dock is an enlargement of this dock which was carried out in the 1890s.

Later docks were constructed as follows:

1807	Basin constructed by Grand Surrey Canal Co
1807	Commercial Dock Co
1809	Baltic Dock
1811	East Country Dock
1860	Albion Dock
1876	Canada Dock
1926	Quebec Dock

26   Globe Wharf, a rice warehouse, 1981. (GLC)

27   Nelson Dock exterior 1979. (GLC)

28   Nelson Dock House 1966. (GLC)

29   Ground floor front room, Nelson Dock House 1958. (GLC)

246

30 Commercial Dock Pier with tug Cricket about 1914. (National Maritime Museum)

31 Surrey Commercial Docks, Canada Dock looking south east 1964. (Museum of London)

32 Canada Dock, Surrey Commercial Docks. A timber pile has been landed and awaits the attention of the deal porters. An esparto grass ship, the Livno, lies off on the buoys. (Museum of London)

33 Albion dry dock for the repair of lighters dewatered 1975. (GLC)

247

Swing bridge remains *TQ 362 793*
Redriff Road, SE16

Remains of the swing bridge which crossed the passage between Greenland Dock and Russia Dock have been preserved to illustrate the mode of operation. A walk leads northwards from here along the former East Quay of Russia Dock to the Lavender Dock area. An interesting redevelopment by the London borough of Southwark.

Lavender Dock Pump House
TQ 363 804

Standard PLA design dated 1929. Formerly housed electrically driven centrifugal pumps for the impounding of the Surrey Commercial Dock system. One of the vertical reciprocating pumps for priming the centrifugal pumps was removed for preservation outside the Brunel Engine House, Rotherhithe, where it may now be seen *(TQ 352 798)*. The remaining plant has gone for scrap. There were plans to use the building as an engineering workshop or for community purposes.

Greenland Dock *TQ 364 791*
Lock listed grade II

Built on the site of Howland Great Wet Dock (see above). During 1893-1904 extensive works enlarged the dock to 2250' by 450'. Difficulty was experienced due to foundation problems. J A Maconnichie, the engineer, died before construction was completed and the work was taken over by Sir John Woolfe Barry. The new entrance lock (550' by 80') enabled the Surrey Commercial Co to compete directly with Millwall Dock and the West India Docks, ships of 12,000 tons gross being accommodated by the new Greenland Dock. Grain traffic with Canada was a principal prize. The formation of the PLA makes it difficult to assess if the capital expenditure was justified. The entrance lock is at present blocked by a (temporary?) dam but there are plans to provide access from the river. The water area is used for recreation (sailing dinghies, canoes etc). There are no impounding pumps. Plans (1982) for redevelopment will make substantial changes if implemented.

The entrance lock, complete with hydraulic capstans, rams etc is still essentially complete. (See the chapter *Hydraulic Power.*) There is a public right of way over the swing footbridge crossing the lock. The Rotherhithe Sailing Club uses the lock entrance to berth small vessels. To the South of the entrance is the 'Surrey Docks Farm'. The swing footbridge across the entrance to South Dock is one of the oldest surviving structures in the Surrey Docks.

Some interesting hydraulic remains have recently been discovered here.

34 Surrey Commercial Docks, floating timber pre-1939. (Museum of London)

35 Dock workers drinking tea at Mr Brewster's mobile canteen, Surrey Commercial Docks 1935. (Museum of London)

Stave, Lavender and Lady Docks were shallow, used by lighters and for floating timber. The Surrey Commercial Dock Co was formed by amalgamation in 1864 and this company was subsequently incorporated into the PLA in 1909.

The docks closed in 1969 having dealt principally in timber. They covered 460 acres. Little is now left on the Dock Estate except at the Southern end.

Dock Offices *TQ 353 794*

Two storey red brick 1892 with fine brick clock tower. Being refurbished.

Lewisham

Squeezed between Southwark and Greenwich this borough has a diminutive riverfront at Deptford. It is also covered by the *Industrial Archaeology of South East London* (see Bibliography).

Grand Surrey Canal

Opened 1807, engineer Ralph Dodd, ran from Surrey Commercial Docks to Camberwell (3 miles). Peckham Branch (½ mile) opened 1826. Originally the entrance lock was at Rotherhithe *(TQ 355 802)*. The Northern part of the canal in the Surrey Commercial Docks was progressively converted to dock use. In later days the canal carried an extensive timber trade to yards along its banks. The Canal closed in 1971 and has since been filled but some of the timber yards remain.

Blackhorse Bridge *TQ 364 782*
Evelyn Street, SE8

Iron plate girder canal bridge with brick abutments, formerly over the Surrey Canal. Iron parapets with brick piers at each end. Cast iron lamp standards.

Disused Laundry *TQ 365 784*
Grove Street, Deptford, SE8

c1900(?) Three storeys in yellow brick with red pilaster strips, bands and window arches.

Victualling Yard *TQ 366 788*
Grove Street, SE8

Founded 1742, known as Royal Victoria Yard after visit by Queen Victoria in 1858. Stored

1   The Grand Surrey Canal (Museum of London)

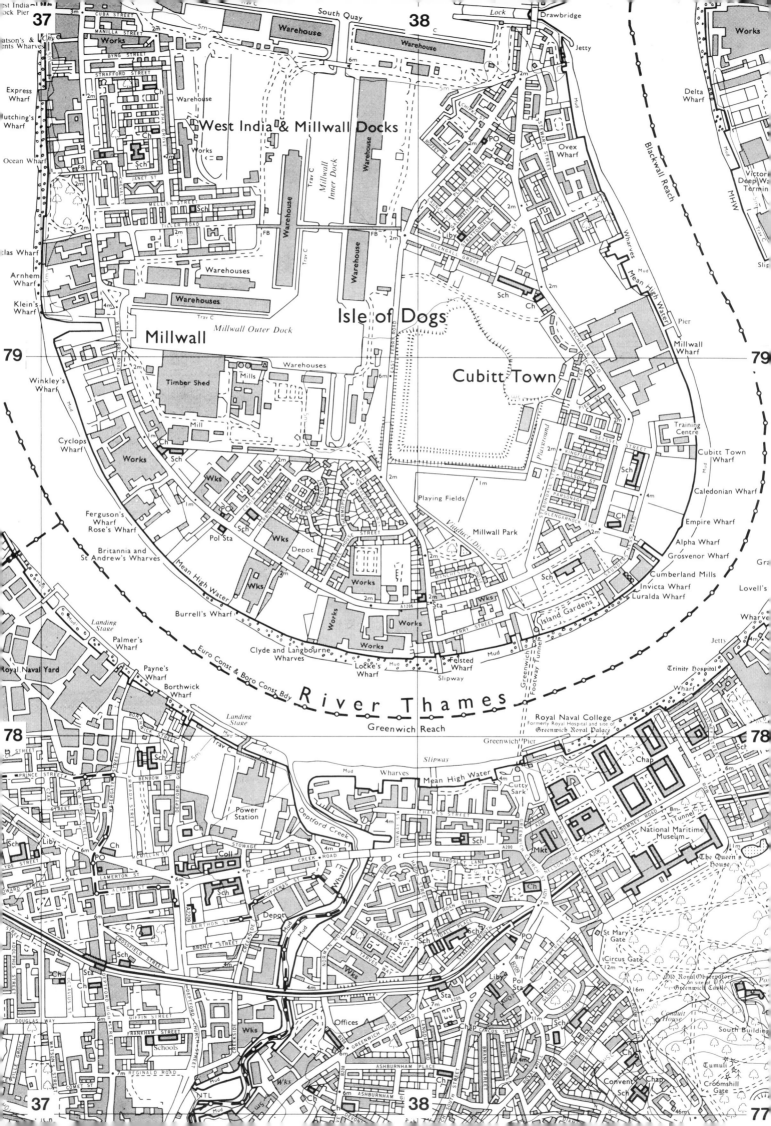

provisions, clothing, rum, etc. Now mostly the GLC Pepys Estate. Gateway and Colonnade (1768). Georgian terrace, Rum Warehouses (1781-89) and Superintendent's House survive. (See the chapter *Royal Dockyards.)*

Victualling Yard, former Gate Piers
TQ 3669 7824
Grove Street, SE8

Early 19th century. Two tall square brick piers with stone cornices, and ball finials. Gateway bricked up.

London and Greenwich Railway

Opened from Spa Road, Bermondsey, to Deptford in February 1836, (see note below on problem of crossing Deptford Creek). The whole railway from London Bridge to Deptford is carried on an 1878 arch brick viaduct, said to be the largest brick structure in the world.
Mechanic's Passage, Deptford, is a surviving fragment of the tree-lined boulevard which originally flanked the railway.
Ref: London's First Railway by R H G Thomas, Batsford 1972.

Deptford Creek Railway Bridge
TQ 377 773

This bridge, on the London & Greenwich Railway (London's first railway), has a moving section to allow navigation. The present structure, installed December 1963, is an electrically operated vertical lift bridge. The centre platform, weighing 40 tons, can be raised in three minutes. Designed by A H Cantrell, Chief Civil Engineer, B R Southern Region. Cost £92,000. Built by Sir William Arrol & Co Ltd of Glasgow. The former bridge of 1884 required twelve men to move it and the operation took over an hour, requiring the removal of a length of rail. Trains were delayed.

The section of the London & Greenwich Railway from Deptford to Greenwich, involving the crossing of Deptford Creek, was not completed until 1838. The first bridge, completed in November 1838, had a drawbridge section of 26 feet span, and was opened by eight men.
Ref: Railway Magazine December 1838.

Relics

A collection of coins and an engraved glass plate giving the history of the railway to 1841 commemorating the start of widening work on the London & Greenwich Railway viaduct. First stone of the new work laid by Colonel George Thomas Landmann RE, 17 March 1841, when the relics were bricked in.
Ref: R H G Thomas p 119.

Greenwich

Running from Deptford in the west to Woolwich in the east, Greenwich is a large borough which also includes Blackwall Point, Greenwich Marshes and Charlton. The industrial area of Greenwich Marshes has become derelict and parts have been characterised by scrapyards: regions where architectural historians and listers of buildings seldom trod. In contrast the centre of Greenwich itself includes the National Maritime Museum, Royal Naval College and Cutty Sark and is a major tourist attraction. Woolwich with its strong military connections has a long established town centre of some standing with notable popular entertainment features.

Deptford

Deptford Royal Dockyard (later Foreign Cattle Market)   *TQ 371 779*

Established by King Henry VIII 1513 as his chief naval dockyard, closed 1869. Converted to foreign cattle market; opened 1871, closed 1913. Some buildings remain. See the chapter on *Royal Dockyards*.

Sir John Franklin departed from here on his ill-fated arctic expedition in 1845.

Covered shipbuilding slipway   *TQ 371 780*
Former Deptford Dockyard

Listed grade II

Large shed for the building of wooden warships dating from 1847. This structure probably ranks with those at Chatham and Portsmouth and was an exciting rediscovery in 1982. At present it is used for the storage of rolls of newsprint imported mainly from Canada and brought on trailers from the adjacent ro-ro berth.

John Penn's Boiler Shop (now Paynes Wharf)   *TQ 372 781*
Borthwick Street, SE8

Building with six-bay façade and semi-circular arched windows. (See *Barry* for more details: engine of *Warrior* installed here. Penn had his engine works on Blackheath Hill. Sheerlegs on the river side of boiler shop were used to install ships' engines). Cast iron bollard with inscription 'J Penn & Son, Deptford' remains.

Ref: Barry P, Dockyard Economy and Naval Power 1863. (Some copies of this book are illustrated).

1   Payne's Wharf August 1979. (R J M Carr)

Deptford Electric Power Generating Station   *TQ 375 779*
Stowage, SE8

Site of the world's first Central Power Station erected to designs of Sebastian de Ferranti for the London Electric Supply Corporation, 1889. Central London was supplied at 10,000 volts AC, and there were plans to serve the whole of Greater London. The idea was ahead of its time and anti-monopolistic opposition prevented its coming into being. Of Ferranti's original station only a set of arches in relief on the South wall of the present East Station survive, the position of the station itself being marked by a lawn. The

West Station was demolished c1980. Coal unloading cranes dating from about the late 1920s survive here. Some power is supplied to British Rail Southern Region for its electric trains.

Mumford's Granary   *TQ 375 771*
Greenwich High Road, SE10

By Aston Webb 1897 for Mumford's Flour Mills (founded 1790); fate uncertain. The only remnant of former complex. Tall building with interior concrete structure, faced in stock brick. One of the more attractive features of this area.

The former mills were supplied by craft navigating Deptford Creek above the moveable bridge on the London and Greenwich Railway.

Deptford Sewage Pumping Station   *TQ 377 772*
Norman Road, SE10

Unlisted

Built to lift sewage 18′ to the level of the Southern Outfall Sewer along which it could then gravitate to Crossness Works (*(TQ 484 811)* for treatment. Opened 1865 with four Slaughter and Gunning 125 hp beam engine pumps having a capacity of 107,000 cubic feet per minute. Cornish Boilers. South wing (rebuilt 1930-31) still houses vertical electric pumps, three Allen diesel engines and two Crossley horizontal gas engines (converted to diesel operation). These latter are of particular interest,. The foregoing plant was all installed in 1934.

Immediately adjacent to the pumping station to the South West at *TQ 376 771* is a most notable coal shed covering 18,000 square feet and consisting of a cast and wrought iron roof with open sides. This was used for the storage of fuel brought to the station along Deptford Creek by lighter. This structure (dating from 1864?) deserves listing. Screens for filtering the incoming sewage are raised for cleaning by hydraulic 'jiggers' similar to those used for warehouse cranes. There is a local hydraulic power system for the station with accumulator etc. This working survivor would be worth filming.

The pumping station is built in light coloured brick in an attractive Italianate style. A (former) central boiler house is flanked by two wings, cf Abbey Mills pumping station (Newham). A notable site.

Greenwich

Greenwich Power Station   *TQ 388 781*
Old Woolwich Road, SE10

Built by the LCC to provide electric power to the whole of its tramway network (68 miles) and opened in 1906 with four 3,400 kW alternators driven by Manhattan type (cylinders at right angles) slow-speed (94 rpm) reciprocating steam engines (plant visually reminiscent of Fritz Lang's film *Metropolis*). By 1922 all replaced by turbines. The building has brick curtain walls with a steel frame. Architect W E Riley FRIBA.

Objections from the nearby Royal Greenwich Observatory caused the two chimneys at the landward side of the station to be reduced in height and the LCC trams in the area were obliged to use special return wires for earthing. Subsequently all the chimneys have been reduced. Now a gas turbine station providing peak-load generation for London Transport railways. It is remotely operated from the LT control room at Lots Road *(TQ 263 769)*.

Previous to the Power Station a horse tram depôt was situated here. It is said that traces remain. Greenwich Power Station is a dominant part of the local landscape.

Ref: R A S Hennessey, The Electric Revolution, Oriel Press 1972, page 29.

Coal unloading jetty   *TQ 388 783*

Massive coal jetty constructed for the adjacent LCC Greenwich Power Station. Large cast iron columns support a substantial platform. Compare with the earlier gasworks' jetties at Rotherhithe *(TQ 354 802)*, East Greenwich *(TQ 396 801)* and Beckton *(TQ 446 811 and TQ 448 813)*. Coal for the Power Station was unloaded by cranes with grabs. These have been removed and the jetty is now used for the import of liquid fuel. Woolwich Power Station *(TQ 433 794)* had a modest wooden jetty.

2   Harbour Master's Office, Ballast Quay 1970. (GLC)

Enderbys' Wharf (Submarine Cables Ltd)
TQ 393 786
Christchurch Way, SE10

The Enderby family who were engaged in whaling (and exploration) set up a rope walk here in 1834, which burnt down in 1845. (Enderby Land in Antarctica was discovered during explorations in one of the family's ships.) A manufactory for the production of submarine telegraph cable was set up by Glass, Elliot and Company in 1854. The company amalgamated with the Gutta Percha Company in 1864 to form the Telegraph Construction and Maintenance Company. The site was active in the early days of this industry and was involved with the first cross-channel telegraph link as well as manufacturing the first successful transatlantic telegraph cable (laid by I K Brunel's *Great Eastern* in 1866). In the last quarter of the 19th century the Thames was pre-eminent in the manufacture of such cable. During World War II, PLUTO (Pipe Line Under The Ocean) was made here. Production of submarine cable ceased c1979, work being transferred to Southampton.

Ref: see the entry for Standard Telephones and Cables in the Library and Archive section.

3 *Enderbys' Wharf looking east August 1979. (R J M Carr)*

4 *Enderby House 1977. (GLC)*

Enderby House *TQ 3914 7876*
Enderbys' Wharf, Christchurch Way, SE10

Listed grade II

The northernmost of the two houses by the river is the original home of the Enderby family, now offices. General Gordon (of Khartoum), the nephew of the first Mr Enderby, spent his last night in England in this building. (He is commemorated by a park in Gravesend.)

Two storey office building *TQ 3914 7874*
Enderbys' Wharf, Christchurch Way, SE10

Immediately to the South of Enderby House is another mid 19th century house with attractive telegraph cable decorations, now used as an office. The front is of yellow stock brick, six bays wide. Segmental-arched windows with stucco keys are decorated with stucco lengths of telegraph cable. Stucco doorcase with telegraph cable moulding to the reveals. Compared with Enderby House this is a more noticeable building. Deserves listing?

Cable loading and coal unloading jetty
TQ 392 787

19th century loading gear for submarine cable. As cable was manufactured in the works it was directly loaded aboard a cable ship in the river to avoid unnecessary handling (and possible damage).

An electric crane and coal conveyor were still used for unloading coal from lighters for the adjacent boiler house until c1984. It is believed from the exhaust that Weir (or similar) feed pumps are installed here. A small hand crane on the jetty is also of interest. A good view of the above items may be obtained from Greenwich — Blackwall Point riverside walk. Recently clearance has taken place.

Cable ship John W Mackay
Formerly at Enderbys' Dolphins, SE10

Laying off Enderbys' Wharf was the 1922 cable ship *John W Mackay* (4, 105 tons gross) powered by a double set of triple expansion steam engines. This vessel is of great interest. She was here several years and has now been moved to the West India Docks.

Ref: Lloyds' register of ships.

5 *The* SS John W Mackay *at Enderbys' Dolphins August 1979. (R J M Carr)*

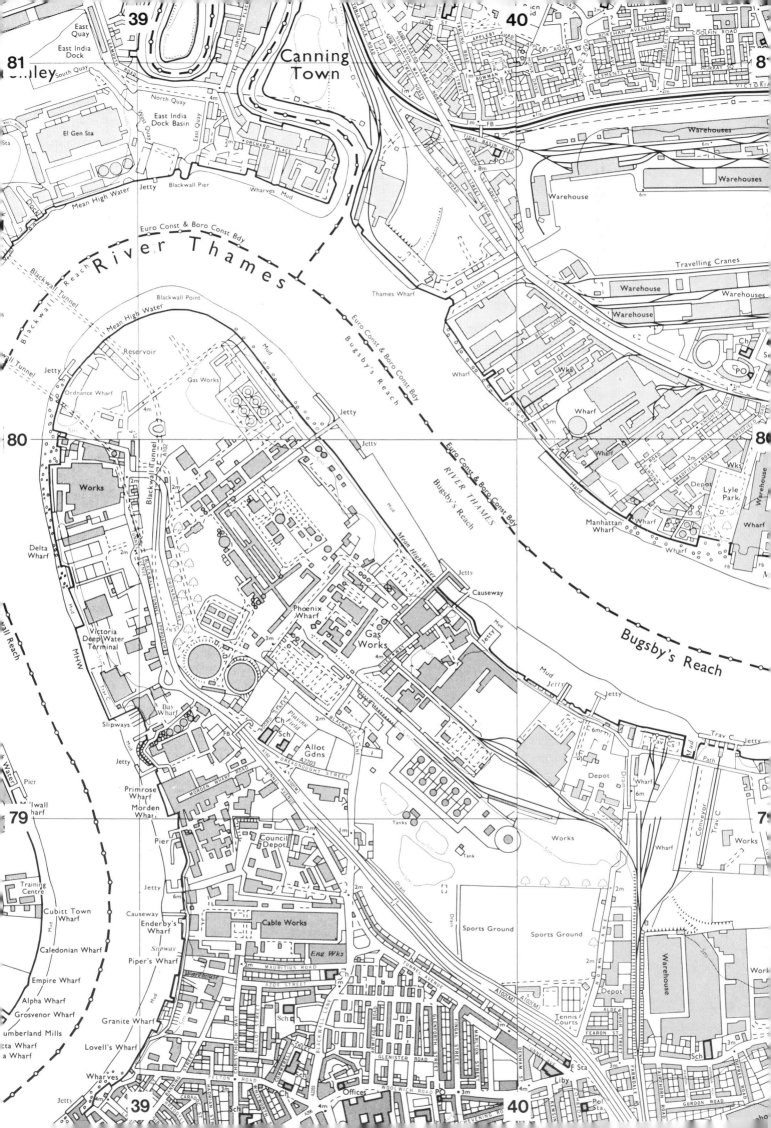

Victoria Deep Water container terminal
TQ 389 796

One of the few flourishing parts of the Port of London up-river. Privately owned. A good view could be obtained from the Greenwich — Blackwall Point riverside walk which passed between the container stacks until recently.

East Greenwich Gasworks   *TQ 395 795*
Grenfell Street, SE10

The works layout was initiated by George and Frank Livesay on a site originally of 96 acres, previously mostly marshland; the first phase of construction lasted from 1881 to 1885. Before this the South Metropolitan Gas Company had made use of works at Vauxhall, Rotherhithe and along the Old Kent Road. During the carbonisation period, 72 million cubic feet of gas per day could be produced (c1955). Later when oil gas plant was introduced the maximum output was increased to something like 400 million cubic feet per day (c1965), which was said to be the world's largest for a single site. This far exceeded the production of the rival Beckton Gas Works in Newham on the North bank which had been the largest in London. A good deal of demolition of the carbonisation plant has taken place but some does still remain. The 1960s oil gas plant was 'mothballed' for possible future uses but is unlikely now to be used again.

This is a large site of some 240 acres (about 1 mile by ½ mile) centred approximately on *TQ 395 797*. Water gas plant installed after nationalisation in 1949 and consisting of eight sets still survived mid-1981. There were by-product plants and tar works. The horizontal retorts were shut down in 1964. The coke ovens closed 1950-68. Nowadays natural gas is drawn from the grid and the site serves as a distribution station.

Refs: Modern Gasworks Practice, Alwyne Meade, Benn Bros (2nd edition 1921). A Century of Gas in South London 1824-1924, South Metropolitan Gas Company (Private Publication) 1924. The Postwar Development of East Greenwich Gasworks, Proceedings of the Institution of Gas Engineers vol **105**, *1955-6, pp 1073-1144.*

Gas Holder No 1   *TQ 393 794*

This was the world's first four lift gas holder, built in 1886. Capacity 8.6 million cubic feet 250′ in diameter, the columns are 198′ high. To the casual observer this holder may appear larger than No 2 (see below) as it is higher. The full height is 200′.

Gas Holder No 2   *TQ 392 794*

Was the world's largest gas holder when built in 1891. Had six lifts. Capacity was originally 12.2 million cubic feet but this was reduced to 8.9 million cubic feet by the removal of the two

flying lifts following damage caused in the great Silvertown Explosion of 1917. It is still the largest gas holder in Britain (see the Guiness Book of Records). The full height is 148′ and the water tank is 303′ in diameter. Bombed by the IRA c1980 it is now back in working order.

Coal and Coke Jetty   *TQ 395 800*

Substantial T-shaped jetty supported on massive cast iron columns built c1890. Used for

6   Southern entrance to the Blackwall Tunnel 1975. (GLC)

7   Inspection of the Blackwall Tunnel 30 October 1895. (GLC)

8 *Hydraulic cranes on coal and coke jetty at East Greenwich gas works August 1979. (R J M Carr)*

the unloading of coal by cranes with grabs and the export of coke. Beneath the deck was accommodation for workshops, mess rooms etc, hence the windows, and a separate staff worked here. Five hydraulic cranes of four tons capacity survive and are of considerable interest. There are also two conveyors 500′ long. The jetty handled 1¼ million tons of coal annually. Railway locomotives were used on the jetty. Coke was exported, largely to Scandinavia, as cast iron notices about the works in several Scandinavian languages testify. Access to the jetty is restricted as it is considered to be a dangerous structure. There is a weighbridge at the Southern end. Two houses close by formerly offices.

Other items

To the south-west of the jetty is an imposing range of (late 19th century?) buildings containing a large washroom complete with fittings, and formerly also a blacksmith's forge and maintenance workshops. These Main Workshops carried out 90% of the work for the South Metropolitan area.

South-west again was a building containing steam driven exhausters (for the water-gas plant?) to designs of Peter Brotherhood, built by Bryan Donkin's. These survived until at least 1981. There were (at least until recently) extensive coke oven remains and a water-gas plant composed of eight sets. This latter had an output of 3.4 million cubic feet per day. Coal etc was transported around the works by rail, traction being provided by a fleet of Peckett steam locomotives. The locomotive shed was demolished c1979. To the West of the jetty, near the river, is a gas washing plant.

Reforming Plant   TQ 396 797

These strikingly dramatic structures were part of a more efficient gas production plant introduced here in 1963, operating on an ICI principle. Compared with previous plant pressures were higher and more by-products obtained. Visually reminiscent of 'cat crackers' in oil refineries.

Ammonium Sulphate Storage Shed
TQ 397 796

Unlisted

Remarkable storage shed with pre-cast concrete parabolic roof constructed 1956 by Demolition & Construction Ltd. In size comparable to an airship shed. For the storage of dry powder (10,000 tons). Unusually sophisticated architecture for this locality. Deserves to be better known.
    Ref: Gas Journal Vol **285**.

Brick Acid Towers   TQ 396 795

Red-brick acid towers (similar to Gay Lussac towers?). A substantial relic. Four? remain. For the Kachkaroff process.

Oil gas plant   TQ 394 795

Introduced 1965-66. 'Mothballed' but unlikely to see further use. To be scrapped? This plant covers a considerable area. Towards the end of gas production at the East Greenwich works new types of plant were introduced at an increasingly rapid rate. The reforming plant era only lasted 10-11 years. The visually exciting oil gas plant may be seen from outside the works from Blackwall lane.

Railway Bridge with Signal Cabin
TQ 396 793
River Way, SE10

Carried the rail connection of 1901 from the South Eastern Railway's Angerstein Wharf to the Gasworks across River Way. This singular structure is a local landmark.

Coalite plant   TQ 398 792

Formerly a retort house. For low temperature carbonisation.

Much demolition has taken place recently at East Greenwich Gasworks.

Blackwall Point Power Station   TQ 398 796
River Way, SE10

Built 1951-53 during the period when the dimensions of turbo-alternators were controlled by law — hence the small size of the sets employed here. Three pulverised-fuel coal-fired boilers supplied steam at a temperature of 454°C and a pressure of 41.4 bars to three 30 MW English Electric turbo-alternators. Generation ceased c1981 and the plant has since been removed. Coal was unloaded at a jetty in the river which still remains.

The layout is unusual in that the control room is separate from the rest of the Station, being to the East of River Way. This control room was to be retained for distribution purposes. Redolent of utility with its tall boiler house and single chimney, but not without beauty, this power station is a unique Dockland landmark. Architects Farmer and Dark, consulting engineers John Bruce and Partners, contractors Peter Lind and Co (as for the aesthetically-different Brunswick Wharf power station).

19th century houses   *TQ 397 795*
River Way, SE10

On local list

Interesting survival of 19th century terraced housing including a public house. Formerly occupied by rivermen's families.

Fire Station   *TQ 401 783*
Woolwich Road, SE10

On local list

Built 1901 by the LCC as East Greenwich Fire Station in Art Nouveau style. Married quarters at rear.

Angerstein Wharf   *TQ 403 792*

At the terminus of a railway built without Act of Parliament in 1852 by the Angerstein family on their own land and leased to the South Eastern Railway. The branch railway runs from the North Kent line not far from Charlton station *(TQ 406 781)* to the Wharf on Bugsby's Reach. The railway branch gave access to G A Harvey's engineering works, the United Glass Bottling Company and the LCC Tramway Repair Depôt as well as to East Greenwich Gasworks. The branch was electrified on the overhead wire system in 1959.

Between the wars the Southern Railway intended to build a power station at Angerstein Wharf for its suburban railway electrification programme. Planning permission for this was refused owing to the already high concentration of electric power stations in the vicinity. The CEGB Deptford East power station provides some of the electricity required locally by British Rail Southern Region.

Former LCC Tramway Repair Depôt
TQ 405 783
Fell Tram Way, SE7

Opened 1909 as the main repair depôt for the LCC tramways. A sizeable building and some tram track remain. The building at *TQ 403 785* is massive, of brick construction, and is many gables deep with four round-arched recesses per gable.

Thames Barrier   *TQ 415 792 — TQ 414 798*
Eastmoor Street, SE7

Massive flood prevention barrier, part of a general scheme for the Thames Estuary now completed. The Thames Barrier was first used on 1 February 1983. Smaller barriers have been erected on tributaries of the Thames, for instance on Bow Creek and at the entrance to Barking Creek. At the same time the river banks have been raised generally.
Ref: Report of Thames Barrier Symposium, Institution of Civil Engineers, 1977.

Woolwich

Woolwich Royal Dockyard   *TQ 427 793*
Woolwich Church Street, London SE18

Dry docks listed grade II

Founded 1513 by Henry VIII. In the 19th century the 'Steam Factory' here was the first plant for the building of engines for steamships in a naval dockyard but had a short life, closing in 1869 due to obsolescence. Part of the site was subsequently used by the Royal Arsenal Co-operative Society.

Two Dry docks (listed) are retained as swimming pools etc, *TQ 428 793*. Built in 1843 there is little of interest now, apart from the battered dock walls, due to excessive tidying.

A large chimney with massive base survives beside the main road. *(TQ 423 790)*, c1840. The adjacent building was the Boiler Works and Iron Foundry. This is a complex site.

Engine Store   *TQ 426 793*

The buildings alongside the river which were latterly used by Albion Sugar to refine glucose were demolished in 1982. It is believed that the roof structure was of interest. The building on the South side was reminiscent of the Boat Store at Sheerness and is earlier.

Smithery

Dating from 1815 and due to J Rennie, The Smithery was demolished in the late 1960s but part of the roof and the cast iron columns have gone to Blist Hill, Ironbridge Gorge Museum

Trust, for eventual re-erection. It is intended to re-create a working puddling furnace and rolling mill making use of the Smithery roof and plant from Thomas Walmsley's Atlas Forge, Bolton. This work is now well under way.

Cubow Ltd, Ship Builders and Repairers
TQ 430 793
51 Woolwich Church Street, SE18

The only shipbuilder in Greater London, on the site of old slips at the East end of Woolwich Royal Dockyard. Recently tugs, trawlers and coasters have been constructed, the latter often being built in sections which are welded together after launching. Shipyard machinery is of interest. Shipbuilding finished about 1982.

Mast Pond Wharf   *TQ 431 783*
Woolwich High Street, SE18

Name self-explanatory, at the East end of Woolwich Royal Dockyard. Small coasters etc still berth here.

Odeon Cinema   *TQ 431 792*
John Wilson Street, SE18

Listed grade II

Large cinema by George Coles 1937. Characteristic late thirties white exterior more noteworthy than that of the slightly earlier Granada Cinema opposite (see below).

Former Granada Cinema   *TQ 432 792*
Powis Street, SE18

Listed grade II

1937; giant cinema to the designs of Massey, Uren and Komisarjevsky. Incredible 'Venetian Gothic' interior by Komisarjevsky has to be seen to be believed — San Marco in Woolwich! The entrance interior is more restrained Romanesque. Wurlitzer organ installed by Frank Holland now removed and premises used as a bingo club. The former seating capacity was almost 3,000. When opened styled as the 'most romantic theatre ever built'.
   Ref: Cathedrals of the Movies, David Atwell, Architectural Press, 1980. Also The Decorator, supp 1937.

Woolwich Free Ferry   *TQ 431 794*

Opened under the auspices of the Metropolitan Board of Works in 1889 after local agitation when tolls on the London bridges up-river were abolished. It was argued that East Londoners should not subsidise river crossings in West and Central London. Woolwich was the first free ferry on the Thames. The three diesel powered craft at present in use have Voith Schneider propulsion and were commissioned in 1963, replacing four paddle steamers of interesting

design, built in the 1920s. New approaches and terminals were constructed in 1966. 3,300 vehicles and 6,500 passengers are carried each day between 8.00 am and 8.00 pm.

9   Cubow's shipyard from the river August 1979. (R J M Carr)

10   The Woolwich free ferry from the air 1954. (Aerofilms)

Woolwich Foot Tunnel   *TQ 432 794*

Built of cast-iron segments with concrete lining using compressed air techniques and a Greathead shield, like the similar Greenwich Foot Tunnel which was constructed a little earlier (1902). The Woolwich tunnel was designed by Sir Maurice Fitzmaurice and opened in 1912. It has been largely used by dockers going to and from work in the Royal Docks. Access is by electric lifts at each end and the shafts are surmounted by attractive cupolas. Length 1,655'. Width of footway 9' 2".

Remains of Woolwich Power Station
TQ 434 793

The local Board of Health established a power
station here in 1891 which was purchased by the
Woolwich Borough Council in 1901. A Low
Pressure Section consisting of four Babcock &
Wilcox boilers and a Fraser & Chalmers/GEC
12.5 MW turbo-alternator was commissioned
1924-28. An Intermediate Pressure Section
was added 1940-48 and a High Pressure
Section 1952-57. Latterly only the High
Pressure Section was in use, steam at 640 psi
and 463°C being supplied to two 30 MW GEC
turbo-alternators by four 'La Mont' type forced
circulation coal-fired boilers.

Two chimneys demolished by explosives in
1979 as a public spectacle.

Royal Arsenal Co-operative Society
Department Store   *TQ 432 791*
Powis Street, SE18

North block built 1903, South block 1935. This
is the headquarters of the Society, one of the
first in South East London. The North block is
ornate and is graced by a statue of Robert
McLeod, a pioneer of the co-operative
movement.

McDonald's Hamburger Restaurant
TQ 435 790
58 Powis Street, SE18

Britain's first McDonald's 1974 and also the
5,000th internationally. The premises were
previously occupied by Burton's the tailor.

Tramway Rails   *TQ 438 790*
Beresford Square, SE18

The last electric tram ran to Woolwich in 1952
but remains of tram rails could still be seen until
recently where granite setts appeared through
the tarmac. The island refuge was once a tram
stop. Electric tram cars operating in Woolwich
used both overhead and buried conductor
current collection systems. Cars could change
their method of working and this change-over
provided something of a spectacle for
passengers and passers by.

*Ref: Brian Bracegirdle, The Archaeology of the
Industrial Revolution, Heinemann 1973, page 75.*

Railway Tunnels
TQ 418 788 — TQ 440 789

The South Eastern Railway built its line
through Woolwich in 1849, when these tunnels
were constructed. Since the electrification of
the railway in the mid 1920s a certain amount of
additional covering-over of the line has taken
place in central Woolwich.

Coffee Tavern   *TQ 437 787*
33 Woolwich New Road, SE18

An inscription reads 'Woolwich and Plumstead Coffee Taverns Co Ltd, 30.10.1880'. The building opened as the Royal Connaught Assembly Rooms and Coffee Tavern but became a Variety Theatre in 1906. Soon after it re-opened as a cinema, closing in the 1930s. The original idea of a Coffee Tavern was to combat excessive drunkenness on the part of workers at the nearby Arsenal by providing congenial surroundings where alcohol was not served. The site is now threatened by a redevelopment scheme for this part of Woolwich (now abandoned but demolition proceeding).

So called 'Tram Shed'   *TQ 436 787*
Woolwich New Road, SE18

Actually a former electricity sub-station for the LCC electric tramways dating from 1908. The architect was E Vincent Harris. Now in use as a local theatre the building is threatened by a redevelopment scheme. Inside, the original travelling crane survives and the structure is of some interest.

Woolwich Arsenal   *TQ 445 793*
Beresford Square, SE18

An ordnance depôt was set up at Woolwich near the site of the present ferry, in the reign of Henry VIII about 1518, when the royal dockyard was established. The depôt was moved a short way down river to the grounds of an old manor house, Tower Place, on the edge of Woolwich Warren in 1671 and was known as The Warren until 1815, when its name was changed to the Royal Arsenal.

Manufacture as opposed to the storage of armaments began with the establishment in 1696 of The Royal Laboratory. The two surviving pavilions of the Royal Laboratory are the only 17th century buildings in the Arsenal. The buildings attributed to Vanbrugh date from 1716-1720.

By the 1914-18 War when the Arsenal was at the height of its activities it covered 1,200 acres. Few buildings now remain, though some survive, including some early buildings and others attributed to Sir John Vanbrugh. It is believed that many interesting 19th century buildings perhaps of comparable interest to those of the Royal Naval Dockyards of Chatham, Portsmouth and Sheerness survived until the 1970s. These escaped the attention of industrial archaeologists owing to the strict security of the site and little of this period was listed.

Woolwich Arsenal was the oldest and largest military arsenal in Britain. During World War II nearly 40,000 workers were employed. Closure commenced in 1963.

Ref: The Royal Arsenal (2 vols), O F G Hogg, Oxford University Press, 1963.

In the Arsenal the following eleven items are particularly noteworthy.

Main Entrance   *TQ 437 789*
Beresford Square

Listed grade II

Built in 1829; originally a gateway flanked by a pair of pavilions. Now has three arches. The upper part of the gate decorated with real mortars dating from 1829 was not constructed until about 1894. Severe style with George IV motifs.

Cadets' Quarters   *TQ 440 790*

Listed grade II

Attractive terrace of mid to late 18th century small houses originally for the accommodation of cadets. In spite of local opposition, the terrace has been demolished for the widening of Plumstead Road. James Wyatt may have designed part of the range.

Brass Gun Foundry

Listed grade I

1717. Said to be by Sir John Vanbrugh. Extensively re-built 1771/2. The building is now restored and used for storage by the National Maritime Museum. The remains of the foundry itself are beneath flooring.

A detailed series of watercolour illustrations was made c1770 of the processes as reorganised by Verbruggen. They were published in *"Eighteenth Century Gunfounding"* by M H Jackson and C de Beer (1973).

Grand Store

Listed grade II

Built 1806-13 as a storehouse. The British Library, Science Reference Library, now uses

14   Casting one of the plates for the Great Steam Hammer at Woolwich. (Illustrated London News 14 December 1872)

15

16

part of the building as an out station to store books and periodicals it is unable to accommodate at Holborn. An impressive building of three ranges by James Wyatt completed by Lewis Wyatt. Much in poor condition.

Canal   *TQ 447 794 — TQ 446 798*

Designed by Lt Col Pilkington and built during the Napoleonic Wars (1812-16) to carry barges from the Thames into the Arsenal. The entrance lock is still in existence. A swing bridge over the lock for the Arsenal light railway survives and is being restored by the GLC. The canal is in effect a narrow dock. It was originally half a mile long. The upper section was filled in before the 1939-45 War. Now part of the Thamesmead site.

The Royal Laboratory

Listed Grade II

The oldest building in The Arsenal, dating from 1696. Once a complete quadrangle. Now only the two central pavilions of the East and

West ranges survive, much altered but still recognisable.

New Laboratory Square

Unlisted

1806-10, possibly to the designs of James Wyatt. Three two-storey ranges built round a courtyard to provide additional laboratory accommodation. Also a single-storey iron-framed building of 1878.

The Dial Square Block

Listed Grade II

The only surviving range of a major courtyard complex built in 1717, possibly to designs by Vanbrugh. The buildings were associated with the washing, turning and engraving processes.

The Model Room

Listed Grade II

Built on the site of Tower Place between 1716 and 1720, probably to designs by Vanburgh. The first Royal Military Academy was housed here in 1720 and the second in 1741 until its transfer to Woolwich Common in 1806.

Verbruggen's House

Listed Grade II

Built 1772/3 for John and Peter Verbruggen, Master Founders.

The New Carriage Store

Listed Grade II

Built 1728, altered 1778; rebuilt 1803 by James Wyatt (after a fire). For gun carriages. Only the façades are old.

15 The Royal Arsenal, building D81 in 1972. (GLC)

16 Interior of D81 showing travelling crane and pits for the annealing of gun barrels. (GLC)

17 Woolwich Arsenal canal entrance lock 1982. (GLC)

17

Library and archive sources

A letter was sent to librarians and achivists who were thought to have in their care material relating to the industrial, social or technological history of London's Dockland, inviting them to contribute a description of relevant parts of their collections to this publication. The replies follow.

Camden, London Borough of
Libraries and Arts Department
Swiss Cottage Library
88 Avenue Road
London NW3 3HA
Tel 01-278 4444

One source which might be valuable are the volumes of Goad Insurance Plans which cover mainly the shopping, commercial and industrial parts of London. The library holds sixteen volumes of maps in stock dating from 1886 to 1947. The maps were usually revised by the addition of pasted alterations to each page, until a new edition of the map was printed. It is therefore often impossible to date the information shown on the maps.

The scales of the maps are usually 40′ or 80′ to the inch and different colours indicate the construction materials used in the buildings, height of buildings are indicated and a description of use of the building shown. Goad plans are also likely to be found in a number of other libraries.

Malcolm Holmes, *Local History Librarian*

The Institution of Civil Engineers
Secretary: J C McKenzie MA MAI MSc
FEng FICE
Great George Street
Westminster
London SW1P 3AA
Tel: 01-222 7722

The relevant material held by the Institution's Library falls into the following four main categories.

Archives: The manuscript reports of the Rennie family and the Telford collection contain material relevant to the 18th century and early 19th century development of the Port of London. The archives also contain material on various schemes for tunnelling under the Thames, including 34 volumes relating to the Brunel's Thames Tunnel.

Periodical holdings: The Institution's Proceedings, dating from 1836 in their earliest form, contain several papers on engineering works associated with the docks. Other relevant periodicals held by the Institution are: the Engineer, Engineering, Dock and Harbour Authority, etc.

Parliamentary reports and Acts of Parliament: A large collection of reports and Acts related to the Port of London from the 18th century onwards.

Books and pamphlets: Material on the Port of London from the 18th century to the present day.

Admission is restricted to members of the Institution and bona fide research workers. Applications to view material should be made to the Librarian or the Archivist.

Doreen J Bayley, *Librarian*

The Institution of Electrical Engineers
Savoy Place
London WC2R OBL
Tel: 01-240 1871

Below are catalogue descriptions of some items in the collection which are relevant to the history of London's Dockland.

Archives Department: Material relating to Deptford power stations and Thames Tunnel as follows:

Autograph letter from Sir Marc Isambard Brunel to Michael Faraday, 24 May 1839, consulting Faraday about gases in the Thames Tunnel which impeded construction work. (SC MSS 2)

Album of photographs taken during the construction of Deptford Generating Station built by Sebastion Ziani de Ferranti, 1888-1892; including a few photographs of the dismantling of the plant in 1933.   (SC MSS 59)

Glass slides and prints of the Deptford West plant, London Electricity Co, including interior and exterior views and various pieces of plant. Undated.   (NAEST 8)

E D P Symons (Mrs), *Archivist*

Greater London Council

Director-General's Department
Greater London History Library
40 Northampton Road
London EC1R OAB
Tel: 01-633 8116/6851

The Greater London Record Office and History Library have considerable source material relating to the development of London's docks. The subject is so big and the holdings so extensive and disparate that it is impracticable to list them. Brief notes below indicate some of the different types of source material held — printed books, photographs, archives. These notes should be regarded as merely introductory; researchers are advised to visit the office to study catalogues and indexes.

Joan Coburn (Miss), *Head Archivist*

London Docklands
Some archive sources in the Greater London Record Office

I   Deposited plans: Under parliamentary standing orders, plans and related books of reference for public undertakings (including construction of docks) had to be deposited with the Clerk of the Peace of any county affected by the works. These plans were duplicates of those presented to Parliament as part of the process of obtaining the relevant powers to acquire land and carry out building works. They are not in the main plans showing structural details, but were drawn up to show land needed for any particular undertaking. They do usually give an idea of the proposed lay-out of a dock, canal, railway, etc.

There are several in our custody.

MR/UP *Old Series* — plans deposited with the Clerk of the Peace of the ancient county of Middlesex c1837-1889. Card index of these available in Catalogue Room arranged by subject.

MR/UP *New Series* — plans deposited with Clerk of the Peace of the administrative county of Middlesex, 1889-1965. Chronologically arranged register of plans available in Catalogue Room.

MBW *Presented plans* — plans placed with Metropolitan Board of Works, 1855-1889. Chronologically arranged list available in Catalogue Room.

LCC LCC/CL/PARL/3.2 — plans deposited with Clerk of the Peace for London, 1890-1930, plans deposited with Clerk to the LCC, 1931-1965. Chronologically arranged list available in Catalogue Room.

Deposited plans relating to proposed docks, alterations and enlargements to existing docks, will be found scattered throughout the above series. Not all these proposed schemes will have gone ahead.

II Thames flooding: MBW 2703-2807. A series of rolled plans of the river frontage with elevations of riparian properties based on surveys carried out 1880-1906 under Thames River (Flood Prevention) Act 1879.

III Crime 1549-1971: The records of the Middlesex Sessions of the Peace and the Gaol Delivery of Newgate and the County of London Sessions will contain numerous references to criminal activity in the docks. However no subject index of such cases exists. A searcher would have to be willing to read through records in the hope of finding such cases or else to pursue cases for which he or she already has certain details, i.e., name of defendant and date of trial.

Other records in charge of the Record Keeper

The following might be mentioned:

The minutes of the London County Council and the minutes and presented papers of its Rivers Committee between 1899 and 1908/9 contain such material on the proposed reform of the Port of London, leading up to the creation of the PLA in supersession to the dock companies and the upper Thames jurisdiction of the Thames Conservancy (by the Port of London Act, 1908)

The following files in the LCC Clerk's Department series

CL/MD/1/87: Miscellaneous printed papers — Port of London, 1894-1902
CL/MD/1/88: Do — Do, 1902-07

CL/MD/1/90: Do — Thames & Lee Conservancies, 1893-1900
CL/MD/1/92: Port of London Dock Accommodation — Reports by LCC Statistical Officer, 1899-1900 (bound vol)
CL/MD/1/93: Royal Commission on Port of London, 1900-02 — Printed LCC reports and minutes of evidence and reports of Royal Commission (bound together)
CL/MD/1/94: Port of London Bill, 1903-04 — Sessional papers (bound vol)
CL/MD/1/95: London Port & Docks Commission Bill, 1905-06 — Petitions (against) praying to be heard by counsel (bound vol)
CL/MD/1/96: Port of London — Miscellaneous printed reports, 1901-05 (bound vol)
CL/MD/1/97: Do — Do, 1906-07 (bound vol)
CL/MD/1/98: Do — Do, 1907 (bound vol)
CL/MD/1/99: Do — Do, 1908 (bound vol)
CL/MD/1/100: Do — Do, 1901-07 (bound vol)
CL/MD/1/101: Do — Transcripts of meetings, discussions, deputations and conferences, 1900-06 (bound vol)
CL/MD/1/102: Thames Conservancy & Post of London — Miscellaneous printed reports, 1872-1902
CL/MD/1/107 to 110: Port of London — Evidence to Royal Commission submitted in writing by persons and bodies other than LCC, 1900-02
CL/CD/3/46: ARP Memorandum No C6 — Air raid precautions for docks, wharves, quays and waterside warehouses (1st ed, 1937)
CL/CD/3/55: ARP Handbook No 7 — Anti-Gas precautions for merchant shipping (4th ed, 1943)

The following files in the LCC Fire Brigade Department series

FB/GEN/2/69: Fires in wharves and docks, 1913-42
FB/GEN/2/85: Fire at Silvertown, 19th January 1917
FB/GEN/2/92: Fire at Rum Quay, West India Docks, E14, 21st April 1933
FB/GEN/2/96: Fire at Colonial Wharf, Wapping, E1, 25th September 1935
FB/GEN/2/128: Lecture on fire at Cottons Wharf, Tooley Street on 22nd June 1861 by Percy E Ridley delivered to Fire Offices Committee, December 1930.

This list is confined to Dockland matters assuming that topics touching on the Thames itself, such as the Woolwich Ferry, the LCC Passenger Steamboat Service, 1905-07, the tunnels and the foot subways, the fireboats, the MAB river ambulances which took smallpox cases from North Wharf, Blackwall and South Wharf, Rotherhithe to Dartford, the Thames Flood Barrier, flood protection generally, etc., are not called for. One could extend the list further to such things as housing, education, etc., in areas within the Dockland boundaries as now statutorily defined.

The office also has the minutes and presented papers of the Docklands Joint Committee and its sub-committees, 1974-81 but these are within the '30-year rule' and access will be given only exceptionally.

Miss Rosemary Heath, *Librarian*
John Phillips, *Maps and Prints*
Christopher Denver, *Photographs*
A R Neate, *Record Keeper*

Department of Architecture and Civic Design
Surveyor of Historic Buildings:
Ashley Barker, OBE, FRIBA
2nd Floor, Chesham House
29/30 Warwick Street
London W1
Tel: 01-734 8144

The Historic Buildings Division has photographs, measured drawings and historical information for a wide range of buildings in Greater London including Dockland subjects.

The Council's *Survey of London* occupies the same premises but so far has covered only a small part of the Dockland area. The *Bankside, Southwark* volume (Vol 22, published 1950) includes the Clink Street/Bankside area; the *Spitalfields* and *Mile End New Town* volume (Vol 27, published 1957) deals with an area on the edge of Dockland.

Contacts
Frank Kelsall, *historical information*
John Sambrook, *measured drawings*
Mike Gilman, *Tower Hamlets, Newham*
Paul Calvocoressi, *Southwark, Lewisham, Greenwich*
Hermione Hobhouse, *Survey of London*

British Library of Political and Economic Science
(London School of Economics and Political Science)
10 Portugal Street
London WC2A 2HD
Tel: 01-405 7686

The Library covers the social sciences in the widest sense of the term, with unique research collections in economics, politics, and sociology. The total number of separate items is estimated at over $2\frac{3}{4}$ million, including over 750,000 bound volumes, over 450,000 pamphlets, and over 24,000 serials (of which over 12,000 are received currently). Material of research value is acquired in the major western and eastern European languages, including Russian.

The Library's holdings can be traced via the printed version of its subject catalogue, *A London Bibliography of the Social Sciences*. Whilst material on the London Docklands is scattered under many headings, very specific material will be found under the headings LONDON — Docks and LONDON — Port.

Among the specific collections housed in the Library are the working papers for Charles Booth's *Labour and Life of the People* and *Life and Labour of the People in London* (1885-1905). Amongst holdings of national and local government publications there is a substantial collection of material from the Greater London Council and its predecessors.

D A Clarke, *Librarian*

Port of London Authority
Units 39/41 Cannon Workshops
Cannon Drive
West India Dock
London E14 9SU
Tel: 01-515 1162 or 538 0209

The Library and archive collection of the Port of London Authority is a specialist library relating to the enclosed docks of London, their history, development, growth and decline: and the administration of the PLA. The material in the Library comprises the minute books of the various dock Companies operating up to 1909 and dating back to 1799; the minute books of the various bodies responsible for the River Thames going back to 1770; a collection of unframed prints; a large photographic collection (mostly on long-term loan to the Museum of London); books on London and Docklands; several old maps of Docklands and a comprehensive set of maps of the enclosed Docks; newspaper cuttings from 1889 onwards; a large collection of historic engineering and architectural drawings; and an extensive collection of miscellaneous archive material relating to the PLA, the private dock companies, and numerous external organisations connected to the Docks, including property leases, minutes and information relating to labour relations in the Docks. Most of our 800 framed paintings and prints are either on display or in store at Tilbury Docks. In a warehouse in Docklands is stored a comprehensive range of cargo-handling equipment.

The Library is for research and reference purposes only, and is open to visitors from 09.00 hours to 16.00 hours Monday to Friday inclusive, strictly by prior appointment with the Librarian, who can be contacted on 01-515 1162 or 01-538 0209.

R R Aspinall, *PLA Librarian*

Public Record Office

Kew
Richmond
Surrey
Tel: 01-876 3444

The following short essay on the holdings of the Public Record Office is necessarily very superficial.

The Public Record Office (PRO) contains the archives of central government in England and Wales from the Norman Conquest onwards. Amidst its vast collections the documents recording the government's involvement in the area now known as London's docklands are too numerous to describe in any detail. Early records of Crown lands and buildings along the Thames, for example, will be found in State Papers Domestic (classes in the SP group) and in records of the Privy Council (PC), Exchequer (E), Treasury (T), Office of Land Revenue Records (LRRO), Crown Estate Commissioners (CRES), Works Department (WORK) and elsewhere. Military and naval undertakings in the Docklands at all periods are documented in records of the War Office and Board of Ordnance (WO) and Admiralty and Navy Board (ADM), as well as in those of the Treasury.

From the late 18th century onwards, Home Office records (HO) touch intermittently on matters of law and order on the riverside and so record the arrival and movement of aliens and the departure of emigrants and of convicts sentenced to transportation. On this latter unhappy side of Docklands history, evidence will also be found in records of the Assize courts (ASS) and of the Metropolitan Police (MEPO) and the Prison Commission (PCOM). Additional records of immigration and emigration through the docks will be found in some classes of Colonial Office (CO) records and, for the period before the development of the docks, in Exchequer and in other classes.

A good hunting ground for the historian of the Docklands is in the records of the Board of Trade (BT) and its Marine and Harbour Departments (MT). Apart from records dealing with commercial and marine policy at all levels, these groups include the records of the Registrar General of Shipping and Seamen and much documentation on business enterprise of all descriptions. Further material on dockland businesses is likely to be found in legal records such as those of the bankruptcy courts (B), Chancery (C), and Supreme Court of Judicature (J). A rich source of the development of the Docklands by railway and canal companies is the former British Transport Historical Records collection, comprising over a thousand separate record classes and now kept by the PRO under the group classification RAIL.

Records of the Local Government Board and other authorities charged with administering the Poor Law, public health and other social policy in the 19th and early 20th centuries are for the most part in the MH and HLG groups (although most of such records for 1900-1919 were later destroyed either by enemy bombing or by fire). Here will be found a wealth of detailed historical material on hospitals, schools, sewers, workhouses, on the use of the river as a thoroughfare for moving the poor and the sick between institutions, and numerous other subjects. For the 20th century there are in addition a great many records of the increasing volume of new government activity. Records of the service departments (ADM, AIR, WO and DEFE) and the Ministries of Supply (SUPP), Home Security (HO), Health (HLG and MH) and others provide evidence on many aspects of Dockland history in war time. They include, to take two examples from the Second World War, such detailed information as bomb censuses (in the class designated HO 198) and papers on the evacuation of children (in HLG 7). The very extensive collection of maps and plans at the PRO is another useful source. It ranges, for instance, from mid 19th century tithe maps, in which the ownership and use of each plot of land in each parish was recorded for the Tithe Commissioners, to plans and drawings of the docks themselves.

Useful works include: *Guide to the Contents of the Public Record Office* (HMSO 3 vols, 1963 and 1968): *Maps and Plans in the Public Record Office 1*, British Isles c1410-1860 (HMSO), 1967; and the following PRO *Handbooks (all also published by HMSO):* No 14, *Records of Interest to Social Scientists 1919 to 1939, Introduction* (1971); No 15, *The Second World War: a guide to documents in the Public Record Office* (1972); No 18, *Record of Interest to Social Scientists 1919 to 1930: Employment and Unemployment;* No 19, *Tracing your Ancestors in the Public Record Office* by Jane Cox and Timothy Padfield (1981). There is also a series of leaflets available from the PRO on particular topics (eg Immigrants, Emigrants, Dockyard Employees). The PRO has reading rooms in Chancery Lane, London WC2A 1LR (for legal records, medieval records and the State Papers), in Ruskin Avenue, Kew, Surrey (for records of modern government departments), and in the Land Registry Building, Portugal Street, London WC2 (for census records). A Reader's ticket will be issued free of charge to anyone over the age of 16, on producing proof of their identity.

Mrs H E Jones, *Assistant Keeper*

Chancery Lane
London WC2A 1LR
Tel: 01-405 0741

Chancery Lane, London WC2A 1LR,
01-405 0741
Ruskin Avenue, Kew, Richmond, Surrey,
01-876 3444

The Public Record Office is the national repository of records deriving from the actions of central government and courts of law, and contains many millions of documents ranging in date from the 11th century to the present day. Public records, with few exceptions, are open to inspection thirty years after the end of the year in which they were created.

Not all official records available to the public are in the Public Record Office (see below), and those which are held by the Office are divided between two buildings, the original repository in Chancery Lane, London WC2A 1LR and a new repository at Ruskin Avenue, Kew, Richmond, Surrey TW9 4DU. In addition, the Census returns for England and Wales for the years 1841, 1851, 1861, 1871 and 1881 are normally available to the public only in the form of microfilm copies in the Land Registry building (entrance in Portugal Street, London WC2). Certain Tithe Redemption Office records are available for inspection only at the Public Record Office's repository at Hayes, Middlesex, where it is necessary to make an appointment in advance by telephone (01-573 3831).

The division of records between the two main buildings has been made as logical as possible (see below), but it is not always easy to forecast which classes of records will prove relevant to any particular piece of research, and readers may find that they have to visit both buildings. Moreover it must be remembered that individual records may be temporarily unavailable because they are in use by other readers or for administrative purposes. Officers in charge of Reading Rooms will be glad to give advice, and readers should ask to see them if they meet any difficulties in the course of their work.

How to get there
Chancery Lane   This building is situated near the south (Fleet Street) end of Chancery Lane. The nearest underground stations are Chancery Lane, Holborn and Temple. Bus service 171 passes the Office, and several services pass the Holborn and Fleet Street ends of Chancery Lane. The Land Registry building entrance in Portugal Street is close by. No car parking space is available at either building.

Kew   The building in Ruskin Avenue is less than 10 minutes walk from Kew Gardens Station, which is served by the District Line (London Transport) and the North London Line (British Rail). Kew Bridge Station (British Rail) is about 15 minutes walk away. There are several bus services to Kew and ample space for parking private cars is available.

Readers' Tickets
Only persons holding a valid Readers Ticket are admitted to the Reading Rooms of the Public Record Office at Chancery Lane or Kew. Tickets are issued (free of charge) at the Enquiry Office at Chancery Lane or at the Reception counter at Kew to applicants who can satisfy the Keeper of Public Records of their suitability to be allowed access to the records and produce documentary proof of identity.

Hours of opening
The Reading Rooms are open from 9.30 am to 5 pm (4.50 pm at Portugal Street) on Mondays to Fridays.

Dates of closures for public holidays, annual stocktaking (normally the first two full weeks in October), etc, are displayed in the Reading Rooms, and a leaflet is available on request.

Official records not in the Public Record Office
For certain classes of public records, including those of Quarter Session, the Lord Chancellor has appointed local repositories as places of deposit *(see Record Repositories in Great Britain, HMSO)*. A few government Departments maintain their own records and provide facilities for their inspection; in particular the Principal Registry of the Family Division, Somerset House, London WC2R 1LP (containing registrations of wills from 1858), and the India Office Library and Records, 197 Blackfriars Road, London SE1 8NG.

The following are the chief places where official documents not covered by the Public Records Act 1958 are preserved:

The Record Office
House of Lords
London SW1A OPW
Records of Parliament.

The Office of Population Censuses and Surveys
General Register Office
St Catherine's House
Kingsway
London WC2B 6JP
Registrations of births, marriages and deaths in England and Wales since 1837; parish registers, which are the main source of earlier genealogical information, are mainly retained locally in parish churches and county record offices, not in the Public Record Office.

The Scottish Record Office
HM General Register House
Edinburgh EH1 3YY
Records of the Kingdom of Scotland to 1707; legal registers, including testaments; records of the Scottish courts and departments; records of the Church of Scotland; certain local records and collections of family monuments.

The General Register Office of Scotland
New Register House
Edinburgh EH1 3YY
Registrations of births, deaths and marriages in Scotland.

The Public Record Office of Northern Ireland
66 Balmoral Avenue
Belfast BT9 6NY
The records of the Northern Ireland courts and departments, and collections of privately deposited papers.

The General Register Office
Oxford House
Chichester Street
Belfast BT1 4HL
Registrations of births, deaths and marriages in Northern Ireland.

Various collections of papers, which a reader might have expected to find in the Public

Record Office, remain in private hands or have been given, sold or lent to institutions, notably to the British Library (Department of Manuscripts), Great Russell Street, London WC1B 3DG. Information on the present whereabouts of such collections should be sought from the Historical Manuscripts Commission, Quality Court, Chancery Lane, London WC2A 1HP.

Division of records between the buildings

Chancery Lane

i   Legal records, etc, described in the *Guide to the Contents of the Public Record Office*, Volume 1 (but excluding Copyright Office records), being records from the Norman Conquest onwards of the King's Court and the divergent branches and offshoots through which it discharged its administrative, financial and judicial functions (ie the Chancery, Exchequer, and the various courts of common law and equity and the prerogative courts down to the present day); other records mainly concerned with judicial matters, including those of the Palatinates of Lancaster, Chester and Durham, of the Duchy of Lancaster, of special jurisdictions, of the High Courts of Admiralty and of Delegates, and of the Judicial Committee of the Privy Council; and certain special collections, being artificially made classes of documents brought together from various sources, including Ancient Correspondence, Ancient Petitions, Court Rolls, the Hundred Rolls, Ministers' and Receivers' Accounts, Papal Bulls and Rentals and Surveys.

ii   Records of some departments, etc, with quasi-legal functions or whose records are relevant to the records above. These are the Crown Estate Commissioners, the Land Revenue Record Office, the Law Officers' Department, the Privy Council Office, the Privy Seal Office, the Director of Public Prosecutions, Queen Anne's Bounty, the Signet Office and the Treasury Solicitor. Records of the Lord Chamberlain's Office, the Lord Steward's Office and the Privy Purse Office are also here.

iii   Records of the State Paper Office, being papers of the Secretaries of State from the 16th to the late 18th centuries, including material from the period 1760 to 1775 described in the *Calendar of Home Office Papers, George III* (4 vols HMSO, 1878-1899), but not the Colonial State Papers.

iv   Certain gifts and deposits mostly relevant by date or content to other records kept in Chancery Lane.

v   The non-parochial registers held by the Office; foreign registers and returns of births, marriages and deaths; the probate records of the Prerogative Court of Canterbury, including original and register copy wills, inventories and exhibits; and the estate duty registers of the Department of Inland Revenue.

Kew

Records of present and defunct government departments, public offices, etc, which are described in the *Guide to the Contents of the Public Record Office*, Volumes II and III, and in unpublished supplements, are (with the exceptions noted above and below) stored at Kew. These records include those of the Cabinet. The Treasury (with records extending back to the 16th century), the Admiralty (including the Navy Board, etc), the Foreign Office, and the War Office. The records of the Colonial Office include Colonial State Papers from the 16th century onwards. Records of the Copyright Office, Stationers' Hall, described in volume 1 of the *Guide* are also at Kew.

Portugal Street

Holds microfilm copies of the Census returns for England and Wales for 1841, 1851, 1861, 1871 and 1881.

Hayes

Certain records of the Tithe Redemption Office, formerly available for inspection at Worthing and Hinchley Wood are now here. Other Tithe Redemption Office records are to be seen at Kew. A separate leaflet on Tithe records, including a list of classes to be seen at the two sites, is available.

Queen Mary College
University of London
The Library
Mile End Road
London E1 4NS
Tel 01-980 4811

The collection is small and by no means rivals the nearby Local History Library of Tower Hamlets Public Libraries.

Queen Mary College Library
Queen Mary College Library has a general collection of books on the history of London and local planning to support teaching programmes in the geography of London and East London from an economic and social viewpoint. Complete runs of *East London Papers* and the *London Journal* are also kept. Archival material consists of documents and papers relating to the People's Palace (1883-1930's) and the early history of the College.

J Neilson (Ms), *History/Politics Librarian*

Science Museum Library
South Kensington
London SW7 5NH
Tel: 01-589 3456

Science Museum Library, South Kensington, London SW7 5NH, telephone, 01-589 3456 (01-581 4734); a national library of pure and applied science, specialising in the history of science and technology. The Library has some printed works relating to London's Docklands, entered in the subject catalogue and also pictorial and archival material, particularly prints and manuscripts of the Thames Tunnel. Reader's tickets are necessary before consulting items in the rare printed books, pictorial and archives collections; tickets are obtainable at the Enquiry Desk or by writing to the Keeper; evidence of identity and address is required. To view items in the Pictorial and Archives collection, prior appointment should be made.

L R Day, *Keeper*

Southwark, London Borough of
Acting Librarian and Curator:
R A Hardern FLA
20-22 Lordship Lane
London SE22 8HN
Tel: 01-693 9221

A brief description of the holdings of the Southwark Local Studies Library relevant to Docklands history follows.

Southwark Local Studies Library, 211 Borough High Street, London SE1 (telephone 01-403 3507). Appointment to view archives advisable.

A comprehensive collection on the area now covered by the London Borough of Southwark, of which Rotherhithe and the former Surrey Docks are in the Dockland area; but the development of most of the Northern part of the borough has been influenced by the Port of London.

Primary source material for buildings and firms includes ratebooks; valuation books and plans; estate records; records of some local wharves and Beatson's, ship repairers of Rotherhithe. About 2,000 unsorted plans (1877?-1960s), formerly belonging to the Port of London Authority and relating to the Surrey Docks are now in the care of the library but an appointment to view them is essential.

Printed material includes maps and plans, eg Ordnance Survey 1870's — to date; Loveday's London Waterside Surveys, 1857; Goad's Insurance plans; London directories; Port of London Authority Monthly; pamphlets and cuttings. Comprehensive Metropolitan Borough of Bermondsey index. Microfilm copies of local newspapers and Census returns. Large photograph and print collection.

Standard Telephones and Cables
STC House
190 Strand
London WC2R 1DU
Tel: 01-836 8055

The site at North Woolwich, where cable had been manufactured since the 1890s, was sold in 1977. On the exodus from North Woolwich records and equipment were abandoned and this still presents problems from an archival point of view. Many of the workforce moved either to Basildon or to Newport, South Wales, so there are plenty of employees, and

pensioners too, who can contribute oral accounts of working life at Woolwich. The company has a number of photographs of the site, both exterior and aerial views, and some interior views showing manufacturing processes in the various shops and also a detailed map of the works. There are copies of contracts for telephone cable between Fowler Waring Cables Co, the previous owners, and the National Telephone Company, 1897, and between Western Electric Company (STC's name pre-1925) and the NTC, 1898; originals of these are in Post Office Records, St Martin's Le Grand. The company also has a shop-by-shop inventory of machinery and description of area etc prepared just after the war.

Several of the more interesting accounts of working life at Woolwich were written by pensioners now dead, and the company has copies of these; STC's company history, "Power of speech" by Peter Young, published in 1983, may be of interest. There are also a number of taped interviews that contain small amounts of information. As the site at Greenwich, formerly occupied by Submarine Cables Ltd and where cable has been made continuously since the 1840s, there is a list of documents and other material compiled in 1977, by NAEST.

National Archive for Electrical Science and Technology
Submarine Systems Division
Standard Telephones and Cables Ltd
Greenwich
London

The history of submarine cable manufacture goes back to the middle of the 19th century: the first successful submarine telegraph cable between England and France was laid in 1851. Some of this cable was made by a Camberwell firm, Kuper & Co, which was re-named Glass, Elliott & Co and moved to premises in East Greenwich, and later to Enderby's Wharf, Greenwich. The core for this Channel cable was made by the Gutta Percha Company of Wharf Road, London. Founded in 1845, it was the first company to exploit the potential of gutta percha as an insulating and proofing compound for electric telegraph wires. In its first 16 years, it completed more than 14,000 nautical miles of cable core, including that for the ill-fated 1857 Atlantic cable.

In 1864 the Gutta Percha Co and Glass Elliott & Co joined forces to become the Telegraph Construction and Maintenance Co Ltd. The new company manufactured and laid the cable for both the 1865 and 1866 Atlantic cables.

The next 60 years were ones of growth and consolidation, during which a large number of cables were completed in all parts of the world. Submarine cable manufacture and laying remained the principal activity, but other gutta percha products were made, eg golf balls and bosses for the linen trade. In 1915 a gutta percha plantation in Malaya was acquired. The company played an important role in the search for a more efficient submarine cable conductor by developing a copper-nickel-iron alloy (Mumetal) in 1923; and improved on the dielectric by introducing 'K-gutta', an artificial plastic made from gutta percha and balata.

In 1935, world depression, and caution on the part of cable companies due to the development of wireless telegraphy, led to a pooling of submarine cable resources for the only surviving British manufacturers, the Telegraph Construction and Maintenance Co Ltd and Siemens Bros & Co Ltd.
A new company, Submarine Cables Ltd was formed, owned jointly by the two firms.

A number of submarine telephone systems had already been completed, but the development of submersible repeaters and a polythene dielectric made possible a vast increase in the submarine telephone cable network: Submarine Cables Ltd began to produce repeaters in the late 1940s. By 1950 the company and its predecessors had made and laid more than 82% of the submarine cable of the world.

Submarine Cables Ltd was taken over by Standard Telephones and Cables Ltd in 1973, and so became part of the American-based ITT Group. Cable manufacture has now been moved to the STC factory at Southampton.

The Telcon Story, 1850-1950, the history and operations of the Telegraph Construction and Maintenance Co Ltd, was published in 1950.

Laurie Dennett, *Company Archivist*

Surrey County Council
Surrey Record Office
County Hall
Kingston upon Thames
KT1 2ND
Tel: 01-546 1050

This is a summary of the kinds of material held relating to the part of the dockland formerly in Surrey.

Surrey Record Office
Until the creation of The London County Council in 1889, Surrey extended eastwards along the Thames as far as Bermondsey, Rotherhithe and a small part (the manor of Hatcham, roughly the New Cross area) of Deptford. Surrey Record Office holds the records, beginning in 1659, of Surrey Court of Quarter Sessions, which administered the county.

These records cover:

Criminal offences — the evidence may throw light on dock work, shipping and social life.

Pauperism — movement of families, illegitimacy.

Highways — upkeep, diversion of line.

Inns and taverns — some licensing powers.

Plans and list of property affected by public undertakings for which Acts of Parliament were sought (from 1791): docks, railways, etc.

Property — holding: Land Tax duplicates, 1780-1832.

Lists of certain classes of inhabitants: freeholders' lists; electoral registers; licensing of victuallers.

The office also holds a small number of title deeds and estate plans relating to the area, and forming part of accumulations of records primarily relating to 'modern' Surrey.

Dr D B Robinson, *County Archivist*

City of Westminster
Archives Department
Victoria Library
160 Buckingham Palace Road
London SW1W 9UD
Tel: 01-730 7371

The Department has only a lease and release relating to Dockland. They are the mortgage of a fourth part of a dock at New Crane, St Paul Shadwell by Lt Tomlinson Henry Bushy to Anthony Pye, 4 and 5 September 1783. The reference is 177/136 and the documents are housed at Marylebone Library, Marylebone Road, London NW1 5PS.

Miss M J Swarbrick, *Chief Archivist*

Lewisham, London Borough of
Lewisham Local History Centre
The Manor House
Old Road
London SE13 5SY
Tel: 01-852 5050

The following list, relating to the Docklands within the Borough of Lewisham, has been compiled:

i The more specialised material:
Maps: Deptford Dockyard
1 View of dockyard [1698]
2 Plan of the Yard before the Revolution in 1688.
3 Some plans and improvements since the Revolution.
[Note — delineated 1698 — photostat copy, three on one sheet — 17" × 22"; original in British Library, Department of MSS]

ii General plans and detailed plans of the buildings at the 'Red House'
[Royal Victoria Victualling Yard] 1743-1790. Mainly by James and Henry James Arrow.

iii Geometrical plan and north-east elevation of His Majesty's Dockyard at Deptford, with part of the town [1753], by Thomas Milton.

iv HM Dockyard and Royal Victoria Victualling Yard, surveyed and drawn by J W Perry [1858].

v Material in manuscript form:
An account of 'charge sustayned' in Deptford Dockyard in November 1618. Refers to wages of storekeepers, clerks, dockyard personnel etc. Total = £87. 12. 6.

vi 'Estimate of charge' Jan-Dec 1712, for Deptford Dockyard [included in volume of Navy Board estimates.]

vii Sale catalogue of provisions etc, 1785 — from the victualling office.

viii Maps: Surrey Canal
'A plan of the Grand Surrey Canal, from Rotherhithe to Camberwell, with the docks and timber ponds' [1810]. Surveyed by Nathaniel Simmons.

ix London and its environs, OS Sheet XI NE [1848 — 5T]. Shows a length of the Canal from Camberwell to Rotherhithe, together with the Dockyard at Deptford.

In addition to the above, the Local History Centre possesses a good collection of late-nineteenth century OS maps of the Deptford riverside area, together with a number of prints, photographs, etc relating to the Navy Dockyard/Victualling Yard. Other relevant material is contained in parish ratebooks and also in local newspapers [which are available on microfilm]. The Centre also has Census Returns on microfilm and a Museums Collection. We have one or two pamphlets, as well as general secondary material, on the London and Greenwich Railway. The magazine of the Port of London Authority is also taken.

C W Harrison, *Archivist*

Newham, London Borough of

Passmore Edwards Museum
Romford Road, London E15 4LZ
Tel: 01-534 4545 ext 5670,
01-519 4296

North Woolwich Old Station Museum
Pier Road
North Woolwich
London E16 2JJ
Tel: 01-474 7244

The Museum's Archival Collections contain material relevant to various aspects of Dockland History. The Essex Pictorial Survey contains photographs of the area from about 1880 until 1935. A range of maps show the development of the area.

There are similar resources relating to the railways in Dockland and various photographs and documents from Beckton Gas Works. More recent photographs have been taken of buildings in the course of the running down of the Docks and Gas Works.

The Parish Registers of St Luke's, Canning Town, have been indexed from 1875, many dock labourers are included.

Objects relating to the history of Dockland have been collected by the main Passmore Edwards Museum since it opened in 1900 and these include the bust of C J Mare, equipment from the Seaman's Hospital, a tidal gauge from Beckton and so on. These have, of course, been augmented by items relating to the history of the Great Eastern Railway in the North Woolwich Old Station Museum opened in 1984.

Ian G Robertson, *Curator*

Patricia Wilkinson, *Principal Assistant Curator*, Archaeology and Local History

Terry Turbin, *Assistant Curator*, Archaeology and Local History (North Woolwich Old Station Museum).

Local Studies Library
Stratford Reference Library
Water Lane
Stratford, E15 4NJ
Tel: 01-534 4545 ext 5661/2

Enquiries to:
Assistant Borough Librarian
Reference & Local Studies, Miss M Lister
Local Studies Librarian, Mr M Bloch

Open:
Mon, Tues, Thurs, Fri: 09.30-19.00
Wed, Sat: 09.30-17.00

Intending readers should telephone first to ensure that the Local Studies Librarian will be on duty. Appointment preferred, especially for access on Saturdays.

Access: Generally open to the public

The Local Studies Library forms part of the Stratford Reference Library but is housed in a separate room. The collection contains material on Essex, London and the former County Boroughs of East and West Ham. The collection covers the London Borough of Newham intensively and Essex and Greater London to a lesser extent. It consists of approximately 6,000 works and 3,500 pamphlets of which about 150 are pre-1851 works relating to Essex. Large amounts of pre-20th century material, especially official records, is in the Essex Record Office (which see). There are approximately 25 directories dated pre-1851 plus a number after that date.

Census returns are available from 1841, some indexed by name and profession, some partially indexed and some with index to streets only. Electoral registers, from 1890 in the case of West Ham, are available.

Among the major collections are archives of Newham Borough and its former constituent authorities; Parochial and religious records, East Ham, 1809-1965, Little Ilford, 1887-1900, West Ham, 1646-1965; Non-Conformist records, 19th and 20th centuries; Air raid precaution files relating to East and West Ham, 1939-1945.

The earliest maps of Newham, complete to a reasonable scale, are the local section of John Rocque's "Survey of London", 1741-45, and the South West Essex sheets of Chapman & Andre's "Map of the County of Essex" 1777. The earliest detailed maps are the locally commissioned "Survey of the parish of West Ham", 1821, 40 ins to 1 mile, and a copy of the "Plan of East Ham for the Tithe Awards", 1838. From this date onward there is a very good range of maps of West Ham and, to a lesser extent, East Ham at successive periods.

There are a large number of publications issued by churches, schools, firms, political groups, libraries, archaeological and historical societies, etc. Important general periodicals include the "Stratford Express", 1858+ on microfilm, 1885 indexed, "East Ham Echo", 1899-1941, "Essex Review", 1892-1957, etc, plus newspaper cuttings. There are non-systematic collections of cuttings on West Ham covering the period 1910-64, Esst Ham 1902-48, plus a systematic service on Newham from 1964 to date. Two earlier volumes on Stratford and Plaistow contain cuttings and illustrations of the 18/19th centuries.

The Library contains a large collection of photographs, among these being a pictorial survey of all docks within the area, this being undertaken in 1984. At the same time a pictorial survey of streets was carried out. A large amount of wartime photographs are contained within the collection.

Specific collections include the "Albion disaster relief fund archives", 1898 and material relating to the Silvertown Explosion. There is also a collection on James Keir Hardie, MP (1856-1915), formed by Herbert Bryan.

To those interested in this area the following publications are recommended:

London Borough of Newham
   Guide to the Local Studies Library, nd, 20pp.

Newham Library Service
   Local Studies notes. Single sheets, examples are:

   Family History Notes, No 1, directories and almanacks;
   Family History Notes, No 3, Census returns;
   Family History Notes, No 5, Newspapers

'Readers' are available for material in microform and photocopying of any material required will be carried out by the library staff, at a cost.

E W Chapman (compiled from information supplied)

The Royal Commission on Historical Manuscripts
Quality House
Quality Court
Chancery Lane
London WC2A 1HP
Tel: 01-242 1198

The Commission collects and disseminates information about the nature and location of historical papers of all kinds outside the Public Records. It maintains the National Register of Archives as a central collecting point for unpublished information on manuscript collections. This is concerned not only with personal and family papers but also the records of local authorities, religious bodies, commercial undertakings, societies and organisations. It contains some 28,000 reports on individual collections of papers which have been brought together from a large number of sources including local, university and other record offices and libraries throughout the United Kingdom.

The Register records details of a wealth of material relating to the industrial, social and technological history of the London docklands. It includes, for example, reports on the records of dock, transport and property companies, ship builders and repairers, local authorities, trade associations, religious organisations, schools and other public amenities, as well as deeds and estate papers. These reports may be approached through the Companies Index and also through the Subject and Personal Indexes. The Search Room is open to the public Monday to Friday 9.30 am to 5 pm and no written introduction or reader's ticket is required. Limited and specific enquiries can be answered by post.

Mrs E P Scarff, *Assistant Keeper*

Tower Hamlets, London Borough of
Directorate of Community Services
Cheviot House
227/233 Commercial Road
London E1 2BU
Tel: 01-790 1818 ext 131, Mr Dellar

London Borough of Tower Hamlets Local History Library
The library, which is housed in the Central Library, Bancroft Road, London E1 4DQ (phone 01-980 4366) comprises the local collections of the former Metropolitan Boroughs of Bethnal Green, Poplar and Stepney, amalgamated to form the present borough in 1965. The collection has been considerably augmented since then, and includes nearly 15,000 books and pamphlets, 1,750 maps, about 7,000 deeds, trade directories, pictures, cuttings, films, and local newspaper files on microfilm from 1857, as well as census returns on microfilm from 1841 to 1881. The collection therefore contains much material on the docklands area on the north

bank of the Thames between the Tower in the west and Bow Creek in the east,

A shipping collection of some 1,600 books, 450 pamphlets, cuttings and 5,000 illustrations forms a separate part of the library, and includes the Bolt Collection, giving details of ships from about 1850 to 1920. Lloyd's Register 1844-1965, Lloyd's Register of Yachts 1904-52 and runs of periodicals (eg *Mariner's Mirror, PLA Monthly, Sea Breezes)* are also held.

Microform readers and a reader printer are available, as well as photocopying facilities. Prints can be arranged through a commercial photographer, the copy negatives being retained by the Library. A reproduction fee may be charged for use of material by publishers, film makers, etc. The Local History Library is normally open from 9 am to 8 pm Monday, Tuesday, Thursday and Friday, and 9 am to 5 pm Wednesday and Saturday.

Correspondence should be addressed to the Assistant Director of Community Services (Libraries, Arts and Entertainments) at the address at the head of this entry.

D T Elliott, *Assistant Director of Community Services*

University College London
The Library
Gower Street
London WC1E 6BT
Tel: 01-387 7050

The London History section of the Library contains some 5,000 volumes, together with about 500 maps and a large pamphlet collection. Some material relating to Docklands is also contained in the Environmental Studies (Architecture anbd Planning) and Geography Libraries.

Michael Jahn, *Assistant Librarian (History and Economics)*

University of London Library
Senate House
Malet Street
London WC1E 7HU
Tel: 01-636 4514

There is a certain amount of material relevant to the history of London's docklands in the following collections:

Goldsmiths' Library of Economic Literature
The Library contains approximately 60,000 volumes in the field of early economic literature (in its widest sense), the majority of items being pre-1851. There is some material on the London docklands, which can be located through the *Catalogue of the Goldsmiths' Library of Economic Literature*, 4 vols 1970-83, and the *London Bibliography of the Social Sciences*, 1931-37 (continued in the Library's own catalogue).

Manuscripts
There are five manuscripts in the Library which are relevant to the history of the Port of London and London's docks:
Charges for victualling ships in London and Chatham, 1596 (MS 380)
Customs duties in the Port of London, 1672 (MS 745)
Customs offices and salaries in London and Outports, 1675 (MS 672)
Commonplace book of James Oldham "Searcher, landing and Coastwaiter" in the Port of London from 1842. [c1828-63] (MS 174)
Memorandum describing the facilities of the London docks, [c1825-30?] (MS 829)

They are described more fully in *Catalogue of the Goldsmiths' Library of Economic Literature*, vol III, 1982.

Bromhead Library
This collection contains about 5,000 volumes, mainly dealing with London and its history. There are a number of books, from the eighteenth to twentieth centuries relating to the London Docks, including material on the Thames Tunnel.

[Staff and students of universities other than London may use the University Library for reference purposes at certain times, in particular during the vacations. Other visitors who wish to use the library for study or research may be allowed access at the discretion of the Director, to whom written application should be made.
The preceding paragraph is taken from 'Guide to the University of London Library' which is a most useful publication to anyone considering using same.]

Miss H M Young, *Palaeography Room*

Miss P M Baker, *Sterling Library*

Corporation of London
Records Office
P O Box 270
Guildhall
London EC2P 2EJ
Tel: 01-606 3030

The Corporation of London Records Office holds the official records of the municipal government of the City of London. These range in date from a charter of William I of 1067 to 20th century documents. They include such classes as royal charters granting privileges to the City; custumals (mostly of medieval date and sometimes illuminated) which are compilations of memoranda and documents thought worthy of remembrance; administrative proceedings of the City government from 1275 (including records of the Courts of Aldermen and Common Council and their committees) and records of admissions to the Freedom of the City; financial accounts (the principal series dating from 1632); property deeds, leases and rentals of land owned by the Corporation both within and without the City; plans; architectural drawings of bridges, prisons and other buildings owned by the Corporation; many records relating to London Bridge and other City bridges and the estgates which maintain them (including medieval deeds and accounts); the City of London Sessions records which include indictments and minutes relating to trials at the Old Bailey; and records of the Husting, Mayor's, the Orphans' and other civic courts.

These records contain much information about the constitution of the civic government (e.g. the election of the mayor and other officers) and civic pageantry; about local government administration in numerous aspects (e.g. public health, markets, watch and ward); about individual citizens as these came in one way or another in contact with the civic machinery; and since the City played a large part in national affairs in earlier centuries there is a good deal about national events and the City's relationship with the crown. The aftermath of the Great Fire and the rebuilding of the City are also very well documented.

A Guide to the Records in the Corporation of London Records Office and the Guildhall Library Muniment Room by P E Jones and R Smith was published in 1951 and, although now out of print, may be available in large reference libraries. Records of particular interest to genealogists are noted in two articles by Betty R Masters entitled *'Some Genealogical Sources in the Corporation of London Records Office'* which were published in June and September 1982 in the *Genealogists' Magazine* (Vol 20, nos 10 and 11).

Various lists, calendars and indexes are available in the search room of the Records Office which is in the North Office Block at Guildhall (second floor, Room 221; entrance to the building is from Basinghall Street at the top of the steps leading from the street tot he piazza). Nearest Underground Stations are: Moorgate, Bank and St Paul's.

The search room is open to the public from 9.30 am to 4.45 pm, Mondays to Fridays inclusive (except Bank Holidays). Appointments are not generally necessary in order to consult the records, but in some cases advance warning of a proposed visit may help both readers and staff. The telephone number of the search room is 01-606 3030 ext 2251. Correspondence should be addressed to: The Deputy Keeper of the Records, Corporation of London Records Office, P O Box 270, Guildhall, London EC2P 2EJ.

James R Sewell, *Deputy Keeper of the Records*

Essex Records Office
County Hall
Chelmsford
Essex CM1 1LX
Tel: 0245 267222 ext 2104

Appointment to view archives desirable.

The West Ham and North Woolwich areas were, until 1964, part of the administrative county of Essex for which the Essex Record Office provides the official archives service. Administrative records of the County Council prior to that date therefore contain material relating to the area.

The principal documents of interest are the minutes of the Victoria Docks Gas Company, 1858-1871 (reference D/F 5/14/1-3).

Printed Guides and Catalogues: F G Emmison, *Guide to the Essex Record Office*, 2nd Edn., 1968; F G Emmison, *Catalogue of Maps in the Essex Record Office* (1947), *First* (1952), *Second* (1964) and *Third* (1968). *Supplements*, include public schemes (railways and docks).

Victor Gray, *County Archivist*

Greenwich, London Borough of
Local History Library
'Woodlands'
90 Mycenae Road
Blackheath, SE3 7SE
Tel: 01-858 4631

The 'docklands' area covers St Nicholas Parish, Deptford, Greenwich, Charlton, Woolwich and Plumstead so forming the longest river boundary of any London Borough. The only commercial docks were in North Woolwich which is now administered by the L B of Newham.

Administrative records include Local Acts, Vestry minutes, Board of Works minutes, Woolwich Board of Health Minutes, Medical Officer of Health reports, Rate books and Borough Council minutes, 1900-.

Population structure and occupation are obtained from the Census returns of 1841, '51, '61, '71, '81 (microfilm). All volumes of the Transactions of the Greenwich and Lewisham Antiquarian Society and the Proceedings of the Woolwich and District Antiquarian Society are held at 'Woodlands' and are fully indexed. Relevant articles include 'The river and marsh at East Greenwich' by W V Bartlett and 'Social conditions on Greenwich Marsh, 1837-1901' by B J Ludlow.

Complete microfilmed runs of local newspapers are available, ie Kentish Independent, 1843-, Kentish Mercury, 1834-, Woolwich and District Labour Notes, 1898-99, Borough of Woolwich Labour Journal, 1901-04 and the Pioneer, 1904-26.

There are some business records in the collection, eg Sykes Pumps Ltd and there are many files on individual companies.

Political archives are Minutes of Greenwich and Woolwich Labour Parties; Woolwich Arsenal Joint Shop Stewards Coimmittee Minutes, c1946-60s; Greenwich Trades Council reports, minutes, 1950s-60s; Journals of Siemans Shop Stewards Committee,

1933-39 and Johnson & Phillips Shop Stewards Journals, 1936-37.

'Woodlands' has a comprehensive collection of maps including Skinner's map of Greenwich Marsh, 1745, OS maps, Tithe Maps and plans by Alfred Roberts, ARIBA. Directories run from 1792-1938 with some gaps. North Woolwich is included in the map and directory holding and there is a file of unpublished material relating to North Woolwich.

The 'Martin Collection' at 'Woodlands' contains a large quantity of maps and plans relating to the Morden College Charity, the main landowner in the industrial area of Greenwich.

Topographically the district is covered by photographs (including aerial), engravings, watercolours, drawings and postcards.

Greenwich Local History Library is open: Monday, Tuesday and Thursday 09.00 am-08.00 pm Saturday 09.00 am-05.00 pm. Closed: Wednesday and Friday.

J Watson, *Local History Librarian*

India Office Library and Records
British Library
197 Blackfriars Road
London SE1 8NG
Tel: 01-928 9531

Currently undertaken is the sorting and listing of a sizeable collection of title deeds and related papers for properties once held by either the East India Company or by the India Office. The majority of these documents concern East India Company premises in the City of London and Middlesex, covering the period from the late fifteenth century until the mid-nineteenth century. The Docklands area is well represented in the collection, which includes deeds for sites at Ratcliff, Poplar, Blackwall, Rotherhithe, Lyon's Quay, Somer's Quay and Hammond's Quay.

A register compiled *circa* 1813 contains abstracts of the title deeds relating to most of the company's pre-nineteenth century property transactions arranged in chronological sequences for the different sites. Brief entries concerning some estates after 1813 were later added at the back of the register, but these groups of deeds are not described in detail. After 1833 the company was obliged to sell its commercial premises, and many of the deeds listed in the register were transferred to the new owners as proof of title.

The IOLR stands at the junction of Blackfriars Road and Union Street, opposite the Cut. Hours of opening are 09.30 to 18.00 Monday to Friday, and 09.30 to 13.00 on Saturday. Temporary entry passes are issued without formality, and regular users may apply for a reader's ticket.

Margaret Meaden, *India Office Records*

Photographic sources

An important source of illustrations is the collection of PLA photographs housed at the Museum of London. These date mostly from c1950. Other photographs will be found in the PLA library and the GLC photographic library. A growing collection of photographs relating to the social history of the Isle of Dogs is kept by the Island History project, 151 Manchester Road, London E14 (telephone 01–987 6014). Phil Dubuque, a member of the Docklands History Group, has submitted the following report of his search for PLA negatives.

Report regarding archival photographic material relating to the Port of London Authority.

In the PLA library is a series of continuous photographs of the Thames river bank from London Bridge to Greenwich Reach taken of both north and south banks. The PLA has no record of the document anywhere. The date and probable purpose are not known nor is there any record of negatives relating to it being received by the PLA. They appear to have been taken in the late 1930s.

I discovered that the company whose name is stamped on these four books of photos stopped trading in 1966. They were Avery Illustrations. On 26 August 1966 Clifford Varnam sold Avery Illustrations as a going concern to 'John Matlby Ltd', photographic company. With the transaction went a half-plate camera and, as far as we know, all the Avery negatives. Two large customers of Avery were the London County Council and the Port of London Authority. In 1972, John Maltby gave the GLC all the Avery-LCC negatives he had for the GLC Photographic Library. Such was the volume of LCC work done by Avery that a separate log book of dates and jobs was kept and all other clients were listed together in another book.

The GLC received just over 5,000 negatives for the period 1956-1966. Recently at 'John Maltby Ltd' the now director George Tanner got the remaining Avery negative and log book out of storage where they had been dust-gathering in photo-paper boxes since 1966. Mr Tanner did not know about the existence of the LCC material. The log book lists, among many others, 2,000 PLA photos taken between 1954 and 1966. A few year's negatives were missing though the main body of it was there. Along with the PLA is listed other clients such as 'Spillers', 'Taylor Woodrow' and the Westminster City Council.

Of the 2,000 PLA negative listed, 763 are missing. So what has come to light are the remaining 1,326 negatives, taken by Avery for the PLA between 1956 and 1966. They are in the possession of George Tanner of John Maltby Ltd (Photographic), Hendon.

Examination was made of the PLA negatives at random. They consist of half-plate and 5" x 4" negatives of sheds, cranes, machinery and river views, sometimes pieces of 'new' technology such as a radio controlled rail system as well as views of work sites and details of welding, pipe joints, vaulting and the like. Entries were also found for forensic purpose such as accident sites. Along with these there are many well detailed architectural and topographical photographs throughout.

Three sample entries are set out below:

(1956) 56/130, PLA, Surrey Dock — shed views

(1961) 61/427 to 442, PLA, London Docks — No 1 Warehouse (views outside and underneath)

(1961) 61/489 to 492, PLA, Victoria Dock — crane jib, fatal accident.

Still not discovered is the fate of the negatives for the continuous river bank photos, so research continues elsewhere.

Phil Dubuque
13-4-83

Bibliography

This list is by no means complete. The editor has not read every work included and would be grateful for additional comments as well as for suggestions of further titles.

Abercrombie, Sir Patrick

Greater London Plan, HMSO, 1944

Account of ships and vessels built in Great Britain from 1790 to 1791 and 1804 to 1805. Parliamentary Papers, 1806, [243] XIII.

Addison, W

Thames Estuary, Hale, 1954

Allen, F H

The Thames Model Investigation, The Dock and Harbour Authority, **32** (1952), 373-8

Allen, F H and Grindley, J

Radioactive Tracers in the Thames Estuary, The Dock and Harbour Authority, **37** (1957), 302-6

Allen, F H, Price, W A and Inglis, Sir Claude

Model Experiments on the Storm Surge of 1953 in the Thames Estuary and the Reduction of Future Surges, Proceedings of the Institution of Civil Engineers, **4** (1955), 48-82

Annual Statement of the Trade of the United Kingdom, Vols 1-4 HM Customs and Excise, HMSO

Atton, H and Holland, H H

The King's Customs, 2 vols, Murray, 1910

Banbury, P

Shipbuilders of the Thames and Medway, David & Charles, 1971 *An important book. Sadly not as complete as might be wished and lacking detailed references. Some errors.*

Barber, T W, et al

The Port of London and the Thames Barrage, Swan, Sonnenschein & Co, 1907

Barker, T C and Robbins, Michael

A history of London transport: passenger travel and the development of the metropolis; 1st edition reprinted with minor revisions, Allen & Urwin for the London Transport Executive, 1976. Originally published 1974.

Barnes, R J

Marc Brunel's Engine House at Rotherhithe, GLIAS Journal **1** (1979), 14-20

Barry, P

Dockyard Economy and Naval Power, 1863 *A most important source, written just before the decline of shipbuilding on the Thames. The copy in the National Maritime Museum has photographs pasted in, said to be by Barry himself, which depict shipyards and works of the period. Few illustrated copies exist and the photographs vary from copy to copy.*

Barton, Nicholas

The Lost Rivers of London, reprinted by
Historical Publications 1982, (original edition
1962)
A classic. Thankfully in print once more.

Bell, A

Port of London 1909-34, PLA, 1934

The Said Noble River, PLA, 1937

Belloc, H

The Historic Thames, Dent, 1907

The River of London, Foulis, 1912

Binns, A

The King George V Dock, London,
Proceedings of the Institution of Civil
Engineers, **216** (1923), 372

The Thames and its Docks, Transactions of
the Institution of Engineers-in-Charge, **42**
(1936-7), 124-40

Mainly Port of London, Proceedings of the
Institution of Mechanical Engineers, **144**
(1940), 50-53

Bird, J

The Geography of the Port of London,
Hutchinson, 1957
*More than its title suggests. Excellent, packs a great
deal into a small space.*

**The Industrial Development of Lower
Thameside,** Geography, **37** (1952), 89-96

Booth, Charles

Life and labour of the people of London,
MacMillan, 1892, 2 vols.

Borley, H V

Chronology of London railways, Railway
and Canal History Society, 1982.

Boucher, Cyril T G

John Rennie, Manchester University Press,
1963
*For Albion Mills, Waterloo Bridge, East India
Docks etc. At the end is a chronological list of
Rennie's works.*

Bowen, F C

London ship types, 1938
The Port of London, Dryden, 1948

The Port of London Guide, Coram, 1955

Bown, A H J

**Ports and Shipping Turn-Round: Causes
of Delay and Suggested Remedies,** The
Dock and Harbour Authority, **33** (1953),
264-7, 270

Port Economics, The Dock and Harbour
Authority, 1953

Bown, A H J and Dove, C A

Port Administration and Operation,
Chapman & Hall, 1950

Braidwood, James

Fire Prevention and fire extinction,
Bell & Daldy, 1866

Reports on docks, 1858
(Guildhall Library, ms 14948)

Brett-James, N G

**Precincts and Trade Quarters: A History of
Use-Zones in the City of London,**
Architectural Review, **100** (1946), 129-50

Bromehead, C E N

**The Influence of its Geography on the
Growth of London,** Geographical Journal, **60**
(1922), 125-35

Broodbank, Sir Joseph

History of the Port of London, 2 vols,
O'Connor, 1921
*A major work but not without errors. Essentially the
administrative history to the formation of the PLA.
The complete history of the Port of London remains
to be written.*

Calvocoressi, Peter

The British experience, 1945-75, Bodley
Head, 1978

Campbell, W A

The Chemical Industry, Longman, 1971
*Good general historical account; makes plain that
many important pilot plants operated in London's
docklands before moving to the provinces for larger
scale production.*

Capper, Charles

**The port and trade of London: historical,
statistical, local and general,** Smith, Elder
and Co, 1862

Carr, R J M

St Paul's Presbyterian Church, West Ferry Road, Isle of Dogs, Industrial Archaeology Review (Oxford University Press) **5** (1981), 264-7
This church, now out of use, is the only significant survival from the launching of the Great Eastern. The foundation stone was laid by John Scott Russell.

Carr, R J M

Ingersoll-Rand Imperial type 10 Air Compressors in London's Docklands, GLIAS Journal 3, 41-46
Three late survivors, one in working order, are reported.

The building of Canada Dock and a dry dock for the repair of lighters — Surrey Commercial Docks, GLIAS Journal 3, 32-40
The dry dock for the repair of lighters was one of the last surviving features on the northern part of the Surrey Commercial Docks estate.

Coleman, A

Landscape and Planning in Relation to the Cement Industry of Thames-side, Town Planning Review, **25** (1954), 216-30

Colquhoun, P

A Treatise on the Commerce and Police of the River Thames, 1800

Colson, C

Notes on docks and dock construction, Longmans Green, 1984
Includes Royal Docks (p 26/7), Green's dry dock at Blackwall (p 179-183)

Cornish, V

The Great Capitals: an Historical Geography, Methuen, 1923

(Administrative) **County of London Development Plan 1951: Analysis,** London County Council, 1951

Course, A G

The Place of Tilbury in the Port of London, PLA, MS, 1946

Cowper, Benjamin H

A description, history and statistical account of Millwall, commonly called the Isle of Dogs, including notices of the founding, opening, etc, of the West India

Docks and City Canal; and notes relating to Limehouse, Poplar, Blackwall and Stepney, Robert Gladding, 1853

Cracknell, B E

The Lower Thames and Medway Petroleum Industry, Geography, **37** (1952), 79-88

The Alluvial Marchlands of the Lower Thames Estuary, Unpublished thesis, PhD, University of London, 1953

Critchell, J T and Raymond J

A History of the Frozen Meat Trade, Constable, 1912

Crouch, A P

Silvertown and Neighbourhood, Burleigh, 1900

Cunningham, B

The Estuarial Embankments of the River Thames, Report of the 16th Congress of Navigation, Brussels, 1935

Denney, M

London's Waterways, Batsford, 1977
Covers the rivers Fleet and Lea, Grand Junction and Regent's Canals, Croydon Canal, Kensington & Grosvenor Canals, as well as smaller creeks and waterways.

Dickinson, H W

Water Supply of Greater London, Newcomen Society, 1954
A great classic. Some account given of the water supply of Dockland areas. Emphasis on steam pumping engines, especially beam engines.

Dobson, E

Foundations and Concrete Work, first published 1850, John Weale, reprinted by Kingsmead Reprints, 1970
Good general background. One of a series.

(The) **Dock and Harbour Authority,** Monthly, 1920 to date.

Docklands Joint Committee

London docklands: a strategic plan, Docklands Joint Committee, 1976. A draft submitted for public consultation and comment.

Dodd, George

Days at the Factories, Charles Knight, 1843 (republished E P 1975)
Visits to manufactories etc.

Dowling, S W

The Exchanges of London, Butterworth, 1929

Dugan, James

The Great Iron Ship, Hamish Hamilton, 1953
A readable, popular account of I K Brunel's giant steamship Great Eastern. Very racy.

Dugdale, Sir William

History of Imbanking and Draining, 2nd Edition, 1772

Dunsheath, Percy

A History of Electrical Enginnering
Faber & Faber, 1962
A general account, makes plain the importance of Thameside as the dominant manufacturing area for submarine cable during the latter part of the 19th century (p 323).

Ellis, A

Three Hundred Years on London River: The Hay's Wharf Story, 1651-1951, Bodley Head, 1952

Elmes, J

A Scientific, Historical and Commercial Survey of the Harbour and Port of London, Weale, 1838

Elton, Julia

Bridges, Docks and Harbours, Ben Weinreb Catalogue, 1982
A priced list with valuable comments on civil engineering books of historic importance.

Emmerson, George S

John Scott Russell, John Murray, 1977
Especially for the building of the Great Eastern (Chaps 4-6) and HMS Warrier (Chap 7). Very much takes the side of Scott Russell in his disagreements with I K Brunel etc.

Exchanges and Commodity Markets, Swiss Bank Corporation, 1955

Fallon, T

River Police, Muller, 1956

Fisher, J A

Reconstruction of the Gallions Lower Entrance Lock at the Royal Docks of the Port of London Autority, Proceedings of the Institution of Civil Engineers, **5** (1956), 136-69

Forshaw, J H and Abercrombie, Sir Patrick

County of London Plan, Macmillan, 1943

Foster, Sir William

East London, Historical Association Pamphlet No 100, Bell, 1935

Glynn, Joseph

Rudimentary Treatise on the Construction of Cranes and Machinery, John Weale, 1854 (reprinted by Kingsmead Reprints, 1970)
Particular references to Woolwich Dockyard (p 21), Blackwall Crane (p 42), West India Docks' cranes (p 43) and chain testing (p 98). Good background material. One of a series.

Gordon, L

The Port of London Authority, Public Enterprise, edited by W A Robson, 13-57, Allen & Unwin, 1937

Green, A F

The Problem of London's Drainage, Geography, **41** (1956), 147-54

Greeves, Ivan S

London Docks 1800-1980, Thomas Telford, 1980
The title is rather a misnomer. The author concentrates on the period after the formation of the PLA in 1908. Makes use of his personal experience. Best from c1940.

Hadfield, Charles and Skempton, A W

William Jessop Engineer, David & Charles, 1979
Especially important for the West India Docks. See Chapters 9 and 10.

Hall, W B

The Origin and History of Trinity High Water, MS, report to the PLA, 1939

Harler, C R

The Culture and Marketing of Tea,
Oxford University Press, 1956

Harris, C D

Electricity Generation in London, England,
Geographical Review, **31** (1941), 127-34

Hennessey, R A S

The Electric Revolution, Oriel Press, 1972
*A stimulating book. Electrical legislation is covered.
Particular references to Greenwich Power Station
(p 20) and Bankside (p 146).*

Herbers, J

The Port of London, Collins, 1947

Hickman, G M

**The Origins and Changing Functions of
Settlement in South-East London, with
Special Reference to the Floodplain
Section of the Borough of Deptford,**
Unpublished Thesis, PhD, University of
London, 1951

Hobson, Sir Oscar

How the City Works, News Chronicle Book,
1955

Hogg, O F G

The Royal Arsenal, (2 volumes)
Oxford University Press, 1963

Holmes, J G

The North Woolwich Branch,
Railway Magazine, May/June 1946

Home, G

Old London Bridge, Bodley Head, 1931

Hoon, E E

**The Organization of the English Customs
System 1696-1786,** Chapter 4, New York,
Appleton-Century, 1938

Hugh-Jones, E M

Wholesale Foods Markets, The New Survey
of London Life and Labour, **Vol 5,** 2, Chapter
3, 115-36, King, 1933

**(The) Industrial Archaeology of South East
London,** SELIA, 1982

Jackson, Alan A

London's Local Railways, David & Charles,
1978
Very detailed and includes more than just railways.

Jones, Gareth S

**Outcast London: a study in the relationship
between classes in Victorian Society,**
Clarendon Press, 1971

*Indispensable background reading, with much of
interest regarding the casual labour system and its
consequencies. Contains a bibliography, 19p*

Jones, L R

The Geography of London River, Methuen,
1931

Kennedy, D and Aldington, H E

**Royal Docks Approaches Improvement,
London,** Journal of the Institution of Civil
Engineers, **2** (1935-6), 4-48

Kingsbury, W J

**Description of the Entrance, Entrance Lock
and Jetty Wall of the Victoria (London)
Docks,** Proceedings of the Institution of Civil
Engineers, **18** (1859), 445

Kirkpatrick, Sir Cyril

The Tidal Thames, Minutes of Proceedings
of the Institution of Civil Engineers, **223**
(1931-2), 2-34

Le Mesurier, H

**The Law relating to the Port of London
Authority,** Butterworth, 1934

Lethaby, W R

Londinium, Architecture and the Crafts,
Duckworth, 1923

Liddell, R R

**Improvements at the Royal Docks, Port of
London Authority,** Journal of the Institution
of Civil Engineers, **10** (1938-9), 283-330

Linney, A G

Peepshow of the Port of London,
Sampson Low, 1930

Lure and Lore of London River,
Sampson Low, 1932

London Street Plan, Geographia, 1977
Useful in that the atlas grid lines coincide with those of the National Grid. Still in print.

London Wharves and Docks, (Directory)
Temple Press, 1954

Longfield, T E

The Subsidence of London, Paper read to the British Association for the Advancement of Science, York, 1932, Professional Papers. New Series, No 14, HMSO, 1932

Lovell, John

Stevedores and dockers: a study of trade unionism in the Port of London 1870-1914, MacMillan, 1969 Contains a bibliography, 4p

Lubbook, Basil

The Blackwall frigates, Brown & Ferguson, 2nd ed, 1950

MacElwee, R S

Ports and Terminal Facilities,
New York: McGraw-Hill, 1918

McNeil, Ian

Hydraulic Power, Longmans, 1972
General account of hydraulic power. Particular references to West India and Victoria Docks (p 69), Millwall Cut Swing Bridge (p 154/5). The history of hydraulic power in London is fairly well covered.

Marshall, John

A Biographical Dictionary of Railway Engineers, David & Charles, 1978
A handy reference book. Worth owning.

Maughan, C

Markets of London, Pitman, 1931

Mayhew, Henry

London labour and the London poor: cyclopaedia of the conditions and earnings of those that will work, those that cannot work and those that will not work, 4 vols, 1861-62.

Originally published 1851, in parts Nos 1-63

(The) Metropolitan Borough of Woolwich,
Woolwich Borough Council, 1949

Morgan, F W

Ports and Harbours,
Hutchinson's University Series, 1952

Morrison, H S

How London is Governed,
People's University Press, 1949

Moss, Michael S and Hume, John R

Workshop of the British Empire,
Heinemann, 1977
Background for heavy machine tools etc, found in ship repair yards.

Mowat, M

Some recent grain handling and storing appliances at the Millwall Docks, Proceedings of the Institution of Civil Engineers, **177** (1909), 58

Munby, D L

Industry and Planning in Stepney,
Oxford University Press, 1951

Ordnam, N N B

The Port of London. Some Engineering Aspects of Post-War Reconstruction and Development, The Dock and Harbour Authority. **33** (1952), 131-6, 170-2

Ormsby, H

London on the Thames, Sifton, Praed, 1924

Owen, Sir David

The Port of London, Yesterday and Today, PLA, 1927

The Origin and Development of the Ports of the United Kingdom, Allman, 1948

Page, W

London: Its Origin and Early Development, Constable, 1923

Pailing, K B

Planning Problems of London's Waterside Areas, Unpublished thesis presented for the Diploma in Planning, 1952. (Copy held at LCC, County Hall)

Passingham, W J

London's Markets: their Origin and History, Sampton Low, 1935

Peacock, T B

PLA Railways, Locomotive Publishing, 1952

Pelham, R A

Medieval Foreign Trade: Eastern Ports, An Historical Geography of England before 1800, edited by H C Darby, Chapter 7, 298-329, Cambridge University Press, 1951

Perrett, D

London and the Steam Engine, Part I, GLIAS Journal 1 (1979), 1-10

London and the Steam Engine, Part II, GLIAS Journal 2 (1980), 24-37
These two articles contain accounts of the history of steam engine builders in London, many of whom were associated with Dockland.

Phillips, H

The Thames about 1750, Collins, 1951

Pollard, S

The Decline of Shipbuilding on the Thames, Economic History Review, 3 (1950), 72-89

PLA Monthly, 1925 to date

Pounds, N J G

Port and Outport in North-West Europe, Geographical Journal, 109 (1947), 216-28

Power, E and Postan, M M

Studies in English Trade in the Fifteenth Century, Routledge, 1933

Preddy, W S

The Mixing and Movement of Water in the Estuary of the Thames, Journal of the Marine Biological Association, 33 (1954), 645-62

Pudney, John

Crossing London's river: the bridges, ferries and tunnels crossing the Thames tideway in London, Dent, 1972

Pudney, John

London's Docks, Thames & Hudson, 1975
An excellent popular introduction. Still in print. Paperback available. Well illustrated.

Purkis, P

RNLI Storeyard at 27 Broomfield Street, Poplar E14, GLIAS Journal 1 (1979), 24-30

Rasmussen, S E

London: The Unique City, Cape, 1937

Rawstron, E M

The Distribution and Location of Steam-Driven Power Stations in Great Britain, Geography, 36 (1951), 249-62

The Salient Geographical Features of Electricity Production in Great Britain, Advancement of Science, 7 (1955), 73-82

Changes in the Geography of Electricity Production, Geography, 40 (1955), 92-7

Rees, H

A Growth Map for North-East London during the Railway Age, Geographical Review, 35 (1945), 458-65

Reports

Report from the Committee appointed to ensure into the **Best Mode of providing Sufficient Accommodation for the Increased Trade and Shipping of the Port of London,** 1796

Report from the Select Committee appointed to consider Evidence taken on Bills for the **Improvement of the Port of London,** 1799

Report from the Select Committee on the **State of London Bridge,** 1821

Report from the Select Committee on the **Port of London,** 1836

Report from the Select Committee on **Thames Conservancy,** 1863

Report of His Majesty's Commissioners Appointed to inquire into the Subject of the **Administration of the Port of London** and other Matters Connected therewith, Cmd 1151, HMSO, 1902

Report of a Committee appointed at a Conference of Public Authorities to consider the Question of **Floods from the River Thames in the County of London,** Cmd 3045, HMSO, 1928

(Joint) Report of Sir George Humphreys and Mr (later Sir) Frederick Palmer on the **Future**

Standard of Thames Flood Prevention works in the County of London, London County Council, 1929

Report of the Departmental Committee on **Thames Flood Prevention,** Cmd 4452, HMSO, 1933

Reports by Dock and Inland Waterways Executive on **Review of Trade Harbours** 1948-50, British Transport Commission, 1951

Report of the Departmental Committee on **Coastal Flooding,** Cmd 9165, HMSO, 1954

Report by the British National Committee of the Permanent International Assocaition of Navigational Congresses, '**Depths to be provided in Seaport Entrance Channels and Berths**'. Excerpt from Bulletin 42 (1955)

(Third) Report of the **Ports Efficiency Committee** to the Ministry of Transport and Civil Aviation, HMSO, 1956

Report of a Court of Inquiry into the causes and circumstances of a strike by members of the National Amalgamated Stevedores and Dockers in the Port of London and with practices relevant thereto, Cmnd 3146, HMSO, 1966

River Thames Wharf Directory, Gaselee, 1954

(The) use of the River Thames in London: Conference papers, July 1985

Robbins, Michael

The North London Railway, Oakwood Press, 1937
The line to Poplar Docks.

Robertson, Ian G

Taking it Further, East London Papers **12** (1969-70), 115-7
A companion piece to Denis Smith's IA of the Lower Lea Valley.

Robinson, A H W

The Changing Navigation Routes of the Thames Estuary, Journal of the Institute of Navigation, 4 (1951), 357-70

The Thames Estuary: A Regional Hydrographic Study, Unpublished thesis, MSc University of London, 1952

The Submarine Morphology of Certain Port Approach Systems, Journal of the Institute of Navigation, **9** (1956), 20-46

Rolt, L T C

Samuel Williams & Sons Ltd, 1855-1955, A Company's Story in its Setting, 41-86, Williams, 1955

Isambard Kingdom Brunel, Longmans Green, 1957
Book one includes the building of the Thames Tunnel.

Tools for the Job, B T Batsford, 1965
Covers Henry Maudslay. A central theme is that a fine machine tool makes possible the construction of other fine machine tools.

Rose, M

The East End of London, Cresset, 1951
A very worthwhile book. Something of a classic.

Royal Commission on Trade Unions

Reports of Commissioners, 1867

Ruegg, R

Summer Evening Rambles Round Woolwich, 1847

Sargent, T E M

The early buildings at the West India Docks up to 1830, unpublished dissertation 1977 (copies in the PLA library and the library of the National Maritime Museum)
A study of the early architectural history of the West India Docks. Illustrated by photographs.

Scott, J F

The Construction and Equipment of the Tilbury Docks, Proceedings of the Institution of Civil Engineers, **120** (1895), 276

Shankland, E C

The Thames Estuary and the Port of London: Channel Development by Dredging. Paper read at the 17th International Navigation Congress, Lisbon, 1949

Sharan, J

Marketing of Tea in the United Kingdom 1939-52, Unpublished thesis, MSc (Econ), University of London, 1954

Shepherd-Baron, W P

The Docks of London, Proceedings of the Institution of Civil Engineers, **3** (1954), 12-42

Sinclair, R

East London, Hale, 1950

Skempton, A W

Engineering in the Port of London 1789-1808, Transactions of the Newcomen Society, **50** (1978-79), 87-108

Engineering in the Port of London 1808-1833, Transactions of the Newcomen Society, **53** (1981-82), 73-96
These two papers by Professor Skempton constitute a very important study. Indispensable.

Smith, Denis

The Industrial Archaeology of the Lower Lea Valley, East London Papers, **12** (1969-70), 83-114
A classic early survey, includes Napier Yard, Thames Ironworks, West Ham Pumping Station, etc.

Smith, H L and Nash, Vaughan

The story of the dockers' strike, (1889): told by two East Londoners, Cedric Chivers Ltd, 1970
First published 1889

Smith, J G

Organised Produce Markets, Longmans, 1922

Smith, T

Commercial Road Goods Depot, GLIAS Journal 2 (1980), 1-12
An account of the large railway goods depot at the London end of the line from Tilbury for the warehousing of goods imported via Tilbury Docks, Much of the site is now occupied by the National Westminster Bank.

Spate, O H K

The Growth of London, AD 1660-1880, An Historical Geography of England before 1800, edited by H C Darby, Chapter 14, 529-47, Cambridge University Press, 1951

Spence, G

Nautical Description of Banks and Channels, 1804

Spurrel, F C J

Early Sites and Embankments on the Margins of the Thames Estuary, Archaeological Journal, **42** (1885), 269-302

Account of an Excursion to Higham, Proceedings of the Geologists' Association, **2** (1889-90), xxii-xxiv

On the Estuary of the Thames and its Alluvium, ut supra, 210-28

Stenton, F M

Norman London, Historical Association leaflets, 93-4, Bell, 1934

Stern, W M

The First London Dock Boom and the Growth of the West India Docks, Economica, **19** (1952), 59-77

Stewart, B

The Library and the Picture Collection of the Port of London authority, Richards, 1955

Stocks, G R

Free Trade Zones and Re-Export Reliefs, The Dock and Harbour Authority, **27** (1946), 137-8

(The) Storm Floods of 1 February 1953, (a symposium), Geography, **38** (1953), 132-89

Stow, J

A Survey of London, 1603, 2 vols, edited by C L Kingsford, Oxford: Clarendon, 1908

Sturt, B

Low-pressure gas storage, GLIAS Journal 2 (1980), 13-23
A general account of gasholders plus a gazetteer which includes a few Dockland examples.

(The) Thames — Waterway of the World, Stratton & Stratton, 1893
Reference to Brown Lenox & Co (p 91-2).

Thompson, A G

The Romance of London River, Bradley, 1934

The Thames from Tower to Tilbury, Bradley, 1939

'Port of London', World Ports, 15 (1953), 32-45

Thompson, R

The Chronicles of Old London Bridge by an Antiquary, 1839

Thornbury, W and Walford, E

Old and New London, (6 vols), Cassell & Co, 1897

Thorne, James

Handbook of the Environs of London, (2 vols), John Murray, 1876, reprinted in the 1970s

Tomlinson, H M

London River, Cassell, 1951

Toothe, E S

Some Modern Trends in Cargo Handling, PLA, 1955

Tucker, M T

Limehouse Lock and the GLIAS winch at Camden Town, GLIAS Journal 1 (1979), 11-13

Tull, G J D

The Port of London Authority, 1909-1959, PLA, 1959

Tull, G J D

Some Observations from a Legal Point of View about the River Thames in the Port of London, PLA, 1956

Vallance, A

The Centre of the World, Hodder & Stoughton, 1935

Vaughan, W

On Wet Docks, Quays and Warehouses for the Port of London, with Hints respecting Trade, 1793

Vernon-Harcourt, L F

Description of the new South Dock in the Isle of Dogs, Proceedings of the Institution of Civil Engineers, 34 (1871), 157

Welch, Charles

History of The Tower Bridge, Smith Elder & Co, 1894

Wheble, C L

The London Lighterage Trade: Its History, Organisation and Economics, Unpublished thesis, MSc (Econ), University of London, 1939

Wheeler, R E M (Sir Mortimer)

'Introduction' **Report of the Royal Commission on Historical Monuments, 3, Roman London,** 1928, 1-67

Williams, H

South London, Hale, 1949

Wilson, Aubrey

London's industrial heritage, David & Charles, 1967
Photographs by Joseph McKeown

Wilson, David F

Dockers: the impact of industrial change, Fontana, 1972
Contains a bibliography, 3½p and some useful appendices, eg Dockers' basic rates, earnings and guarantee, 1947-70; Summary of major dock strikes, 1945-71

Wilson, G A

Port of London Authority Engineering Works, 1952, Proceedings of the Institution of Civil Engineers, 2 II (1953), 551-604

Wilson, G and Grace, H

Settlement of London due to Under-drainage of the London Clay, Journal of the Institution of Civil Engineers, 19 (1942-3), 100-27

Wooding, J W

As to the Origin and Meaning of 'Trinity High Water' and its Evaluation to Ordnance Datum, Newlyn, Mimeographed, PLA, 1943

Wooldridge, S W

The Geographer as Scientist, Nelson, 1956

Wooldridge, S W and Hutchings, G E

London's Countryside, Methuen, 1957

Wooldridge, S W and Linton, D L

Structure Surface and Drainage in South-east England, Philip, 1955

Yamey, B S

Futures Trading in Cocoa, Rubber and Wool Tops, The Three Banks Review, **23** (1954), 28-41

The Metal Exchange, The Three Banks Review, **30** (1956), 21-39

Young, Peter

Power of Speech, A History of Standard Telephones and Cables 1883-1983, George Allen & Unwin, 1983

Much relevant material will be found in the periodicals:
Engineering, The Engineer, Proceedings of the Institution of Civil Engineers, The Builder and the **PLA magazines,** etc, and of course the Ordnance Survey and Nikolaus Pevsner's **The Buildings of England** should not be forgotten.

Abbreviations

When consideration was first given to the provision of definitions to abbreviations used within the text of this work it was thought that offence might be given to some, particularly the specialist readers. However, it was also thought, perhaps hopefully, that many non-specialists might read and find the book of interest and that among such readers a teenager might well be aware of the meaning of 'rpm' but 'LCC' would be a mystery. On the other hand a reader of a much older generation might well find the reverse — therefore the following list.

c
Circa, meaning 'approximately' or 'about', eg c1850, 'about 1850'

cf
compare

GLC
The Greater London Council, a democratically-elected body devoted to the interests of Londoners, came into being with the London Government Act, 1963 and the disbandment of the LCC (see below). It covered an area of 600 square miles, extending far beyond the boundaries of the old country, in recognition of the realition of Greater London's continued expansion. The LCC and other pre-existing local authorities remained side by side with the new authority until April 1 1965.

GLIAS
Greater London Industrial Archaeology Society. 'Greater London' in this context refers to the geographical area and not to the GLC as a parent body.

LCC
The London County Council. Created in 1889, to provide London with a unified elected government and cope with problems arising from the vast expansion of the metropolis. The LCC was succeeded in 1965 by the GLC (see above).

LPTB
London Passenger Transport Board. A variety of competing agencies, street congestion, and a lack of capital investment to develop the underground railways, led to considerable dissatisfaction regarding public passenger-carrying transport in London. Largely due to Herbert (later Lord) Morrison the amalgamated undertakings were put under the control of a public board, the LPTB, which was set up in 1933. The LPTB existed until 1948 when it was replaced by the London Transport Executive, itself later replaced by the London Transport Board.

LTE
London Transport Executive.

MBW
Metropolitan Board of Works. Established in 1856 and the first local government body to have an overview of the capital. It was succeeded by the LCC (see above).

OS
Ordnance Survey (maps)

PLA
Port of London Authority. Formed in 1908, largely on the model of the Mersey Docks and Harbour Board, to bring some order to the management and finances of London's docks. The PLA is an indirectly-elected body with representatives of port interests and local authorities. Its main duties, as laid down, were the administration and improvement of London's docks, the conservancy of the Thames from Teddington Lock to the sea and certain licensing powers, eg of river craft and lightermen.

psi
pounds per square inch

rpm
revolutions per minute

STOLPORT
Short take-off and landing (port). A landing and take-off area for aircraft requiring only short runways.

In view of the variety of topics covered by this book it was decided that the compilation of a

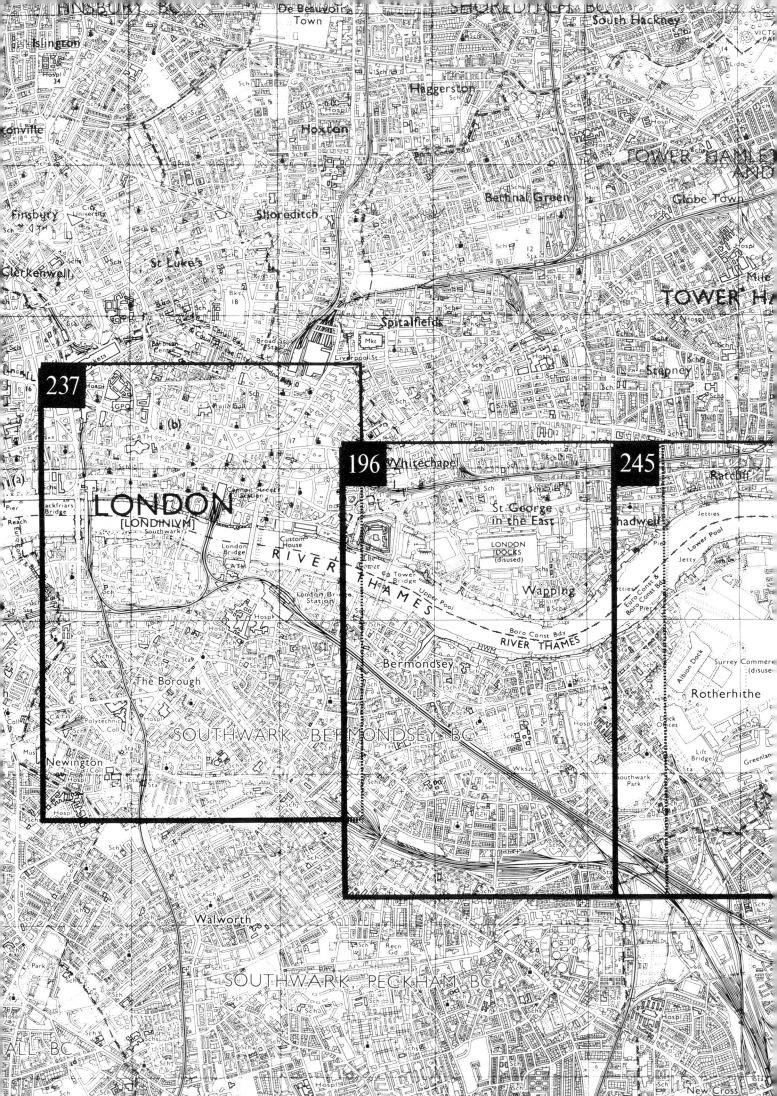

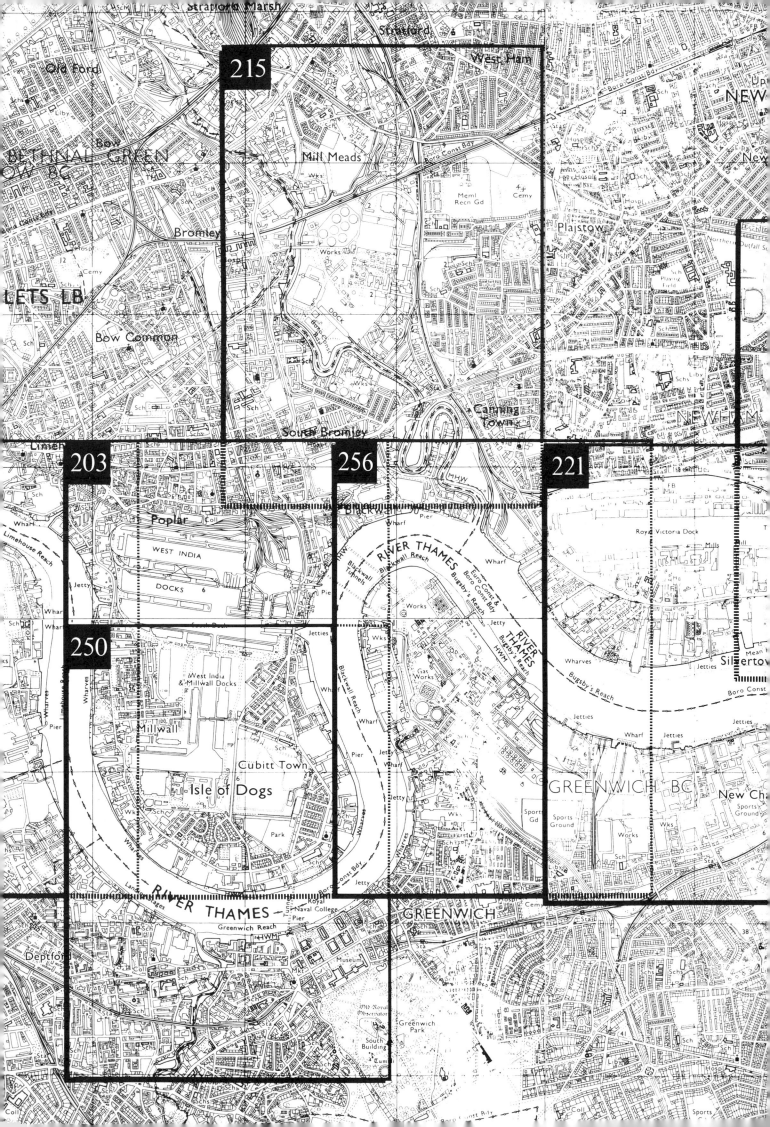

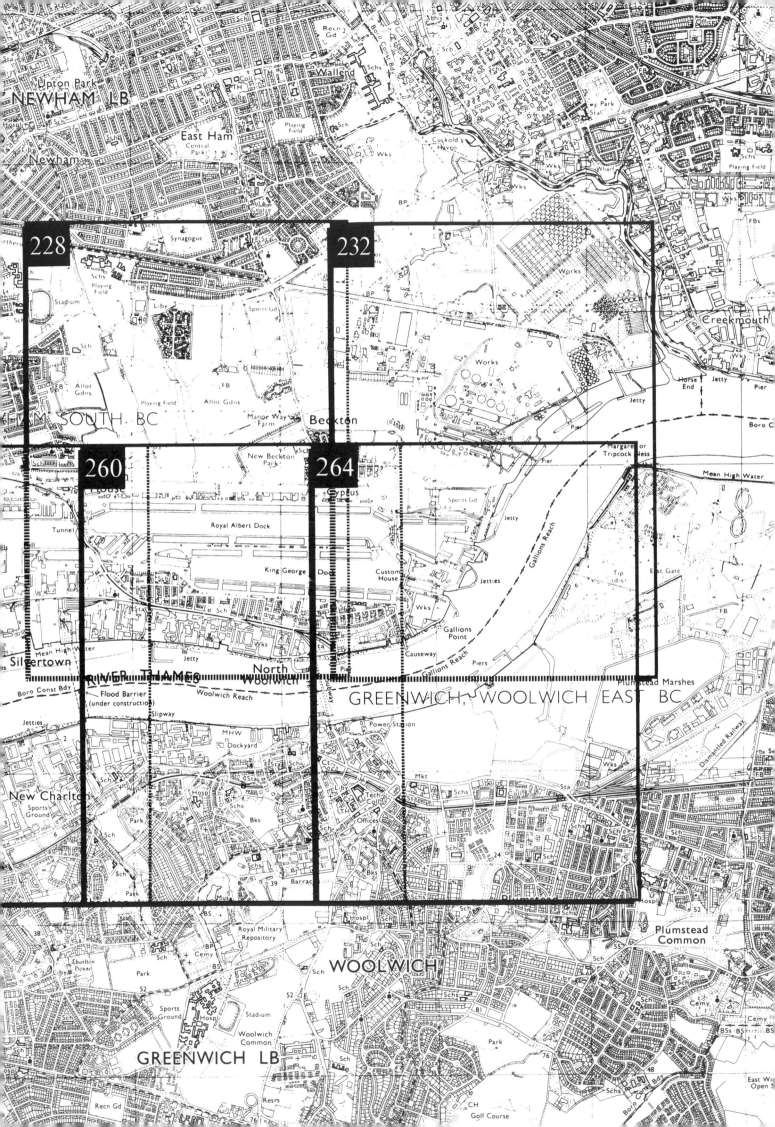

Index

Acknowledgements

This book is the result of a generous grant and substantial support given to the Polytechnic by the Greater London Council (GLC) to continue research into London's Dockland History previously carried out in the Department of Civil Engineering at North East London Polytechnic.

The Polytechnic wishes to record deepest thanks to Mr George Nicholson, Chairman of the Planning Committee, and other GLC members and officers for their initiative and determination in establishing a proper record of Dockland heritage for London and the rest of the World.

Special thanks are due to Mr John Earl, of the Historic Buildings Division of the GLC for his enthusiasm and unstinting support throughout the project.

Work on this publication has been overseen and helped greatly by the Dockland History Survey Committee consisting of the following:

Dr D P Smith
Chairman

Dr S K Al Naib, Project Director
North East London Polytechnic

Mr C Ellmers
Museum of London

Mr A Pearsall
National Maritime Museum

Mr J Earl
GLC observer

Mr P Calvocoressi
GLC observer, Secretary

Dr R J M Carr, in attendance
Research Fellow

We would like to thank the Museum of London for providing accommodation and facilities for the meetings of the Survey Committee.

The editorial assistance on this publication is substantially that of Dr R J M Carr who was appointed by the Polytechnic as a part-time Research Fellow to assist me and work on this project under my supervision from January 1985 until March 1986.

Special thanks are due to John Beake and Joe Hale, graphic designers of the GLC for their help and advice in designing this volume and to Gloria Shayler of NELP for her assistance with the preparation of illustrations.

For the supply of information and help generally we are indebted to many but special mention should be made of George Adams, Robert Aspinall, Robert Baldwin, R J Barnes, Jim Barr, Professor James Bird, Howard Bloch, Colin Bowden, Louise Brodie, T E Browne, Paul Calvocoressi, E W Chapman, Henry Cleary, Robin Craig, D K Cross, Denis Delay, Faith Dewhurst, Philip Dubuque, Chris Ellmers, Miss Julia Elton, David Eversley, Caroline Fitton, Oliver Green, Mr I S S Greeves, Rick Hogben, Michael Jones, John Jupp, Chris Lloyd, Mary Mills, Patricia O'Driscoll, Barbara Orrett, Mrs Carmel Ortega, Ilana Pergam, David Perrett, Tom Ridge, Mr Ian G Robertson, Mrs Elizabeth Rolfe, Christopher Rule, Mike Seaborne, James Smith, Tim Smith, Brian Sturt, Mr R J M Sutherland, Mrs Mary Thurston, Malcolm Tucker, Julian Watson, Mr E W Weedon, Alex Werner, Mrs Audrey White and David and Elizabeth Wood. We would also like to thank the many Librarians and Archivists who have contributed descriptions of material in their care.

We are very grateful to Professor James Bird for permission to reproduce the diagram showing the role of lighterage (fig 5 page 184) from his book *The Major Seaports of the United Kingdom*, Hutchinson 1986.

As the person responsible for the organisation of the whole enterprise and the editing of this book, I must accept the blame for shortcomings. The reception of the first edition, however, has been very generous and comments have been most favourable.

Dr S K Al Naib
Head of Department of Civil Engineering
North East London Polytechnic
Longbridge Road
Dagenham
Essex RM8 2AS